GPS: A Case Study in Generality

and

Problem Solving

ACM MONOGRAPH SERIES

*Published under the auspices of the Association for
Computing Machinery Inc.*

Edited by ROBERT L. ASHENHURST *The University of Chicago*

A. FINERMAN (Ed.) University Education in Computing Science, 1968
A. GINZBURG Algebraic Theory of Automata, 1968
E. F. CODD Cellular Automata, 1968
G. ERNST AND A. NEWELL GPS: A Case Study in Generality and Problem Solving

In preparation
M. A. GAVRILOV AND A. D. ZAKREVSKII LYaPAS: A Programming Language
for Logic and Switching

Previously published and available from The Macmillan Company,
New York City
G. SEBESTYN Decision Making Processes in Pattern Recognition, 1963
M. YOVITS (Ed.) Large Capacity Memory Techniques for Computing Systems, 1962
V. KRYLOV Approximate Calculation of Integrals (Translated by A. H. Stroud), 1962

GPS: A Case Study in Generality and Problem Solving

GEORGE W. ERNST

Andrew R. Jennings Computing Center
Case Western Reserve University
Cleveland, Ohio

ALLEN NEWELL

Carnegie-Mellon University
Pittsburgh, Pennsylvania

ACADEMIC PRESS   New York   London   1969

ACADEMIC PRESS, INC.
111 Fifth Avenue, New York, New York 10003

United Kingdom Edition published by
ACADEMIC PRESS, INC. (LONDON) LTD.
Berkeley Square House, London W.1

LIBRARY OF CONGRESS CATALOG CARD NUMBER: 69-12276

PRINTED IN THE UNITED STATES OF AMERICA

To Herb and Cliff
whose program this also is

PREFACE

The material of this monograph constitutes the culmination of work on a single problem solving program, GPS (for General Problem Solver), that stretches back to 1957. The origination of the program was the joint work of J. C. Shaw, H. A. Simon, and A. Newell. During the "middle years," the continuing efforts on reorganization and reprogramming fell to A. Newell; the attempts to exploit the program and its ideas were pursued jointly with H. A. Simon. The results of the last several explorations into modified organizations have never been reported. The final phase, reported here, consists of two intertwined parts. One is the description of the final organization of GPS (i.e., GPS-2-5). This is covered in Chapter III and part of Chapter IV. The responsibility for most of the programming details of this organization must rest with the second author (A. Newell); the first author came on the scene much too late to do anything but be frustrated by them. The second part of this research is the attempt to get this program (perhaps "this thing" expresses our feelings more precisely) to live up to its name, at least marginally. Taking GPS and getting it to be general enough to do a number of different tasks has been the primary responsibility of G. Ernst, and constitutes the substance of his doctoral dissertation at Carnegie Institute of Technology. Chapter II and part of Chapters IV, V, and VI cover this research. The present volume is a somewhat revised version of the original dissertation (Ernst and Newell, 1966).

We have used the term "final" in several places above. This does not indicate any feeling that this document marks a terminus to our research on general problem solvers; quite the contrary is true. However, we do feel that this particular aggregate of IPL-V code should be laid to rest, as having done its part in advancing our understanding of the mechanisms of intelligence.

We would like to acknowledge the continued advice, support, and criticism of our colleague, H. A. Simon. Both he and J. C. Shaw were involved in the first several years of research on GPS, and their contribution to the present form of the program is pervasive. The extent of our debt is indicated by our dedication of the book to them. However, they are not to be held responsible for the errors and vagaries of this book or the final form that GPS has taken. In addition, we would like to thank L. W. Gregg and R. W. Floyd who served on G. Ernst's Dissertation Committee. Finally, we express our appreciation to Mildred Sisko, who handled the typing of the book through innumerable drafts.

The research reported here has been supported in part by contract SD-146 from the Advanced Research Projects Agency to Carnegie Institute of Technology. It has also been supported by the RAND Corporation, both in the support of A. Newell, first as an employee and more recently as a consultant, and through the award by Carnegie to G. Ernst of the RAND Fellowship in Systems and Communication Sciences. The preparation of this book was partially supported by the Air Force Office of Scientific Research under grant AF-OSR-125-67 and the National Science Foundation under grant GK-1386.

G. W. ERNST
A. NEWELL

March 1969

CONTENTS

CHAPTER I

INTRODUCTION

The research reported here is an investigation into the development of a computer program with general problem solving capabilities. It lies within that part of computer science known as artificial intelligence, defined generally as the attempt to construct mechanisms that perform tasks requiring intelligence when performed by humans. The term *artificial intelligence* is usually taken broadly enough to encompass all such efforts, whether done via programming a computer or in any other technology. More narrowly, then, this research lies within the area of *heuristic programming*—a term that has come to mean the programming of computers that solve problems and accomplish complex tasks by the exercise of intelligence.

The term *problem solving* is not altogether clear. In English the term has a broad and indefinite scope, as do such similar terms as *recognition, understanding, learning,* and *searching.* Behind this vagueness, of course, lies the absence of a science of problem solving that would support the definition of a technical term. In this respect the work in artificial intelligence is to be viewed as an effort to obtain such a science. Thus, programs that are labeled problem-solving programs are really proposals for how the term is to be taken in a more precise sense.

There is an additional source of ambiguity in the normal use of the term *problem solving*. A typical user of a computer has a problem he wants solved, and the computer, appropriately programmed, produces the answer. We ambiguously attribute problem solving both to the man and to the computer (that is, to the instrument). We say "the man solved his problem," and also "the computer solved his problem." The ambiguity is fostered by chains of instrumental action in which a man (or computer) is both the instrument and initiator. Thus, Man X has a problem, and gives it to his assistant, Man Y to solve. Man Y uses the computer to solve it. The computer program, in turn, uses some other programs to solve the problem, and perhaps also a human operator to mount tapes. Who is now the problem solver? English lets us avoid such decisions by permitting us to use the term *problem solver* for any link in the chain.

We recognize that problems come in a variety of forms, that some are big problems and some little problems, and that the difficulty of a problem is related both to the information given the problem solver and to the knowledge and abilities of the problem solver. When a program's input statements are problems of sufficient difficulty to cause a human to remark (say), "Well now, that *is* a problem. Let's see, how does one do it?" it is natural to call such a program a problem solver. The instrumental meaning, whereby any program is a problem solver, is not intended. Such a program is different from the usual program, at least in part because it must discover how to produce the solution as well as actually produce it. What else it might have to do—and thus how different from more familiar programs it might end up being—is of course an object of research on problem-solving programs.

In sum, this research is concerned with problem-solving programs and not with programs to solve anyone else's immediate problems. It is of the nature of a case study, since it attempts to make use of a single program, called the General Problem Solver (GPS, hereafter), as an experimental vehicle. The end result is not a problem solver that can be used, but rather a series of lessons that give a more perfect view of the nature of problem solving and what is required to construct processes that accomplish it.

This sort of empirical activity is very much akin to the construction of an engineering prototype, except that its goal is scientific knowledge rather than the demonstration of feasibility for an application. It appears that such activity will constitute a substantial part of the experimental side of computer science for some time to come. Certainly, it has been the major avenue to knowledge in artificial intelligence.[*] For example, almost all the references in this book to work in artificial intelligence are to case studies, similar to the present one in their methodology.

The program used in this investigation should properly be called GPS-2-6, rather than GPS, since it was constructed by modifying an earlier program called GPS-2-5. Both these programs are derived ultimately from a program conceived in 1957 by Newell *et al.* (1957b). Throughout its history the various versions of GPS have been used for diverse purposes. In particular, one of the main concerns has been with natural intelligence, rather than artificial intelligence—that is, with trying to understand how humans solve problems. The approach has been to shape a version of GPS to simulate the detailed behavior of a single human problem solver for a short period of time (Newell and Simon, 1961c). The present research—that is, the present version of GPS—is governed entirely by concern about how to attain generality. Therefore, we have labeled it artificial intelligence rather than psychology. There is no conflict, much less contradiction, between these two aims. Nevertheless, one will not find in this monograph any treatment of human data or any direct discussions of whether it is plausible for humans to behave or be structured in ways suggested by the present research. We do not consider such concerns to be irrelevant. After all, the history of GPS has been an alternation between questions of artificial and natural intelligence. However, it awaits additional positive research before anything of substance can be said.

The emphasis in this research is on the generality of GPS—on the variety of problems that GPS can attempt to solve. The quality of the problem solving exhibited by GPS is only a secondary consideration. Hence, the kinds of problem for which GPS was designed are simple according to human standards, although they still require intellectual effort. A typical problem is the Missionaries and Cannibals task in which there are three missionaries and three cannibals who want to cross a river. The only means of conveyance is a small boat with a capacity of two people, which all six know how to operate. If, at any time, there are more cannibals than missionaries on either side of the river, those missionaries will be eaten by the cannibals. How can all six get across the river without any missionaries being eaten?

[*] The exceptions are a few places where some mathematical support has been possible, e.g., theorem proving in the predicate calculus and pattern recognition (although the latter is hardly referenced here).

Another sample task is that of integrating, symbolically, a simple integral such as

$$\int t e^{t^2} \, dt.$$

This problem is apparently quite different from the Missionaries and Cannibals task, but GPS has the generality, as well as the ability, to solve both of these problems.

Although GPS-2-5 was designed to be general, it, together with its predecessors, only solved three different kinds of problem mainly because of inadequate facilities for representing tasks. The central problem of this research is to generalize GPS-2-5 so that it can attempt a wider variety of problems. We also demand that the formulation of a problem for GPS require no knowledge of the internal structure of the program. Underlying this specific objective is the desire to shed light on some of the issues involved in designing better representations for problem solvers.

This research does not endeavor to construct an impressive problem solver. Difficulties in reworking an existing program, such as GPS-2-5, make this infeasible. For example, the representation of tasks in GPS is somewhat *ad hoc*, having been introduced in several stages. (The representation of GPS-2-5 is a modification of the representation of a previous version of the program.) Thus, GPS is an experimental program used to investigate representational issues. No attempt to redesign the basic internal representation of GPS was attempted.

We have given only a brief informal statement of the problem. Chapter II gives a more precise statement. It starts by discussing some possible approaches to generality, so that the present effort can be placed in context. Although a number of related studies are touched upon, it should be evident by now that no attempt is being made to present or analyze the entire field of heuristic programming. With the context set, a problem of generality is posed with sufficient precision to make the plan of research plausible. We round out Chapter II by giving a brief history of GPS.

Chapter III describes in detail the problem-solving structure of GPS. This consists of the goals and the means of attempting to attain them, called methods. GPS has a special language for describing methods, so that its main executive routine is really an interpreter for this method language. Once this language and the central interpreter are described, the methods are easily presented.

Chapter IV describes the components of a task and their internal representation in GPS so that the methods can work on them. As the analysis of Chapter II suggests, there is a clean interface between the problem-solving structure and the environment with which it deals— or, more precisely, with how the parts of that environment are represented and manipulated. The main things to be represented are objects, operators, goals, and differences; and each is discussed in detail. There are also several minor items: a table of connections that relates differences to operators; an ordering of the differences; the information on how to compare objects; and declarations of the type of each symbol used. Besides a discussion of the internal representation, Chapter IV contains a description of an external representation for giving a new task to GPS. Since the focus of the research effort is on the internal representation, the external one is directly isomorphic to the internal one. Nevertheless, it does permit increased readability and provide a convenient way of viewing the amount of specification for a task as a single package of information.

Chapter V provides the main conceptual content of the study. Chapters III and IV give a reasonably straightforward description of GPS, along lines familiar to anyone who has ever had to describe a complex program. Chapter V attempts to recast this so as to highlight the role that representation plays in permitting—and hence limiting— the generality of GPS. Thus, the basic problem of generality, as posed in Chapter II, is restated in quite particular terms. This leads to a set of specific issues to be overcome to make GPS general enough to perform a range of tasks. Each of these issues is described in detail: generalizing the desired object; generalizing the operator; representing unordered sets; working with large objects; and the expressive power of the differences. Not all of these issues were dealt with satisfactorily. For some we agreed to leave the generality of GPS limited. But they form the central concerns with which we struggled in this case study.

In Chapter VI we provide the evidence for the success—and limitation thereof—of the modifications analyzed in Chapter V. We were able to give GPS eleven different tasks. Taken all in all they represent considerable diversity. Each of these tasks is described, its formal presentation to GPS given, and its behavior exhibited. A number of additional, though minor, points about generality come out in the discussions.

In the last chapter, Chapter VII, we recapitulate the entire course of events and discuss critically the lessons that seem to have emerged.

The generalization of GPS focused on the properties of a group of tasks. These tasks were singled out for reasons that are neither arbitrary nor entirely justified. Some of these tasks were successfully solved by GPS, while others could not be solved by GPS. Several of the tasks were selected because they have been solved by other problems solvers. The reason for giving such tasks to GPS is not to compare the quality of its performance with the performance of other problem solvers. Indeed, in all such cases, GPS is the least efficient. However, giving such tasks to GPS is instructive because it helps to reveal the structure of the tasks, as well as the differences and similarities between GPS and other problem solvers.

GPS is programmed in IPL-V (Newell *et al.*, 1961) language. This monograph does not require the reader to have an intimate knowledge of IPL-V. However, the reader should understand the concept of list processing [see Rosen (1967), which reprints a number of articles on list processing systems].

CHAPTER II

THE ISSUE OF GENERALITY

This chapter states more precisely the problem of generality. We start by illustrating the various approaches of current research to the contruction of a general problem solver. With this background we formulate a version of the "problem of generality" that allows us to outline this research. Finally, we provide some appropriate historical background.

APPROACHES TO GENERALITY

How might one go about creating a general problem solver? Consider the simple model of a problem solver shown in Fig. 1. The problem is initially expressed in some external representation, which is converted by a translator into an internal representation—an encoding of the external representation inside the computer. The internal representation is processed by a set of problem-solving techniques, and the result of this processing is (hopefully) the solution.

According to this simple view, generality can be limited by the generality of any of these three parts: the external representation, the internal representation, or the collection of techniques. Although

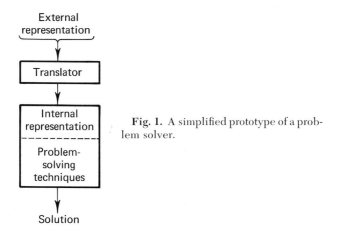

Fig. 1. A simplified prototype of a problem solver.

eventually all three parts must be dealt with, an approach can start by emphasizing a single one: to adopt a general external representation that is similar to the way problems occur in the real world; to adopt a general internal representation so that all problems can be homogeneously represented inside of the computer; or to develop a set of problem-solving methods of universal applicability. Each of these approaches focuses on one of the three parts of the model of a problem solver in Fig. 1 and considers the other two to be subordinate. To clarify these different approaches, a discussion of each follows that includes some examples of research efforts that use the approach. The research here adopts a variant of the third approach (heuristic search). We shall discuss it in great detail, the discussion of the other approaches serving to place matters in context.

EXTERNAL REPRESENTATION

Two quite different possibilities seem to be appropriate for a "natural" representation of problems.

NATURAL LANGUAGE INPUT. Assuming that problems are posed to the computer by people, a natural language is a good choice for an external representation of problems. Prior to the actual problem solving, the meaning must be extracted from sentences (and paragraphs) and encoded in the internal representation. The earlier work on question-answering programs [SAD SAM in Lindsay (1963), and BASEBALL in Green *et al.* (1961)] focused on this problem and purposely avoided any problem solving on the internal representation (although they did do sophisticated information retrieval). Recently, however, several programs have endeavored to do problem solving on the meaning extracted from natural language inputs. The input language has had to be a much cruder approximation to a natural language than in the earlier question-answering programs. A brief discussion of two of these gives some flavor of their structure.

SIR [Semantic Information Retriever (Raphael, 1964)] is a program that answers questions about a data base it has accumulated from interaction with a human. A typical protocol is shown in Fig. 2. SIR answers the first two equations (signified by Q rather than ?) YES, because it knows that set inclusion is both transitive and reflexive.

SIR extracts the semantics of statements and questions by matching each to a number of standard sentence forms. Associated with each form is a LISP (McCarthy et al., 1963) routine that stores information in the internal representation of the environment or retrieves information from it as the case may be.

SIR's internal representation is a network in which the nodes

MAN: EVERY KEYPUNCH-OPERATOR IS A GIRL

SIR: I UNDERSTAND

MAN: ANY GIRL IS AN EXAMPLE OF A PERSON

SIR: I UNDERSTAND

MAN: IS A KEYPUNCH-OPERATOR A PERSON Q

SIR: YES

MAN: IS A PERSON A PERSON Q

SIR: YES

MAN: IS A PERSON A GIRL Q

SIR: SOMETIMES

MAN: IS A MONKEY A KEYPUNCH-OPERATOR Q

SIR: INSUFFICIENT INFORMATION

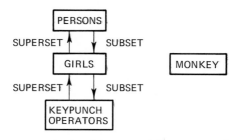

Fig. 2. A SIR conversation (top) and the internal data structure (bottom).

THE GAS CONSUMPTION OF MY CAR IS 15 MILES PER GALLON . THE DIS-
TANCE BETWEEN BOSTON AND NEW YORK IS 250 MILES . WHAT IS THE
NUMBER OF GALLONS OF GAS USED ON A TRIP BETWEEN NEW YORK AND
BOSTON Q

(a)

1. (EQUAL (DISTANCE BETWEEN BOSTON AND NEW YORK)
    (TIMES (250 (MILES))))
2. (EQUAL X1 (NUMBER OF GALLONS OF GAS USED ON TRIP BETWEEN
    NEW YORK AND BOSTON))
3. (EQUAL (GAS CONSUMPTION OF MY CAR) (QUOTIENT
    (TIMES 15 (MILES)) (TIMES 1 (GALLONS))))
4. (EQUAL (DISTANCE) (TIMES (GAS CONSUMPTION)
    (NUMBER OF GALLONS OF GAS USED)))

(b)

1. GAS CONSUMPTION = GAS CONSUMPTION OF MY CAR
2. DISTANCE = DISTANCE BETWEEN BOSTON AND NEW YORK
3. NUMBER OF GALLONS OF GAS USED = NUMBER OF GALLONS
    OF GAS USED ON A TRIP BETWEEN NEW YORK AND BOSTON

(c)

THE NUMBER OF GALLONS OF GAS USED ON A TRIP BETWEEN
NEW YORK AND BOSTON IS 16.66 GALLONS

(d)

Fig. 3. A typical problem for STUDENT: (a) statement of the problem; (b) the set of equations derived from (a); (c) assumptions made by STUDENT in order to solve (a); (d) the answer obtained. A prefix notation is used; e.g., (EQUAL X Y) is $X=Y$; (TIMES (250 (MILES))) is 250 miles.

represent nouns of English sentences and the branches between the nodes represent relationships between nouns. For example, the SIR model of the conversation in Fig. 2 is given at the bottom of the figure. The nodes of the network represent GIRLS, PERSONS, and KEYPUNCH OPERATORS. The branch between GIRLS and PERSONS, which is labeled SUBSET, represents the fact that the set of all girls is contained in the set of all persons. There are no connections between MONKEY and any other node, hence the answer INSUFFI-CIENT INFORMATION.

A program called STUDENT (Bobrow, 1964) provides a second

example of a program focused on natural-language problem solving. It attempts to solve story algebra problems found in a high school algebra textbook. While problems are posed to both STUDENT and SIR in a restricted subset of English, STUDENT unlike SIR is strongly oriented to a particular type of problem. Figure 3a gives a typical question that was posed to STUDENT, together with STUDENT's answer.

The internal representation of problems in STUDENT is a set of algebraic equations. For example, Fig. 3b is the set of equations that STUDENT arrives at for the problem in Fig. 3a. Before solving the equation, STUDENT must recognize that the pairs of phrases in Fig. 3c represent the same entities.

The main emphasis in STUDENT is translating the external representation. Since the internal representation is strongly task oriented, an algorithm can be used to solve the problem from its internal representation.

VISUAL PERCEPTION. The other "natural" external representation for many problems is the world itself. This external representation places large constraints on the problem solver. For example, to perceive the world it must be capable of accepting parallel inputs. In addition, answers must be produced quickly in order to solve problems in real time. Models of pseudoneural nets, e.g., *perceptrons* (Rosenblatt, 1962) accept parallel inputs and produce answers in real time.

The basic element of pseudoneural nets is usually an "adaptive threshold element" illustrated in Fig. 4a. Each of the stimulus signals $s_1, s_2, \ldots, s_n$ may have either 1 or 0 as a value. The response signal r is determined by the sum of the stimulus signals times their corresponding weights, $w_1, w_2, \ldots, w_n$. If

$$\sum_{i=1}^{n} w_i s_i > w_{n+1},$$

then r is 1; otherwise r is 0. A pseudoneural net is a number of interconnected adaptive threshold elements such as the fragment illustrated in Fig. 4b.

A problem for such a net takes the form of discriminating between two (or more) sets of stimulus patterns—those for which the correct response is 1 and those for which the correct response is 0. If the net has a large enough capacity, there may exist a set of weights such that, for every input stimulus, the net will produce the correct response. To find such a set of weights, stimulus patterns are presented

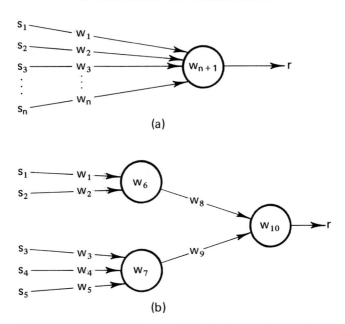

(a)

(b)

Fig. 4. (a) A threshold element; (b) a simple pseudoneural net.

to the neural net and, depending upon the correctness of the response, the weights are adjusted so as to reinforce the net either posi-
tively or negatively.

It has been proven that, if a net has the capability of discriminating
between two sets of stimulus patterns, certain simple reinforcement
rules will eventually lead to a correct assignment of weights. However, the training sequence required to arrive at a correct assignment
of weights may be arbitrarily long.

Adaptive pseudoneural nets can be viewed as the type of problem
solver depicted in Fig. 1. The external representation of a problem is
the two sets of stimulus patterns—those for which the correct response
is 0 and those for which the correct response is 1. The internal representation of the problem is the values assigned to weights of the
adaptive threshold elements, since the values of these weights determine the response for any particular stimulus. In general, different
weight assignments cause a net to discriminate between different sets
of stimulus patterns. The single problem-solving technique employed
by the adaptive net is the calculation of the final response from the
input according to the weights. Each reinforcement of the weights
changes the internal representation of the problem, and hopefully,
after a sufficiently large number of reinforcements, the weights will

have values that cause the method to perform the correct discrimination.

INTERNAL REPRESENTATION

In focusing on internal representation, we look for one that permits many different problems to be expressed in it. In addition, the internal representation should have a simple formal structure so that problem-solving techniques that process the internal representation can be programmed. The first-order predicate calculus is a general, formal system for expressing problems and, as such, is a good candidate for the internal representation of a general solver. In many cases, the formulation of problems in the predicate calculus is somewhat clumsy. But the structure of this calculus is specific enough so that several programs that attempt to prove theorems expressed in the predicate calculus have been implemented (Davis and Putman, 1960; Friedman, 1963; Gilmore, 1960; Robinson, 1963, 1965; Wang, 1960, 1961; Wos et al., 1964).

It is known that no mechanical proof procedure for the first-order predicate calculus can guarantee an answer in a finite amount of time. However, the proof procedures have undergone successive reductions and purifications, so that by now they have a simple and definite structure. The internal representation of some recent theorem provers, such as in Robinson (1965), and their proof process is described on pp. 164–168, since GPS used this formulation in proving a theorem in the predicate calculus.

The predicate calculus can be viewed conveniently as an internal representation because it does not contain information peculiar to any particular task. For example, the tasks for the theorem prover described in Robinson (1963) are taken from group theory and number theory, and the predicate calculus contains no information peculiar to either of these mathematical theories. Similarly, the proof process contains no task-dependent information. The theorem prover in Robinson contains a single rule of inference that combines two predicate calculus statements to form a new statement. A theorem is proved by assuming the negation of the theorem and inferring a contradiction.

Most of the work in theorem-proving programs in the predicate calculus has focused on the problem of attaining proof. However, there has been some effort, identified mainly with work on the Advice Taker (McCarthy, 1959), to extend the domain of problems for which the predicate calculus can be used as a representation. This work has focused on problems on everyday reasoning and so far has

English	Internal Representation

CORPUS:

I am at the desk.	AT(I, DESK)
The desk is at home.	AT(DESK, HOME)
If x is at y and y is at z, then x is at z.	AT(X, Y), AT(Y, Z) → AT(X, Z)

QUESTION:

| Am I at home? | AT(I, HOME) |

(a)

| If desk is at home, I am at home. | AT(DESK, HOME) → AT(I, HOME) |

(b)

Fig. 5. (a) A simple problem for Black's program; (b) a "conditional statement" deduced by the program in finding a solution to (a).

been limited to toy problems. An example is a program by Black (1964). Figure 5 is a simple problem that might be posed to Black's program.

A problem statement consists of (1) a "corpus," which is a set of "unconditional statements" and "conditional statements" (statements that contain the symbol "→"), and (2) a "question," which is an unconditional statement. The external representation of Black's program is very similar to its internal representation, and the translation from one to the other is simple.

Black's program can deduce a new statement from a "conditional statement" and an "unconditional statement." For example, to solve the problem in Fig. 5a, the program would substitute I for X and HOME for Z in the third statement. From the first and third statements it would deduce the statement in Fig. 5b. The problem would be solved by deducing the question from the statement in Fig. 5b and the second statement in Fig. 5a.

PROBLEM-SOLVING TECHNIQUES

As the third alternative, we can focus on the techniques used to solve problems, ignoring temporarily both what internal representation will be used and the translation of the original problem into it. There may be many highly particular techniques; alternatively, the techniques may be small in number with wide applicability. We shall consider an example of each possibility. The latter one, heuristic search, provides the basis of the approach of this research.

PROGRAMMING LANGUAGES. From the user's point of view a computer is a problem solver, consisting of a set of specific techniques (its operations and subroutines) plus a language for determining the circumstances in which each technique is to be applied. Should we also view such a system as a problem solver in the sense of Fig. 1? The external representation would be the program as written by the user; and the translator would perform both the translation of the program and data into internal form and the interpretation of the user's program. The reaction is generally negative. We feel that the user specifies to the computer not only "what" the problem is, but "how" it is to be solved. As support for this we note that programs are given in the imperative mode, whereas problems are given primarily in the declarative mode. (There is usually one statement that commands findings or solving.) Furthermore, we feel that many of the instructions in a program can be eliminated without withdrawing any information that is essential to the specification of the problem that the program solves.

These feelings deserve critical examination. For instance, a problem solver (in the sense of Fig. 1) surely derives its behavior— that is, "how" it attempts to solve the problem—from the external representation of the problem. Its behavior does not totally determine the external behavior, of course, since its internal structure plays an equally important role. But the same is to be said of the program— the total behavior of the system is determined jointly by the user's program and the internal structure of the system (the raw computer plus translators plus subroutines).

More revealing is the evolution of systems (i.e., computers with programming languages), starting with machine language, then assembly language, procedure-oriented languages such as ALGOL, ALGOL plus subroutines libraries, and on toward problem-oriented languages. Each of these systems remains clearly in the domain of programming languages, but each requires less and less specification to get the same problem solved. In fact, the goal of problem-oriented languages is to eliminate as specification everything that is unnecessary for the problem externally conceived. If this evolution comes close to success, it may be difficult to deny such systems the status of problem solvers.

To illustrate more concretely the relation of a programming language to problem-solving techniques, consider the programming language, GPL [Game Playing Language in Williams (1965)*], that was designed for expressing procedures for playing board games and card games. The specifications of a game in GPL consist of (1) data structures that describe the objects used in playing the game, and (2) a procedure for playing the game. For example, the specification of tic-tac-toe consists of a description of a tic-tac-toe board that is initially empty and the following procedure, expressed in GPL, for playing the game:

1. *If* there is a winning move, *then* make it;
   else

2. *If* there is a winning move for the opponent,
   then block the opponent by making the move;
   else

3. Make any legal move.

This procedure contains a definition of the legal moves of tic-tac-toe as well as a simple strategy for playing the game.

GPL is designed so that games can be described in it as briefly as they are described in a book of Hoyle, such as Morehead and Mott-Smith (1963). Strategy statements like "make a winning move" can also be specified briefly in GPL because the ability to search a board for a particular pattern is a primitive operation of the language. In the tic-tac-toe example, a winning pattern is a rank, file, or diagonal that has X's (or O's as the case may be) on two squares and nothing on the third square. Thus, the primitives of GPL are general problem-solving techniques for card and board games, and they can be combined readily to form a specialized problem-solving technique for a particular game.

DEDUCOM (Slagle, 1965) is another work that confounds the distinction between programming and problem solving. In many respects, DEDUCOM is similar to Black's program, discussed earlier. In part, the specification of a problem for DEDUCOM is a group of linguistic expressions that are combined to form new expressions during problem solving. However, the specification of a problem may also contain LISP (McCarthy *et al.*, 1963) expressions (which are programs) freely intermixed with other expressions. When they occur as sub-expressions within a linguistic expression, they are executed by the standard LISP interpreter. When they contain linguistic expressions

---

° An interpreter for GPL has been implemented in IPL-V.

as subparts, interpretation is held up until the linguistic expressions can be solved. Consequently, the problem-solving power of DEDUCOM stems in part from the power of the LISP interpreter and in part from the freedom never to distinguish whether one is programming or specifying a problem.

HEURISTIC SEARCH. A final way to focus on the generality of a problem-solving technique is first to find a paradigm of a problem and then develop methods that are applicable to the paradigm. The generality of the paradigm determines the generality of the methods that are applicable to the paradigm. The paradigm need not imply a uniform representation of problems, but only that all problems that fit the paradigm have some common structure.

One general paradigm, which we shall call *heuristic search* (Newell and Ernst, 1965), consists of two basic kinds of entities—operators and objects. An operator, when applied to an object, produces a new object or indicates inapplicability. A heuristic-search problem is:

> Given: An initial situation represented as an object.
> A desired situation represented as an object.
> A set of operators.
>
> Find: A sequence of operators that will transform
> the initial situation into the desired situation.

The first operator of the solution sequence is applied to the initial situation, the other operators are applied to the result of the application of the preceding operator, and the result of the application of the last operator in the sequence is the desired situation.

The operators are rules for generating objects and thus define a tree of objects. Each node of the tree represents an object, and each branch from a node represents the application of an operator to the object represented by the node. The node to which a branch leads represents the object produced by the application of the operator. In Fig. 6, for example, node $A1$ represents the object $A1$, and branch $X5$ from $A1$ represents the application of the operator $X5$ to $A1$ which produces the object $A5$.

A method for solving a heuristic search problem is searching the tree defined by the initial situation and the operators for a path from the initial situation to the desired situation. For example, if a problem has $A0$ as the initial situation and $X1$, $X2$, . . . as operators, the problem can be solved by searching the tree in Fig. 6 for a path from the top node to the desired situation. If the problem's desired situation is $A7$, a solution is $(X1, X5, X3)$ (others might exist).

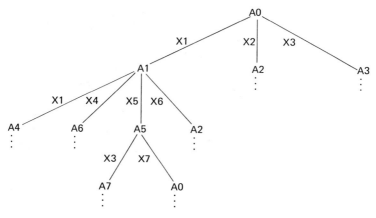

Fig. 6. A typical object tree defined by a simple heuristic-search problem.

An operator can, in general, be applied only to certain objects; it is infeasible to apply it to others. For example, in arithmetic it is feasible to apply the operator

$$x + y = y + x, \tag{1}$$

in which x and y are variables, to the object

$$2 + 5.$$

In the extreme case, each operator of a task could be applicable to only a single object. For example, the commutativity of addition could be represented as the list of expressions

$$1 + 2 = 2 + 1 \tag{2}$$
$$1 + 3 = 3 + 1 \tag{3}$$

and so on, assuming that numbers are bounded. Each expression such as (2) and (3) is considered a separate operator, even though they all perform the same function. In general, an operator is any function whose domain and range are objects, provided that the function is represented as a *single entity* (e.g., a single routine, a single data structure, etc.). The reason for this unusual definition of operators is that the problem solvers process representations, not what is represented. Thus, in applying the commutativity of addition represented as the list (2), (3), and so on, a problem solver must match the input object to the left side of many different operators in order to find the feasible member. On the other hand, when the commutativity of addition is represented as (1), the input object need only be matched to

$$x + y.$$

The effectiveness of a heuristic-search problem solver is determined by its rules for selecting operators to be tried (rules for guiding the search). There are two basic criteria for selecting operators:

Desirability The operator should produce an object that is similar to the desired situation.

Feasibility The operator should be applicable to its input object.

The problem solver must face the dilemma that in general only one of these criteria can be satisfied; i.e., operators that are seemingly desirable are infeasible.

Some problem solvers that use heuristic search insist on the perfect desirability of operators; i.e., only those operators that produce the object desired are applied. Such problem solvers do not search the tree defined by the initial situation and the operator for the desired situation, but, rather, search the tree defined by the inverse operators and the desired situation for the initial situation. (Q' is the inverse of the operator Q, if $Q(A) = A'$ implies that $Q'(A') = A$ for all A and A'.) In this case, the problem solver works "backwards" and the desirability of the "forward problem" is nothing more than the feasibility of the backward problem. In general, there can be no gain in such a formulation because the backward, backward problem is the original forward problem. But for particular problems working in one direction can be considerably easier than working in the other direction, because the space to be searched is smaller.

Many different problems can be formulated in the heuristic-search model, and it provides the underlying conceptual framework of many problem-solving programs. All of the early game-playing programs and theorem-proving programs use the heuristic-search model. We give below brief discussions of several efforts to indicate how widespread the paradigm is. To do this we need the following generalization of the heuristic search paradigm:

The initial situation may be more than one object that can be represented by an object schema* or a list of objects and object schemas.

* A schema is an expression containing variables. An instance of the schema can be obtained by the substitution of constants for variables.

The desired situation may be more than one object. It can be represented by an object schema, a list of objects and object schemas, by a more complex description, or by a testing procedure that can recognize it.

The operators may be given by schemas.

Some of the operators may have several objects as an input or may produce several objects as output.

The solution to the problem may be more complex than the simple sequence of operators described above. For example, if an operator has several objects as an output, for each output object, a sequence of operators that transforms it into the desired situation may be required. In this case, the solution is a tree of operators.

1. Chess. Playing chess is an example of a problem that can easily be cast into the heuristic search paradigm. The initial situation is the chess position at the point of play, and the operators are the legal chess moves. The desired situation is a chess position in which the opponent is checkmated. The move to be made from the initial position is the first move in the solution sequence.

To find such a move involves exploring the tree of possibilities. That is, for any move, explore the possibilities that are available to the opponent, and for each of these, explore the possible responses, etc. This tree is so large that for most chess positions it is not possible to find a forced checkmate. However, exploring the tree does reveal important features hidden in a chess position and is a powerful method for evaluating a chess position.

Several programs that play chess (Baylor and Simon, 1966; Bernstein *et al.*, 1958; Greenblatt *et al.*, 1967; Kister *et al.*, 1957; Kotok, 1962; Newell, *et al.*, 1958) have been constructed. All of them use as their basic problem-solving technique searching the tree defined by the initial chess position and the legal chess moves. These programs do not look for a checkmate but instead look for good positions. The goodness of a chess position is determined by an evaluation function that is designed to rate a position according to standard features, e.g., material advantage, mobility, center control, and so on. Some programs have more elaborate evaluation functions than others, and some use heuristic rules to guide the search. But all of the programs play chess by generating possible chess positions and using an evaluating function to determine the goodness of the position.

2. *Other games.* In addition to chess programs, there exist several other game-playing programs that use heuristic search; one plays checkers (Samuel, 1959, 1967); one plays Kahla (McCarthy, 1966); one plays three dimensional tic-tac-toe (Gilbert, 1966); and one plays five-in-a-row (Weizenbaum, 1962). The framework of all of these programs is quite similar to that of the chess programs. The game positions are the objects and the legal moves are the operators. The initial situation is the initial game position, and the desired situation is a class of objects. The desired situation is, in general, too remote and the program looks for a good move instead. A small part of the tree defined by the initial situation and the operators is searched, and the best move is determined by using an evaluation function and a minimax procedure.

3. *Proposition calculus.* LT [Logic Theory Machine, Newell *et al.* (1957a)] proves theorems in the sentential calculus of Whitehead and Russell. The initial situation is a set of objects, each of which represents an axiom or a previously proved theorem. Each object is a group of primitive propositions combined according to the logical connectives negation ($\sim$), conjunction ($\vee$), disjunction ($\wedge$), and implication ($\supset$). The desired situation is an object that represents the theorem to be proven. The operators are the rules of inference:

a. *Modus ponens* From A and $A \supset B$, B can be inferred.

b. *Syllogism* From $A \supset B$ and $B \supset C$, $A \supset C$ can be inferred.

(A, B, C are variables for which propositions can be substituted.) LT does not work forward but instead searches for a member of the initial situation in the tree defined by the desired situation and the inverse of the operators.

4. *Geometry.* Many of the theorems found in a high school Euclidian geometry textbook can be proven by the Geometry Machine (Gelernter, 1959), a program that uses heuristic search. Like LT, it also works backwards. The initial situation is a set of objects, each of which represents an axiom or a premise of the theorem to be proven, e.g., *angle ABC equals angle ABD*. The conclusion of the theorem to be proven is the desired situation. Those theorems accepted as already proven are the operators. Theorems are proven by working backwards. Consider, for example, the desired situation that triangle *ABC* and triangle *EFG* are congruent. The inverse of the oper-

ator—if the three corresponding sides of two triangles are equal, then the triangles are congruent—could be applied to the desired situation, producing three new objects:

> segment *AB* equals segment *EF*;
> segment *BC* equals segment *FG*;
> segment *CA* equals segment *GE*.

Each of these three objects must be inferred from the axioms and the premises of the theorem in order for the theorem to be proven.

All the inverse operators have a single object as an input and one or more objects as an output. In this formulation a proof is not a simple path from the desired situation to the initial situation. Instead, it is a tree in which (1) the top node is the desired situation; (2) all of the terminal nodes are objects that are members of the set of objects representing the initial situation; and (3) the immediate subnodes of a node represent the objects produced by the application of an inverse operator to the object represented by the node.

5. *Integration.* SAINT (Slagle, 1963) is a computer program that integrates expressions symbolically. The initial situation is the expression to be integrated, and the desired situation is a set of objects, each of which represents a standard integral form. The operators are "heuristic transformations" for changing the form of an object. One of the operators, for example, is the substitution of tan *u* for *x* in an object in which *x* is the variable of integration. If the initial situation were

$$\int \frac{dx}{1 + x^2},$$

the application of this operator to it would result in the new object

$$\int du.$$

In applying an operator SAINT automatically performs "algorithm-like transformations" such as algebraic simplification and differentiation.

6. *Programming.* Amarel (1962) developed a program that constructs programs in a highly task-oriented programming language. The objects are flow-diagram schemas—flow diagrams in which some of the actions might be variables. The operators are rules for flow-diagram modification—substitution of a specific action or an "elementary" flow-diagram schema for a variable action in a flow-diagram schema.

The program to be constructed is described by listing all its inputs along with their corresponding outputs; thus, the desired situation is an object that, when executed on the inputs, produces the corresponding outputs. (There are special mechanisms to deal with the facts that some of the actions may be variables and that there may be a large number of input–output pairs.)

7. *Everyday reasoning.* Even some of the research efforts focusing on internal representation use heuristic search as their basic problem solving method. Black's program (described on pp. 13–14) treats "unconditional statements" as objects and "conditional statements" as operators. The desired situation is the "question," and the initial situation is the set of "unconditional statements" in the "corpus."

Black's program works backwards. The inverse operators all have a single object for an input and produce one or more objects as a result of their application. For this reason a solution is not a simple path from the desired situation to the initial situation, but a tree that has the same form as a solution found by the Geometry Machine.

8. *Predicate calculus.* The proof process of some programs that prove theorems in the first-order predicate calculus (e.g., the one described on pp. 164–168) can be viewed as heuristic search. The objects are statements and the single rule of inference is the only operator. The initial situation is the set of statements whose conjunction is the negation of the theorem to be proven. The desired situation is a contradictory statement.

The operator has two objects as an input and produces a single object as a result. The input objects must be in the set of objects representing the initial situation or be the result of a previous application of the operator.

9. *Story algebra problems.* STUDENT's only problem solving technique is an algorithm for solving a set of simultaneous equations symbolically (see p. 11). Thus, STUDENT does not use heuristic search. However, the problem of solving a set of simultaneous equations can be formulated easily as a heuristic-search problem by treating the equations as objects and algebraic manipulations as operators.*

GPS. All of the programs discussed above use heuristic search because it is a convenient framework for the particular problem, not because it is a general paradigm for solving problems. GPS, on the other hand, is an attempt to implement problem-solving techniques that have general applicability to heuristic search problems. GPS uses the heuristic search paradigm directly; a problem is given to GPS in terms of objects and operators.

* This formulation is used in Krulee and Kuck (1964).

GPS attempts problems by tree search, as in any heuristic search program. But GPS employs a general technique called means–ends analysis to guide the search, which involves subdividing a problem into easier subproblems. Means–ends analysis is accomplished by taking differences between what is given and what is wanted, e.g., between two objects, or between an object and the class of objects to which an operator can be applied. A difference designates some feature of an object that is incorrect. GPS uses the difference to select a desirable operator—one that is relevant to reducing the difference. For example, in attempting the original problem, GPS detects a difference, if one exists, between the initial situation and the desired situation. Assuming that a desirable operator exists and that it can be applied to the initial situation, GPS applies the operator to the initial situation, which results in a new object. GPS rephrases the original problem by replacing the initial situation with the new object and then recycles. As usual, the problem is solved when an object is generated that is identical to the desired situation.

If an operator is not applicable to an object, an attempt to apply it will result in a difference—the reason it is not applicable. If the difference is not too difficult, GPS will attempt to alleviate the difference in the same way that it attempts to reduce a difference between two objects. If the attempt to reduce the difference is success-

(a) Initial Situation: $(R \supset \sim P) \cdot (\sim R \supset Q)$

     Desired Situation: $\sim(\sim Q \cdot P)$

(b) Operators:

     R1 $A \vee B \to B \vee A, A \cdot B \to B \cdot A$

     R2 $A \supset B \to \sim B \supset \sim A$

     R3 $A \vee A \leftrightarrow A, A \cdot A \leftrightarrow A$

     R4 $A \vee (B \vee C) \leftrightarrow (A \vee B) \vee C, A \cdot (B \cdot C) \leftrightarrow (A \cdot B) \cdot C$

     R5 $A \vee B \leftrightarrow \sim(\sim A \cdot \sim B)$

     R6 $A \supset B \leftrightarrow \sim A \vee B$

     R7 $A \vee (B \cdot C) \leftrightarrow (A \vee B) \cdot (A \vee C), A \cdot (B \vee C) \leftrightarrow (A \cdot B) \vee (A \cdot C)$

     R8 $A \cdot B \to A, A \cdot B \to B$

     R9 $A \to A \vee X$ (X is any expression)

     R10 $[A, B] \to A \cdot B$ (Two expressions input)

     R11 $[A \supset B, A] \to B$ (Two expressions input)

     R12 $[A \supset B, B \supset C] \to A \supset C$ (Two expressions input)

Fig. 7. A problem in propositional calculus solved by GPS: (a) problem statement; (b) information given to GPS in addition to the problem; (c) internal representation of the initial situation; (d) internal representation of the first part of operator R1.

(b, cont.)   Difference Ordering:

TABLE-OF-CONNECTIONS

Difference ordering	R1	R2	R3	R4	R5	R6	R7	R8	R9	R10	R11	R12
Add variables									X	X		X
Decrease variables								X			X	X
Increase number of variables			X				X		X	X		X
Decrease number of variables			X				X				X	X
Change connective					X	X	X					
Change sign		X			X	X						
Change grouping				X			X					
Change position	X	X										

(c)

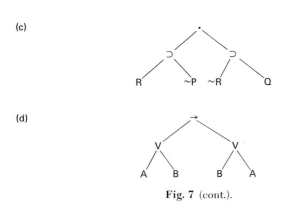

(d)

Fig. 7 (cont.).

ful, a new object will be produced and, hopefully, the operator can be applied to the new object.

Previous versions of GPS solved several tasks. The first task was a formulation of proving theorems in the propositional calculus designed by Moore and Anderson (1954). Figure 7a shows a typical problem that GPS solved. In addition to the problem statement in Fig. 7a, GPS was given the information in Fig. 7b (called the task environment). The differences are ordered according to their relative difficulty; there is a Table of Connections that associates with each difference those operators (rules of inference) that are relevant to reducing it. The objects and operators are represented by schemas. Figure 7c illustrates the internal representation of an object and Fig. 7d illustrates the internal representation of an operator.

Another task solved by a previous version of GPS is the Missionaries and Cannibals task (stated in Chapter I). The objects were configurations of people on the river banks and were represented by schemas. The operators, which moved people across the river, could not be completely represented by schemas; instead they were represented by expressions together with a special routine that interpreted the semantics of the expression. For example, the expression

L: MC

represents the operator that moved one missionary, one cannibal, and the boat from the right bank to the left bank. Given an object and this expression, the special routine created a new object in which one missionary, one cannibal, and the boat were moved across the river. The new object would be produced only if the boat was originally on the right bank and if no missionaries would be eaten, etc. One disadvantage of using a special routine is that its construction requires knowledge of the internal structure of GPS.

The only other task given to GPS previous to this report is a task found in a psychological experiment designed to investigate the mathematical ability of children (approximately age 7). The problem is to transform one string of *I*'s and *O*'s into another by

    a.   adding two *I*'s to the right end of the string;

    b.   adding two *O*'s to the right end of the string;

    c.   deleting one *I*;

    d.   deleting one *O*.

GPS solved the problem of transforming

IOIIOIOOI

into

IOOIOOOII.

The objects are the strings of *I*'s and *O*'s, which were represented by schemas. The operators are the rules for modifying the strings and were also represented by schemas.

Several tasks have been formulated for GPS but never carried through to completion. Proving trigonometric identities was proposed and hand simulated (Newell *et al.*, 1960a). The problem of balancing an assembly line [the task solved by another heuristic program (Tonge, 1961)] was formulated in terms of GPS (Tonge, 1963). A formulation for GPS of the problem of discovering a good set of differences for a task was proposed in Newell *et al.* (1960b).

Two programs have been constructed that have deliberately adapted the problem-solving techniques of GPS to a particular task.*

1. Heuristic Compiler. The Heuristic Compiler (Simon, 1963) is a program that constructs programs in IPL-V. It consists of three basic parts, each of which corresponds to a GPS task environment (a type of task for GPS). A description of one, the State Description Compiler, is sufficient to illustrate how the problem-solving techniques of GPS can be applied to a programming task.

In the state description of a programming task, the initial situation is the list of cells affected by the execution of the program together with the contents of each cell prior to execution. The desired situation is the contents of the affected cells after the execution of the program. For example, Fig. 8a represents the programming task of replacing the contents of the SIGNAL-CELL by MINUS. (IPL-V is a list-processing language and PUSHDOWN 1 represents the second symbol on the list, SIGN-CELL.) In Fig. 8b, PUSHDOWN 1 and SYMB 1 represent an arbitrary symbol. An operator is a previously compiled routine and is represented by a list of the cells affected by its execution together with the contents of these cells before and after its execution, e.g., the operator shown in Fig. 8b.

In attempting to construct the program represented in Fig. 8a, the Heuristic Compiler notices the difference that the contents of the SIGNAL-CELL is not MINUS. According to its TABLE-OF-CONNECTIONS, the operator shown in Fig. 8b is relevant to reducing this difference. After substituting MINUS for SYMB 2, so that the operator will perform a desirable function, the Heuristic Compiler notices that the operator cannot be applied because of the difference that the contents of the ACCUMULATOR is not MINUS. This difference is reduced by applying the operator in Fig. 8c after substituting MINUS for SYMB 1. The

---

* Recently a GPS-like program has been developed in FORTRAN (Quinlan and Hunt, 1968). The program has been used on a variety of tasks in logic, algebra, and inequalities. The performance appears to be quite impressive. Both the generality and the power of the program imply that it will be highly relevant to the questions that the present case study with GPS attempts to bring out.

The problem statement:

(a) Affected cell   SIGNAL-CELL
        Input   SYMB1, PUSHDOWN1
        Output   MINUS, PUSHDOWN1

Operators:

(b) Affected cell   ACCUMULATOR   CELL1
        Input   SYMB2, PUSHDOWN1   SYMB1, PUSHDOWN2
        Output   PUSHDOWN1   SYMB2, PUSHDOWN2

(c) Affected cell   ACCUMULATOR
        Input   PUSHDOWN1
        Output   SYMB1

Fig. 8. Heuristic compiler formulation of the problem of setting the SIGNAL-CELL to be MINUS: (a) state description of the task; (b) and (c) state descriptions of two previously compiled routines.

operator in Fig. 8b can be applied to the resulting object and the task is solved.

2. Binary-Choice experiment. In the Binary-Choice task, the subject is asked to predict which of two events will occur in each of a series of trials. The subject is told which event occurs after he makes his prediction. A program that uses the problem-solving methods of GPS was constructed to simulate human behavior in the Binary-Choice experiment (Feldman *et al.*, 1963). The assumption underlying this simulation is that the subject is entertaining hypotheses about the patterns of events that have occurred. (In fact, the experimenter normally uses a randomly generated sequence.)

The objects of this task are hypotheses about the pattern of events and the operators are rules for forming hypotheses according to the actual sequence of events. The differences are features of hypotheses, which, according to the actual sequence of events, seem to be incorrect. Thus, the GPS methods are not used to predict events but to form a model of the environment that is used to predict events.

POSING A PROBLEM OF GENERALITY

As we have seen, there are several quite distinct approaches to constructing a problem solver with some degree of generality. Their diversity underscores the fact that the decision to work with GPS entails selecting a particular approach: one that derives its appeal from the wide applicability of heuristic search, but that ignores, by and large, the way problems are represented externally or internally. The importance of the internal representation will become evident in what follows. Nevertheless, the internal representation used in GPS was chosen *ad hoc,* within the framework of the problem-solving techniques to be used, and not as the primary consideration in implementing GPS.

It is clear that generality has to do with the size of the domain of problems that can be handled by a problem solver. Still it is not enough to specify just the problem domain in evaluating the generality of a program. It is the purpose of this section to clarify some of the additional considerations so that we can finally state a meaningful problem of generality.

AMOUNT OF SPECIFICATION

If we were to take seriously that generality is defined by the domain of problems that are solvable, then many perfectly general problem solvers exist: Turing Machines, ALGOL compilers, etc. But the generality of a Turing Machine (for example) stems from the fact that the amount of information in the specification of a problem to a Turing Machine is not limited. For example, the problem of playing perfect chess could be represented by all possible chess positions together with the best move for each position. It is theoretically possible to give this information to a Turing Machine, since the number of different chess positions is finite. But this specification, being impractical, does not qualify a Turing Machine as a chess player.

The advantage that ALGOL has over a Turing Machine (or an assembly language) is most problems of interest can be specified more briefly in ALGOL. Consider the problem of evaluating a polynomial. To describe this problem to a Turing Machine, it would be necessary also to describe numerical operations (multiplication, addition, etc.). The problem can be specified in ALGOL by a single declarative statement. The information in the specification of a problem determines whether the problem solving is done endogenously or exogenously. In describing the evaluation of a polynomial to a Turing Machine most of the problem-solving techniques were contained in the specification of the problem. On the other hand, an ALGOL translator has built into it problem-solving techniques that are sufficient to evaluate polynomials.

Thus, the generality of a problem solver must be defined relative to the amount of information it takes to specify a problem. An ALGOL translator would appear to be more general than an assembly language or a Turing Machine because in ALGOL problems can be described in terms of more sophisticated concepts such as iteration statements.

Problems are specified in terms of the concepts built into the problem solver. In constructing a general problem solver, we face the dilemma that the concepts built into it should be both sophisticated and general. The sophistication of the concepts allows the problem specification to be brief, while the generality of the concepts allows them to be useful in specifying more than one problem. Chess programs, for example, contain the concept of playing chess, and the problem of finding a move for a particular chess position is specified by specifying the chess position. Although the concept of playing chess is a very sophisticated concept, it is also very specialized. The concept of playing a game on a chess board is a more general concept; both chess and checkers could be specified in terms of this concept. However, the specification of chess in terms of a game on a chess board would necessarily include the definition of the legal chess moves as well as the chess position.

We know of no way to determine, for any particular task, what information should be built into the problem solver and what information should be contained in the specification of the task. But clearly this issue is relevant to the evaluation of a general problem solver.

QUALITY OF PROBLEM SOLVING

An outstanding property of the various efforts to construct a general problem solver is that the quality of the problem solving suffers as the generality of the problem solver is increased. For example, the best chess program (Greenblatt *et al.*, 1967) in existence plays a good* game of chess. Although GPS can attempt more than one kind of problem, the only kinds of problem that it can solve are much easier than chess. The representation in GPS of the chess board and the legal chess moves would be cumbersome, and GPS's problem-solving techniques are not sufficient to play even poor chess.

The power of a problem solver is determined by the effectiveness of its problem-solving techniques, while its generality is determined by the domain of problems to which the techniques are applicable. Each technique requires that certain information be abstracted from the internal representation. The techniques are applicable if pro-

---

* It has been rated a class D player (with a chess rating of 1400) after playing several correspondence tournaments. This is good enough to beat most casual players.

cesses can be found that abstract the necessary information from the internal representation. For example, one of the requirements of the techniques of GPS is that in attempting to apply an operator to an object, a new object is produced if the operator is applicable to the object; otherwise, a difference is produced. Thus, there must be a process that given the internal representation of an operator and an object, will produce either a difference or an object, depending on the applicability of the operator to the object.

The internal representation is pulled in two directions: on the one hand, it must be general so that problems can be translated into it; on the other hand, it must be specific enough for the problem-solving techniques to be applicable. Thus, there are many different generality problems—one for each set of problem-solving techniques. The difficulty of a particular generality problem depends upon the variety and complexity of the techniques. If this were not the case, a problem solver more general than any in existence could be constructed by using a natural language for its internal representation and giving it no problem solving techniques. Of course, it would never solve a problem, no matter how trivial, but it would be very general.

More cogently, it would be much easier to achieve generality with a problem solver that did only forward search (by applying the operators in a fixed order) than with GPS. Conversely, it would be more difficult to achieve the level of generality that we have achieved with GPS for a problem solver that is more adequate than GPS.

ROLE OF REPRESENTATION

A problem is expressed quite differently for different problem solvers. For example, a story algebra problem is expressed in English for STUDENT. A story algebra problem can also be expressed in the first-order predicate calculus or as a heuristic-search problem in terms of objects and operators. Although in some sense each of these formulations represents the same problem, are they really the same? A human presented with these formulations would probably exhibit considerably different behavior in finding a solution for each, and would probably not reconize that they were really the same problem.

More generally, changes in the representation of a problem can have problem-solving significance. To choose a simple example, each of the lines below is simply a different representation of a quadratic equation, but the first poses a problem, and the last does not.

find x such that $x^2 - 2x - 8 = 0$
$$x^2 - 2x + 1 = 9$$
$$(x - 1)^2 = 9$$
$$x - 1 = +3, -3$$
$$x = +4, -2$$

One is tempted to assert that each different representation is a different problem and that there is no way to compare different problem solvers that make use of different internal representations. While this is clearly too pessimistic, it does indicate the wisdom of confining a study of generality to the case study of a single problem solver with a single representation.

SUMMARY

A meaningful problem for this research can finally be formulated—to extend the generality of GPS while holding its power at a fixed level. This involves extending the internal representation of GPS in such a way that its problem-solving methods remain applicable and in a way that increases the domain of problems that can be translated into its internal representation. Thus, this research is mainly concerned with representational issues. We would not expect the issues to be the same in generalizing the internal representation of a problem solver that employed different techniques than those of GPS. In this respect, this research has the nature of a case study.

Two other representational issues were discussed in this section: (1) the amount of information that is required to specify a problem; and (2) which of several equivalent representations is a neutral representation of a problem. These issues, although important, are only secondary concerns of this research. The primary concerns are to discover the way in which the problem-solving techniques interact with the internal representation, and to learn something about the properties of a good internal representation for the problem-solving techniques of GPS.

Let us recapitulate the outline of this monograph, now that the task is clear. Chapter III describes the problem-solving techniques of GPS and Chapter IV the generalized internal representation. We keep these quite distinct so that we can hold the techniques constant, so to speak, while modifying the internal representation to meet the demands of generality. In Chapter V, the interaction between the internal representation and the techniques is illustrated by examining the nature of modifications necessary to get GPS to work on different tasks. Chapter VI describes the different tasks actually given to GPS;

these illustrate the generality of GPS as well as its power. Finally, Chapter VII provides a conclusion and summary.

HISTORY OF GPS

Since this report is concerned intensively with GPS, a brief description of the different versions of GPS is appropriate.* GPS grew out of the Logic Theory Machine (described on p. 21), a program for proving theorems in the sentential calculus of Whitehead and Russell. The first version, called GPS-1 was coded in IPL-IV for JOHNIAC, a Princeton class computer at the RAND Corporation. All of the other versions have been coded in IPL-V (Newell *et al.*, 1961). The successor of GPS-1, called GPS-2-1, was similar to GPS-1 functionally, but the program was organized quite differently. The change to GPS-2-2, the next version of GPS, involved smaller organizational changes but required a separate designation since, for a short period, both versions were operational. This version is rather completely documented (Newell, 1963).

GPS-2-3 changed the internal representation. Objects and operators were now represented by description lists—attribute–values pairs— instead of by conventional lists, which were used in previous versions. GPS-2-4 was obtained by revising the mechanism for testing the identity of two data structures. In the predecessors of GPS-2-4, there were several *ad hoc* processes for testing whether two data structures of a particular type were identical, e.g., two goals or two objects. In GPS-2-4 these *ad hoc* processes were replaced by a general process for testing the identity of any two data structures regardless of whether they were goals, objects, or whatever.†

GPS-2-5 introduced a language for describing problem-solving methods that allowed the application of a method to be monitored by the problem-solving executive. Thus it incorporated both a major change in internal representation and in problem-solving organization over GPS-2-2.

The version of the program used in this research started with GPS-2-5. The problem-solving structure was not altered, but the internal representation was generalized under the impact of new tasks. Al-

---

* The following is the primary published material either describing GPS or discussing its use in the simulation of cognitive processes; Ernst and Newell (1966, 1967); Newell (1962a, 1962b, 1963); Newell *et al.*, (1957b, 1960a, 1960b, 1962); and Newell and Simon (1961a, 1961b, 1961c).

† This process is described on pp. 48–50.

though this current version should be called GPS-2-6, for expediency it is called simply GPS.

All the IPL-V versions of GPS (GPS-2-1 to GPS-2-5) were run on the IBM 7090. The current version has been run on the CDC G21, a machine with 65K of 32-bit memory (requiring two words per IPL symbol).

GPS was produced by five successive modifications of GPS-2-1 over a five-year period (and still contains parts of the original code). Some of the programming conventions have become confusing and a significant portion of the code is *ad hoc*. This makes description more difficult and muddies somewhat the lessons to be drawn from generalizing GPS-2-5. In fact, there now seems little further profit in continuing with this version rather than constructing an entirely new GPS program.

A certain degree of success has been guaranteed because the previous versions of GPS had moderate problem-solving capabilities. On the other hand, serious programming difficulties had already been encountered, and modification could be expected to introduce more. Consequently, no high expectations were held for the power of the problem solving to be shown by GPS across many tasks.

One serious limitation on the expected performance of GPS is the size of the program and the size of its rather elaborate data structure. The program itself occupies a significant portion of the computer memory, and the generation of new data structures during problem solving quickly exhausts the remaining memory. Thus, GPS is designed to solve only modest problems whose representation is not too elaborate. Although larger computer memories would alleviate the extravagances of GPS's use of memory, conceptual difficulties would still remain. Some of these are touched on later (pp. 117–120).

CHAPTER III

THE PROBLEM-SOLVING STRUCTURE OF GPS

The structure of GPS exhibits the simple scheme of Fig. 1, with its sharp division among external representation, internal representation, and problem-solving techniques. Indeed, it was the separation of internal representation from the problem solving that gave rise initially to the vision of generality and to the name GPS. Now the internal representation is data and the problem-solving techniques are programs, so in one respect they are quite distinct in any event. But the two become welded together firmly if the processes make use of intimate details of the problem being represented. A good example of this is LT, described in the preceding chapter. Its methods embody the rules of inference in the propositional calculus; thus, they are of no use whatsoever in dealing with any other task. In contrast, in GPS all of the methods appear to be content free. There is no way of telling by looking at the problem-solving part of the system what kind of task is being worked on, except for some very general features, such as the fact that objects are being manipulated.

Thus, the description of GPS can be divided into two main parts: the description of the problem-solving techniques, covered in this chapter; and the description of the internal representation, covered in the next chapter. For this chapter all we need to know about the in-

35

ternal representation is that there exists some encoding of objects, operators, and differences.

The third part of the scheme of Fig. 1, the external representation and its translation, has never been of concern in the research on GPS. In order to be clear about what specifications are given to GPS, we shall need an external representation. However, this will mirror the internal representation, and is described as an adjunct to it in Chapter IV.

The problem-solving techniques are organized by goals. That is, the main function of the problem-solving techniques is to achieve goals, and in the process other goals may be generated to which the problem-solving techniques are also applied. Goals, which are discussed in the first section of this chapter, are achieved by applying relevant *methods.** The methods are expressed in a special *method language*, which is described in the second section. The PROBLEM-SOLVING-EXECUTIVE,† described in the third section of this chapter, selects and applies methods. In the last section, each method is described individually.

GOALS

A goal is a data structure that provides sufficient information to carry out problem-solving activity. It defines a desired state of affairs, the current situation, and a history of previous attempts to achieve the goal. Thus, in any context GPS can stop what it is doing and start working on a new goal or on a previous goal, from where it left off. The statement of a problem must be formulated as a GPS goal, and is called TOP-GOAL.

GPS uses only four types of goals (the necessity for others has not arisen):

> *Transform object A into object B.*   To achieve
> this goal a series of objects, which are derived‡

---

* We have used the word *techniques* rather than *method* in the preceding discussion, since the methods in GPS have a special technical definition.

† Words printed in small capitals denote IPL symbols within GPS. These symbols often identify types of data structures; for example, MOVE-OPERATOR is the IPL symbol that identifies a class of operators satisfying certain conventions. The most general terms—e.g., goal, operator, object, and difference—are not so capitalized, since they are used in the text both in general and special ways (though they do have IPL symbols associated with them).

‡ Object A is derived from object B if it is produced by the application of an operator either to B or an object derived from B.

from A, is generated. The final member of the
series is identical to B.

Reduce difference D on object A.   To achieve this
goal GPS produces a new object A', which is derived
from A. The feature of A to which D refers is
modified in A'.

Apply operator Q to object A.   To achieve this
goal a new object is generated by applying Q
to A or some object derived form A.

Goal: Transform object A into object B.

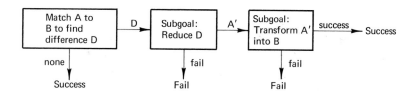

Goal: Reduce difference D between object A and object B.

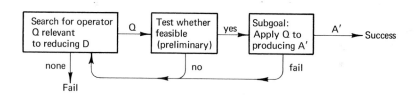

Goal: Apply operator Q to object A.

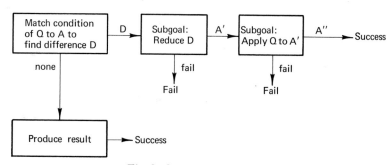

Fig. 9. GPS main methods.

Select the elements of set S which best fulfill criterion C. To achieve this goal an element of S is selected. C is stated with respect to an object; e.g., select the element of S most similar to object A.

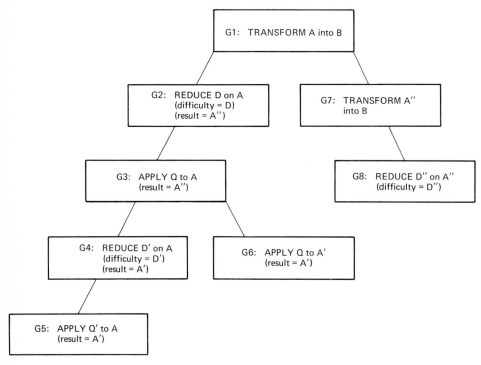

Fig. 10. A typical goal tree, showing the difficulty and the results of the goals.

With each goal there are methods that attempt to attain the goal. In earlier work with GPS only the first three goals, TRANSFORM, REDUCE, and APPLY, were used. In the written descriptions (e.g., Newell *et al.*, 1960a) a flow diagram, shown in Fig. 9, was given to describe the main problem-solving activity. In the present organization, as we shall see in a moment, these three methods are expressed in a method language,* along with a number of additional methods that define GPS's behavior in situations not covered by these main methods—e.g., what to do if all goals have been rejected.

---

* As the TRANSFORM-METHOD, REDUCE-METHOD, and FORM-OPERATOR, METHOD, respectively.

A typical example of how GPS subdivides goals into simpler goals according to the methods of Fig. 9 is represented by the tree of goals in Fig. 10. The original is G1. In attempting to achieve this goal, GPS notices the difference, D, between A and B and creates G2. GPS attempts to modify A by creating G3. The operator Q in not applicable to A, but the difference D' is detected and G4 is created. (Note that D' is related to applying Q, not to the original goal, G1.) G4 is achieved by the solution of G5. GPS then continues working on G3 by creating G6, which uses the result of G4, A'. The successful application of Q to A' results in the solution of G3 and G2, both of which use the result of G6, A'' as their results. In reattempting the original goal, G7 is created and G1 will be achieved, if G7 is successful. However, the difference D'' between A'' and B is detected, and the process continues.

If GPS finds a sufficiently undesirable situation while attempting G7, the previous goals may be retried in hope of finding new results. But, the basic strategy of GPS is to continue on the current approach, rather than to do an exhaustive search for results.

METHOD LANGUAGE

The methods for achieving goals are expressed in a method language, and the PROBLEM-SOLVING-EXECUTIVE is an interpreter for this language. A system of signals provides the main means of communication between the methods and the PROBLEM-SOLVING-EXECUTIVE. A signal is an IPL symbol. Each method, when executed, assigns to the variable CURRENT-SIGNAL* a signal that summarizes the result of the method's execution. The next action of the PROBLEM-SOLVING-EXECUTIVE, following the execution of a method, depends on the value of the CURRENT-SIGNAL.

The signal system is a generalization of the notion of having each routine whose outcome is conditional set a signal to + (succeed) or − (fail). In IPL all tests operate in this fashion, making use of a common test cell ($H5$).† Often however, there are more than two conditions that result. For example, a method may succeed, fail (but be

---

* CURRENT-SIGNAL is the name of the *IPL cell* in which the methods put the signal that summarizes their execution. However, it may be convenient to think of CURRENT-SIGNAL as a variable that is assigned a value during the execution of a method. More generally, we shall often refer to a cell as a variable and to its contents as the value assigned to the variable.

† Some machines also operate this way; e.g., the IBM 360 has a two-bit condition code, providing for four possible signals.

capable of being retried), or fail absolutely. Another example is the result of examining a new method to determine that it is one of four syntactic types. Such a signal system is still highly restrictive, however. One could admit much more complex summaries of the actions. These would then require both effort to compose them and effort to interpret them. The present system is a compromise between communicative power and processing costs.*

In the method language there are four different method structures, as far as interpretation is concerned. Three of these correspond to the primitive term, the unconditional expression, and the conditional expression, which are incorporated in almost all programming languages. The fourth, goal construction, is somewhat peculiar to problem solving.

An IPL method, the primitive term in the method language, is an IPL subroutine. This type of method is executed by calling the IPL interpreter to execute it. No further methods occur inside an IPL method.

A SEQUENTIAL method is a list of methods to be executed in the order of their occurrence. The execution of the sequence may be terminated part way through, but otherwise is unconditional. Both in a SEQUENTIAL method and a SIGNAL-LIST method (described next) any of the four types of method can occur; thus full phrase structure is permitted.

A SIGNAL-LIST method is used for conditional operation. It consists of a list of pairs, each of which is a signal followed by a method. A SIGNAL-LIST method is executed by executing the submethod that is paired with the same signal as the CURRENT-SIGNAL. If none of the signals associated with the submethods is identical to the CURRENT-SIGNAL, then no submethod is executed. Thus, this type of method performs a general *n*-way branch conditional on the CURRENT-SIGNAL.

A GOAL-SCHEMA method is a request for the construction of a goal. It has the form of the goal to be constructed, stated relative to the CURRENT-GOAL context. (CURRENT-GOAL is a variable whose value is the goal that GPS is currently attempting.) An example of a GOAL-SCHEMA method is

> TRANSFORM the result of the last subgoal into
> the second object of the CURRENT-GOAL.

The result of the last subgoal and the second object of the CURRENT-

* This is discussed further in Newell (1962a).

GOAL depend on the context of the CURRENT-GOAL and, thus, a goal constructed according to this GOAL-SCHEMA depends on the CUR-RENT-GOAL context. The PROBLEM-SOLVING-EXECUTIVE executes a GOAL-SCHEMA method by constructing the goal, evaluating it, and if acceptable attempting it.

A SIGNAL-LIST method can be used to perform iterations by recursive execution of its submethods.* However, iterations can be performed more directly by having the PROBLEM-SOLVING-EXECUTIVE repeatedly execute a method as long as a certain condition is satisfied. For example, if a method is marked to repeat on SUCCESS, it will be repeated as long as the CURRENT-SIGNAL is a signal that indicates SUCCESS. Several different signals indicate the different degrees of SUCCESS, while several other signals indicate the different kinds of FAILURE. Any type of method except a GOAL-SCHEMA method can be designated as repeatable. The conditions on which repetition can occur are as follows:

a change in the CURRENT-SIGNAL;

the CURRENT-SIGNAL indicates FAILURE;

the CURRENT-SIGNAL indicates SUCCESS;

the CURRENT-SIGNAL does not indicate either SUCCESS or FAILURE.

Normally, whenever the CURRENT-SIGNAL indicates SUCCESS or FAILURE, the execution of a method is terminated. However, any nonrepeatable method, except a GOAL-SCHEMA method, can be marked to continue on SUCCESS or FAILURE.

An example of a method, the GENERATE-AND-TEST-METHOD, is shown in Fig. 11. It is used to achieve a SELECT goal. Our standard way of writing the methods is at the top of the figure. The GENERATE-AND-TEST-METHOD is a SEQUENTIAL method, and the submethods are given as a vertical list. The middle submethod, SELECT-MEMBER, is also a SEQUENTIAL method, and its definition is given below that of the GENERATE-AND-TEST-METHOD. The other two submethods, SET-CONTENT and RECORD-RESULT, are IPL methods, and no additional definitions are provided. Their functions are clear; their details depend on IPL data structures. SELECT-MEMBER has one IPL method and one SIGNAL-LIST method, the latter again being defined

---

* It is a recursion because the submethod is executed with subsequent return of control to the main method, rather than control being transferred to the submethod.

```
GENERATE-AND-TEST-METHOD:    SET-CONTEXT
                             SELECT-MEMBER
                             RECORD-RESULT

       SELECT-MEMBER:        FIND-NEXT-MEMBER-OF-SET
                             IS-IT-OK
                             (repeat on FAILURE)

           IS-IT-OK:         BEGIN, TEST PASSED → FIND-NEXT-TEST
                             TEST-FOUND → APPLY-TEST
                             TEST-FAILED → FAILURE
```

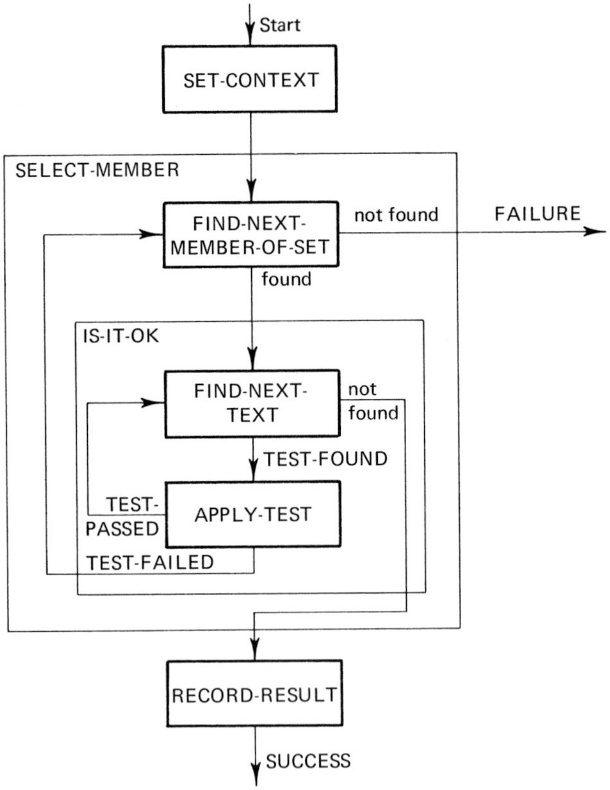

Fig. 11. Flow-chart representation of the GENERATE-AND-TEXT-METHOD.

in the figure. SELECT-MEMBER also has an iteration condition, repeat on FAILURE, and this is given in parentheses at the end of the list. The defining list for a SIGNAL-LIST method consists of the signal (or signals), then an arrow (→), then the submethod that will be executed if the CURRENT-SIGNAL is any of the signals. For instance, in IS-IT-OK, BEGIN, and TEST-PASSED both lead to executing the IPL method

FIND-NEXT-TEST. A signal can occur as a submethod of a SEQUENTIAL or SIGNAL-LIST method (e.g., FAILURE in IS-IT-OK). It is processed as if it were the IPL method that assigns the signal to be the value of the CURRENT-SIGNAL. Unless otherwise noted, the SEQUENTIAL and SIGNAL-LIST submethods that occur in the main method are also defined in the figure.

The GENERATE-AND-TEST-METHOD generates the elements of the SET one at a time and applies to each a series of tests. The first element that passes all of them is the element that is selected and marks the termination of the method.

An equivalent flow diagram for the GENERATE-AND-TEST-METHOD is also given in Fig. 11 below the method. Additional signals that are implicit in the structure of the method language, but required to be explicit in the flow diagram, are written in lower case. The method consists of three processes, executed in sequence: SET-CONTEXT, SELECT-MEMBER, and RECORD-RESULT. However, if SELECT-MEMBER fails, then RECORD-RESULT is not executed, since the convention is that any failure signal terminates a method. SELECT-MEMBER consists of repeated attempts to find a member and test it. Since repetition should occur upon failure of the test, SELECT-MEMBER is explicitly marked to repeat on FAILURE. However, there is a hierarchy of failure, and UNCONDITIONAL-FAILURE will terminate a method, overriding instructions to repeat or continue on FAILURE. Thus, since FIND-NEXT-MEMBER-OF-SET fails with UNCONDITIONAL-FAILURE, it terminates the iteration. The oscillation between the two subprocesses of SELECT-MEMBER is not explicit in the structure of the method, but is governed by the signals that the two submethods output. IS-IT-OK is itself repeated through the sequence of tests until one is found that fails. Note that both FIND-NEXT-MEMBER-OF-SET and FIND-NEXT-TEST find the first member as well as the next one.

PROBLEM-SOLVING-EXECUTIVE

Since all of the actions of GPS are expressed as methods written in a special language, the main function of the PROBLEM-SOLVING-EXECUTIVE is to interpret this language. It must perform all the functions that are normal to language interpretation: fetching the next expression to be interpreted; determining its syntactic type; and keeping track of the hierarchy of subexpressions. In addition to these interpretive tasks, the PROBLEM-SOLVING-EXECUTIVE also has a number of functions directly related to problem solving. These are

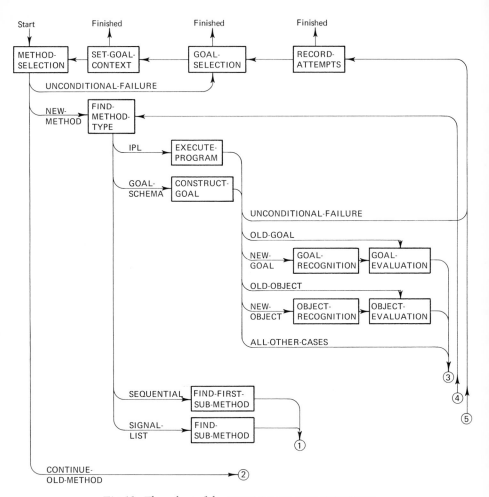

Fig. 12. Flow chart of the PROBLEM-SOLVING-EXECUTIVE.

METHOD-SELECTION	OBJECT-EVALUATION
GOAL-RECOGNITION	GOAL-SELECTION
GOAL-EVALUATION	RECORD-ATTEMPTS
OBJECT-RECOGNITION	SET-GOAL-CONTEXT

Each of these functions is a box in Fig. 12, a flow chart of the PROB-
LEM-SOLVING-EXECUTIVE, and is discussed individually later in
this section. All of the other boxes in Fig. 12 pertain to the interpretation of the method language. All of the discriminations in Fig. 12

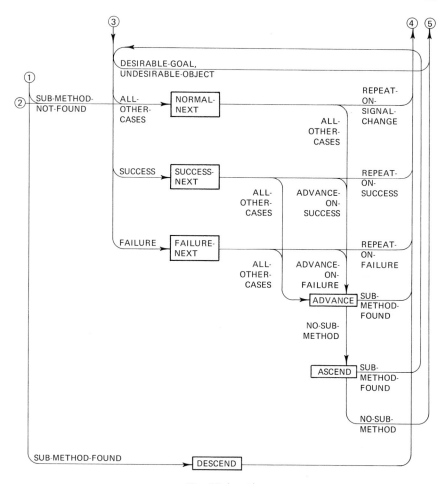

Fig. 12 (cont.).

are on the SIGNAL-CELL* and represent the communication to the PROBLEM-SOLVING-EXECUTIVE by the methods of the results of their actions.

The PROBLEM-SOLVING-EXECUTIVE is always in the context of a single goal, CURRENT-GOAL. Initially it is in the context of the TOP-GOAL, which is the statement of the problem given in the specification of a task.

The PROBLEM-SOLVING-EXECUTIVE starts off by trying to select a

---

*Except the discrimination on syntactic type.

method (METHOD-SELECTION in Fig. 12). If one is selected, it is attempted by first discriminating on the type of the method (i.e., on grammatical type). SEQUENTIAL and SIGNAL-LIST methods are attempted by trying their submethods one at a time. Thus, this processing is pure interpretation. On the other hand, the PROBLEM-SOLVING-EXECUTIVE constructs a goal in order to attempt a GOAL-SCHEMA method. After constructing the goal, the PROBLEM-SOLVING-EXECUTIVE files it (this process will be described in detail in GOAL-RECOGNITION) and recognizes whether or not it is equivalent to a goal filed previously. If the goal passes an evaluation, the executive abandons the CURRENT-GOAL, after recording its status, and initializes the context for the new goal. The new goal is then attempted by selecting a method that is relevant to achieving it.

The executive uses the IPL interpreter to execute an IPL method. In principle an IPL method can do anything, but only certain types of results are expected. An IPL method can select an old goal, which the executive then evaluates, and on the basis of its evaluation decides whether this goal should be attempted. IPL methods can also produce objects, which are then evaluated by the executive. An undesirable object will cause the executive to abandon the goal. If the object produced is a new one, the executive will file and recognize it (in the same way that it recognizes goals) before evaluating it.

METHOD-SELECTION

METHOD-SELECTION is done by a discrimination tree, shown in Fig. 13. The terminal nodes of the tree are methods. The selection is performed by discriminating, first at the top node (on CURRENT-SIGNAL), and then at each node resulting from the previous discrimination, until arriving at a terminal node. The method at the terminal node is the one selected, provided that its status for the CURRENT-GOAL is not EXHAUSTED. If the discrimination at any node does not yield a new node, or if the method at the terminal node is EXHAUSTED, all methods are EXHAUSTED and the selection results in UNCONDITIONAL-FAILURE.

At every node the discrimination is on the feature of the current context, enclosed in the box representing the node. For example, if a method is being selected for a new goal, the first discrimination detects a goal (NEW-GOAL), and the next discrimination will be on the GOAL-TYPE of the CURRENT-GOAL. If it is a TRANSFORM GOAL whose given object is a SET of objects, the TRANSFORM-SET-METHOD will be selected.

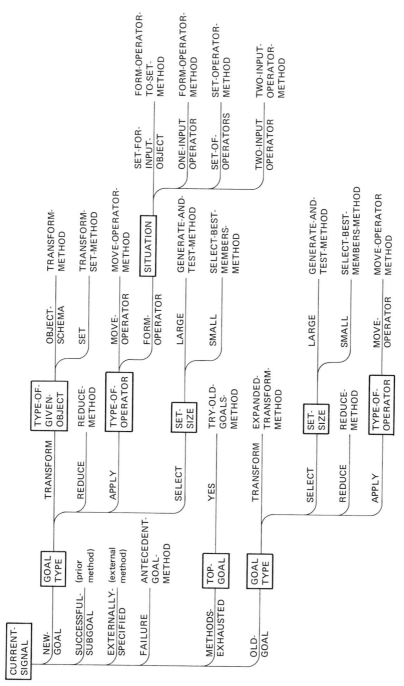

Fig. 13. Discrimination net used for METHOD-SELECTION.

Some of the discriminations depend on the representation of the task, e.g., TYPE-OF-OPERATOR. Such discriminations will be clarified in the next chapter, which discusses the details of the representation of a task.

GOAL-RECOGNITION

In GPS the philosophy for comparing two data structures that are not atomic symbols, such as goals, is to assign to them canonical names and compare only their names. Whenever a new data structure (one without a canonical name) is encountered, it is entered in a file. If the data structure is identical to one already filed, it is replaced by the filed structure which, by definition, is the canonical structure; otherwise, it is filed and becomes a canonical structure.

The canonization is accomplished by a discrimination net, which is similar to an EPAM net (Feigenbaum, 1961). An example is shown in Fig. 14a. The nodes of the tree, execpt for terminal nodes, are properties of data structures, and the branches represent values of the properties. The terminal nodes represent filed data structures. Filing a data structure involves sorting it through the tree and, if necessary, growing the tree so that it can be filed at a terminal node.

Consider filing in the net in Fig. 14a the goal

G5:   TRANSFORM $A1$ into $B1$.

Discrimination on the property at the top node of the tree sorts G5 to the leftmost subnode of the top node because G5 is a GOAL. The discrimination on the GOAL-TYPE sorts G5 to the node G1. Since G1 is a terminal node, the tree does not contain sufficient discrimination to distinguish between G1 and G5. G1 and G5 are matched, and if they are identical, G1 is used as the canonical form of G5. (In this case, G5 is not filed.) On the other hand, if a difference is detected between G1 and G5, it is used to grow the tree so that G5 can be filed. The tree shown in Fig. 14b is the result of filing G5 in the tree in Fig. 14a, assuming that G1 is the goal

G1:   TRANSFORM $A2$ into $B2$.

There are two essential properties of this process. First, the data structure being filed will be matched to at most one other data structure. (The matching is done by the IDENTITY-MATCH-METHOD in Fig. 17 described later in this chapter.) This keeps the amount of processing small, since matching is the most expensive part of the

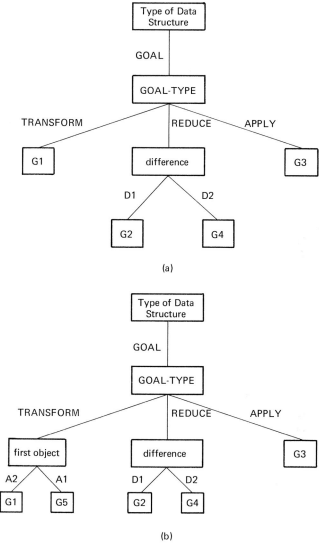

Fig. 14. The net at (b) is the result of filing G5 in the discrimination net at (a).

process when the data structure being filed is large. The other essential property of the filing process is its generality; i.e., the process can deal with other types of data structures in addition to goals. Both objects and differences are filed in the same tree.

If goals were not canonized, every goal (except the goal that is the statement of the problem) would have a unique supergoal. However,

since goals are canonized, a goal may have several supergoals. To
see this, suppose that goal G1 is created to simplify goal G2 and that a
previously generated goal, G3, is equivalent to G1. In canonizing G1,
it is replaced by its equivalent, G3, and consequently, G3 has two
supergoals: G2 and the original supergoal of G3. Thus, the canonization of goals causes the goal structure of GPS to be a goal network
instead of a goal tree.

GOAL-EVALUATION

GOAL-EVALUATION rejects goals from immediate consideration.
However, they do become part of the goal tree, and immediate
rejection does not imply that they will never be considered.

Two principles are used to evaluate goals. The first is the notion
that a subgoal should be easier than its supergoal. Supposedly this
is why one sets up subgoals. Consequently, GPS considers any goal
undesirable if its supergoal is easier than the goal.

The second principle is that problem solving should proceed from
the difficult to the easy. Thus GPS always generates the most difficult
subgoal first. A consequence of this is that if one subgoal has been
successfully attained, and another one generated on the basis of its
result, then the latter should be easier. If it is not, then GPS considers the new goal to be undesirable. To realize this principle, we
introduce the notion of the *antecedent* goal of a goal G which is
defined as the goal whose result is used in the statement of G and
whose supergoal is the same as the supergoal of G. (Currently, there
is no need for more than a single antecedent.) In Fig. 10 for example,
G2 is the antecedent goal of G7, and G4 is the antecedent goal of G6.
No other goal in Fig. 10 has an antecedent. Thus the principle is that
the antecedent of a goal be no easier than the goal.

The difficulty of a goal is determined by the difficulty of the difference associated with the goal. Since REDUCE goals are the only
type of goals that have differences associated with them, they are the
only goals that can be evaluated according to their difficulty. However, other goals are considered to be as difficult as their most difficult subgoal.

For example, G7 in Fig. 10 does not have a difference associated
with it. But GPS considers it as difficult as G8 because D'' is the most
difficult difference detected in matching A'' and B; hence G8 is the
most difficult subgoal of G7. GPS considers G8 desirable only if D''
is less difficult than D, because G2 is the antecedent goal of G7.

Similarly, G4 is desirable only if D' is not more difficult than D, because the supergoal of G3 is G2.

OBJECT-RECOGNITION

All newly generated objects are canonized in the same way that goals are canonized, using the same discrimination tree and filing processes. The main reason for canonizing objects is to simplify the canonization of goals. Since the names of objects appear in goals, matching two goals would necessitate matching objects that appear in the goals, if the canonical names of objects were not used.

OBJECT-EVALUATION

The evaluation of an object as undesirable leads to abandoning the approach being taken, and thus serves to guide the heuristic search. Throughout this research the evaluation has been held constant, consisting of a rejection of an object that is considerably larger than any of the objects in the TOP-GOAL.

GOAL-SELECTION

Only simple goal selection is done directly by the problem-solving executive; more complicated goal selection is accomplished by the execution of a method whose purpose is to select a goal.*

If a new desirable goal G is generated, the PROBLEM-SOLVING-EXECUTIVE will abandon the CURRENT-GOAL and work on G. The supergoal is selected whenever a method for achieving a goal is completed (SUCCESS, NO-PROGRESS, or FAILURE). The PROBLEM-SOLVING-EXECUTIVE has no fixed search strategy built into it, e.g., neither breadth first nor depth first. Instead, goals are attempted iteratively by working on one goal until deciding to abandon it in order to work on another goal. However, if only the two rules above were used to select goals, they would be attempted in the recursive order in which they were generated.

The only other goal-selection rule employed directly by the PROBLEM-SOLVING-EXECUTIVE is that TOP-GOAL is selected whenever a newly generated goal is identical to a previously generated goal. This rule prevents GPS from entering an endless loop.

* The only methods whose purpose is to select goals are the TRY-OLD-GOALS-METHOD and the ANTECEDENT-GOAL-METHOD.

RECORD-ATTEMPTS

Before abandoning a goal, the PROBLEM-SOLVING-EXECUTIVE records certain information that summarizes the attempt to achieve the goal. For example, the methods that have been tried together with their status—EXHAUSTED or NOT-EXHAUSTED—are recorded.

SET-GOAL-CONTEXT

After selecting the next goal to be attempted, the context of this goal is initialized before selecting a method relevant to achieving the goal.

METHODS

Each of GPS's methods, except for the GENERATE-AND-TEST-METHOD (already discussed on pp. 41–43) is described below. The details of some of the methods will not be entirely clear because they are dependent upon the representation of tasks, which is discussed in the next chapter.

TRANSFORM-METHOD

The TRANSFORM-METHOD is used for achieving the goal of transforming object A into object B and is defined in Fig. 15. After the context for the method is initialized, the two objects are matched by the MATCH-DIFF-METHOD which is defined in Fig. 16. If the two objects are not identical, MATCH-DIFF-METHOD detects the differences

```
TRANSFORM-METHOD:

        SET-CONTEXT
        MATCH-DIFF-METHOD
        SELECT-DIFFERENCE
        REPORT-SUCCESS
        GOAL-SCHEMA:    REDUCE the difference selected on the first
                        object of the CURRENT-GOAL.
        GOAL-SCHEMA:    TRANSFORM the result of the last subgoal into
                        the second object of the CURRENT-GOAL.
        REPORT-RESULT

    REPORT-SUCCESS:

        NO-DIFFERENCES → SUCCESS
```

Fig. 15. Definition of the TRANSFORM-METHOD used for achieving a TRANSFORM GOAL.

```
MATCH-DIFF-METHOD:

    BEGIN, PARTS-MATCHED.
    ONLY-ONE-PART-FOUND → FIND-NEXT-PART
    PARTS-FOUND,
    CONTINUE-MATCHING → FIND-DIFFERENCE-BETWEEN-PARTS
    DIFFERENCE-FOUND → PROCESS-DIFFERENCE
    (repeat on signal change)

PROCESS-DIFFERENCE:

    TRY-IMMEDIATE-OPERATORS
    RECORD

RECORD:

    DIFFERENCE-FOUND → REPORT-DIFFERENCE
```

Fig. 16. Definition of the MATCH-DIFF-METHOD, which matches two data structures for all of the differences between them.

and the most difficult difference is determined by SELECT-DIFFER-ENCE. If no differences are found, SUCCESS is reported by REPORT-SUCCESS, which terminates the method.

On finding differences, the construction of a goal to reduce the most difficult difference on A is requested. If the goal fails, the method terminates with FAILURE; otherwise, the goal results in a new object C and the goal of transforming C into B is constructed. The result of this goal is used as the result of the CURRENT-GOAL.

MATCH-DIFF-METHOD

The MATCH-DIFF-METHOD, defined in Fig. 16, detects all of the differences between two data structures. It is a submethod both of the TRANSFORM-METHOD and the FORM-OPERATOR-METHOD. The strategy of this method is to decompose data structures into parts and then match corresponding parts. On finding a difference, it tries to alleviate the difference with an *immediate operator*. These operators are applied in context in the middle of the match, at the point where the difference is found. If successful in eliminating the difference (determined by the operator itself), then the match is able to continue just as if no difference had been detected at all. For example, if the type of difference, *variable versus term*, were detected, the immediate operator of substitution would be applied. The term would be substituted for the variable (throughout both total expressions), the difference would vanish, and matching would resume.

Immediate operators do on a small scale what GPS does as a whole: detected differences lead to operators to reduce these differences. However, no goal structure is created to capture the situation; thus, it is not possible to return at a later time to try a different immediate operator, if the first one proves inadequate. Moreover, unlike the main GPS, no process of getting into context is required in order to apply an operator; immediate operators are applied in the situation in which the difference was found—i.e., "immediately." Thus immediate operators are useful where it is known that a unique operator is required in order to eliminate a difference (hence, to make the match successful). It provides a convenient way of mechanizing such general operations as substitution and some varieties of replacement, e.g., deleting two negation signs in forms of logic where $\sim\sim X$ is always replaced by X.

Immediate operators are task dependent, and are given as IPL routines, since they need to know the full context in which the match is taking place. There are two other parameters to the MATCH-DIFF-METHOD besides the immediate operators: a scheme for determining which parts of two data structures are to be placed in correspondence; and a list of the differences to be detected between two corresponding parts.

In Fig. 16, the first parts of the two data structures are found by FIND-NEXT-PART. The parts are matched by checking for each type of difference, one at a time. When detected, a difference is reported, provided that the immediate operators cannot alleviate it. After checking for all types of differences the next parts are found and matched, and so on. The method is finished when all of the parts are matched, because CURRENT-SIGNAL does not change after this condition arises.

IDENTITY-MATCH-METHOD

The IDENTITY-MATCH-METHOD, defined in Fig. 17, is very similar to MATCH-DIFF-METHOD. In fact, the two submethods of the IDENTITY-

```
IDENTITY-MATCH-METHOD:

    BEGINS, PARTS-MATCHED,
    ONLY-ONE-PART-FOUND → FIND-NEXT-PART

    PARTS-FOUND,
    CONTINUE-MATCHING → FIND-DIFFERENCE-BETWEEN-PARTS
    (repeat on signal change)
```

Fig. 17. Definition of the IDENTITY-MATCH-METHOD, which is used to test the identity of two data structures.

MATCH-METHOD are also used in the MATCH-DIFF-METHOD. The IDENTITY-MATCH-METHOD is used by the canonization process to compare the identity of two data structures (see pp. 48–50). It differs from the MATCH-DIFF-METHOD in two ways: It does not use immediate operators, and it terminates upon detecting a single difference, whereas the MATCH-DIFF-METHOD detects all of the differences.

REDUCE-METHOD

The REDUCE-METHOD, defined in Fig. 18, is the only method for achieving the goal of reducing a difference on an object. First, it

```
REDUCE-METHOD:

    SET-CONTEXT
    SELECT-OPERATOR
    GOAL-SCHEMA:   APPLY the operator selected to the object
                   of the CURRENT-GOAL.
    REPORT-RESULT

SELECT-OPERATOR:

    FIND-OPERATOR
    APPLY-DESIRABILITY-FILTER
    (repeat on FAILURE)
```

Fig. 18. Definition of the REDUCE-METHOD for achieving a REDUCE GOAL.

selects a desirable operator by finding the next operator and testing its desirability. If the operator is undesirable, it finds the next operator, etc. On finding a desirable operator, the goal of applying the operator to the object of the REDUCE goal is constructed, which, if successful, will result in a new object. The new object is used as the result of the REDUCE goal.

Since there may be several desirable operators, all of which produce different objects, a REDUCE goal may have several results. However, the REDUCE-METHOD is terminated when an operator is successfully applied. The other results are found only by retrying the method.

FORM-OPERATOR-METHOD

In general, any operator can be legally applied only to certain objects. A FORM-OPERATOR can be applied to an object whose form

FORM-OPERATOR-METHOD:

    SET-CONTEXT
    EXECUTE-PRETESTS
    MATCH-DIFF-METHOD
    SELECT-DIFFERENCE
    CONTINUE

CONTINUE:

    NO-DIFFERENCE → PRODUCE-RESULT
    DIFFERENCE-FOUND → MODIFY-AND-APPLY

MODIFY-AND-APPLY:

    GOAL-SCHEMA: REDUCE the difference selected on the
                       object of the APPLY goal.
    GOAL-SCHEMA: APPLY the operator of the CURRENT-GOAL
                       to the result of the previous method.
    REPORT-RESULT

Fig. 19. Definition of the FORM-OPERATOR-METHOD for achieving an APPLY GOAL whose operator is a FORM-OPERATOR.

is the same as the *input form* of the operator, and which satisfies the pretests of the operator (given as IPL routines).

The FORM-OPERATOR-METHOD, defined in Fig. 19, is the method for achieving an APPLY goal whose operator is expressed as a FORM-OPERATOR. After the context is initialized, the applicability of the operator is tested by EXECUTE-PRETESTS and by matching the object to the input form. If no differences are detected, the operator is applicable, and its result, which is used as the result of the CURRENT-GOAL, is produced. If differences are detected, a goal to reduce the most difficult one is constructed.

If the REDUCE goal is successful, it results in a new object, and a goal to apply the operator to the new object is constructed. The result of the latter goal, if it is successful, becomes the result of the CURRENT-GOAL. (Figure 10 illustrates the way in which the result of a goal is also used as the result of its supergoal.)

FORM-OPERATOR-TO-SET-METHOD

The method for achieving the goal of applying a FORM-OPERATOR to a SET of objects is the FORM-OPERATOR-TO-SET-METHOD which is defined in Fig. 20. First, the object most similar to the input form of the operator is selected by a goal constructed for that purpose. Then, the goal of applying the operator to the object selected is generated, and its result is also the result of the CURRENT-GOAL.

FORM-OPERATOR-TO-SET-METHOD:

GOAL-SCHEMA: SELECT an object from the SET of the
CURRENT-GOAL that is similar to the input
form of the operator.

GOAL-SCHEMA: APPLY the operator of the CURRENT-GOAL
to the object selected.

REPORT-RESULT

Fig. 20. Definition of the FORM-OPERATOR-TO-SET-METHOD for achieving an APPLY GOAL whose operator is a FORM-OPERATOR and whose input object is a SET of objects.

SET-OPERATOR-METHOD

The SET-OPERATOR-METHOD, defined in Fig. 21, is used to achieve an APPLY goal whose operator is a SET of FORM-OPERATORs. This

SET-OPERATOR-METHOD:

GOAL-SCHEMA: SELECT an operator whose input form is
similar to the object of the CURRENT-GOAL.

GOAL-SCHEMA: APPLY the operator selected to the object
of the CURRENT-GOAL.

REPORT-RESULT

Fig. 21. Definition of SET-OPERATOR-METHOD for achieving an APPLY GOAL whose operator is a SET of FORM-OPERATORs.

method is the same as the FORM-OPERATOR-TO-SET-METHOD, except that an operator whose input form is similar to the object is selected instead of the converse.

TWO-INPUT-OPERATOR-METHOD

Some form operators have two input forms instead of one. Such operators are applied to a pair of objects, both of which are derived from the same objects, e.g., both derived from the axioms of a theory. Each object has the same form as one of the input forms.*

The TWO-INPUT-OPERATOR-METHOD, defined in Fig. 22, is used to achieve an APPLY goal whose operator has two input forms. By the way GPS operates, any operator will be applied to a single object (that of the CURRENT-GOAL). Thus the first step is to select which of two input forms of the operator is to correspond to this object. The criterion of this SELECT goal is the similarity of the two objects. In applying the operator to the object, the operator is modified if it is

---

* The logic operators $R10$, $R11$, and $R12$ in Fig. 7 are examples of operators that have two objects as input.

TWO-INPUT-OPERATOR-METHOD:

GOAL-SCHEMA: SELECT the input form that is more similar
                to the object of the CURRENT-GOAL.
GOAL-SCHEMA: APPLY the input form selected to the
                object of the CURRENT-GOAL.
GOAL-SCHEMA: SELECT an object similar to the
                second input form.
GOAL-SCHEMA: APPLY the second input form to the
                object selected.
REPORT-RESULT

Fig. 22. Definition of the TWO-INPUT-OPERATOR-METHOD for achieving an APPLY GOAL whose operator is a FORM-OPERATOR that has two inputs.

necessary to substitute for some of the variables in the operator. The modified operator is the result of applying the operator to the first input. The other input object is selected from the SET of objects that are derived from the same object from which the first input object is derived. After applying the modified operator to the second input, the new object is produced.

MOVE-OPERATOR-METHOD

The above methods for achieving APPLY goals all assume that the operator is represented as a FORM-OPERATOR. A MOVE-OPERATOR is an alternative representation for an operator. Unlike a FORM-OPER-ATOR, a MOVE-OPERATOR may produce more than one result, each obtained from a different specification of the variables in the operator. The MOVE-OPERATOR-METHOD terminates on finding a single result, but may be retried to produce the other results.

Figure 23 is the definition of the MOVE-OPERATOR-METHOD for achieving a goal whose operator is a MOVE-OPERATOR. After specifying the variables in the operator, the feasibility of the operator is tested. If feasible, i.e., if no difference is found, the resultant object is produced and tested for legality by executing the POST-TESTS. If the POST-TESTS fail, the result is rejected; otherwise, it is used as a result of the goal. On the other hand, if a difference is found, a goal is set up to reduce the difference, provided that it is not too difficult. If the REDUCE goal is successful, a goal is constructed to apply the operator to its result.

Upon retrying APPLY-FEASIBLE-OPERATOR a different specification of the variables is used, and the method may be retried for as long as a new specification of variables is found.

```
MOVE-OPERATOR-METHOD:

      SET-CONTEXT
      APPLY-FEASIBLE-OPERATOR

  APPLY-FEASIBLE-OPERATOR:

      SPECIFY-VARIABLES
      EXECUTE-PRETESTS-AND-TEST-LEGALITY-OF-MOVES
      SELECT-DIFFERENCE
      APPLY-OPERATOR-IF-POSSIBLE
      (repeat on FAILURE)

  APPLY-OPERATOR-IF-POSSIBLE:

      NO-DIFFERENCE → APPLY-OPERATOR
      DIFFERENCE-FOUND → MODIFY-IF-NOT-TOO-DIFFICULT

  MODIFY-IF-NOT-TOO-DIFFICULT:

      TEST-DIFFICULTY-OF-DIFFERENCE
      GOAL-SCHEMA:    REDUCE the difference selected on the
                      object of the CURRENT-GOAL.
      GOAL-SCHEMA:    APPLY the operator of the CURRENT-GOAL
                      to the result of the previous method.
      REPORT-RESULT

  APPLY-OPERATOR:

      APPLY-MOVES-AND-POST-TESTS
      RECORD-RESULT
```

Fig. 23. Definition of the MOVE-OPERATOR-METHOD for achieving an APPLY GOAL whose operator is a MOVE-OPERATOR.

TRANSFORM-SET-METHOD

The TRANSFORM-SET-METHOD, defined in Fig. 24, is used to achieve the goal of transforming a SET of objects into an object. It is very similar to the FORM-OPERATOR-TO-SET-METHOD in that the CURRENT-GOAL is rephrased by replacing the SET of objects by one of its members.

```
TRANSFORM-SET-METHOD:

      GOAL-SCHEMA:   SELECT a member of the SET.
      GOAL-SCHEMA:   TRANSFORM the member selected into the second
                     object of the CURRENT-GOAL.
      REPORT-RESULT
```

Fig. 24. Definition of the TRANSFORM-SET-METHOD for achieving a TRANSFORM GOAL whose first object is a SET of objects.

EXPANDED-TRANSFORM-METHOD

The EXPANDED-TRANSFORM-METHOD, defined in Fig. 25, is a method for achieving the TOP-GOAL. It replaces the initial situation of the TOP-GOAL by the SET of all objects derived from the initial situation. The rationale for this method is that the goal of transforming one of these objects into the desired situation might be easier than the TOP-GOAL. Since all of the objects are derived from the same objects, the solution of one goal is equivalent to the solution of another.

EXPANDED-TRANSFORM-METHOD:

GOAL-SCHEMA: TRANSFORM the SET of objects that are derived
                from the initial situation into the desired situation.
REPORT-RESULT

Fig. 25. Definition of the EXPANDED-TRANSFORM-METHOD for achieving the TOP-GOAL.

SELECT-BEST-MEMBERS-METHOD

Figure 26 gives the definition of the SELECT-BEST-MEMBERS-METHOD, which is used to achieve a SELECT GOAL whose SET is "small." The SELECT-MEMBERS-METHOD applies a test to each member of the SET that passed all of the previous tests. If only one member passes the test, it is the member selected; if no members pass the test, those members that passed the previous test are selected; if more than one member passes the test, the procedure is repeated with the next test.

The SELECT-BEST-MEMBERS-METHOD applies a test to all members of the SET. Only those members that fail the test are eliminated. On

SELECT-BEST-MEMBERS-METHOD:

SET-CONTEXT
SELECT-MEMBERS

SELECT-MEMBERS:

BEGIN, SEVERAL-MEMBERS-PASSED → FIND-NEXT-TEST
TEST-FOUND → APPLY TEST
ONLY-ONE-MEMBER-PASSED → RESULT-IS-PREVIOUSLY-PASSED-MEMBERS
(repeat on signal change)

Fig. 26. Definition of SELECT-BEST-MEMBERS-METHOD for achieving a SELECT GOAL whose SET is small.

the other hand, the GENERATE-AND-TEST-METHOD (Fig. 27) applies tests to one member at a time. Whenever a member is found that passes all of the tests, it is the member selected. However, there may be several other members that also would pass all of the tests, and one of these members may fulfill the criterion better than the one selected. The GENERATE-AND-TEST-METHOD is used for "large" SETs because in many cases only a few members of the SET need to be processed.

```
GENERATE-AND-TEST-METHOD:

    SET-CONTEXT
    SELECT-MEMBER
    RECORD-RESULT

SELECT-MEMBER:

    FIND-NEXT-MEMBER-OF-SET
    IS-IT-OK
    (repeat on FAILURE)

IS-IT-OK:

    BEGIN, TEST-PASSED → FIND-NEXT-TEST
    TEST-FOUND → APPLY-TEST
    TEST-FAILED → FAILURE
    (repeat until no signal change; terminate on FAILURE)
```

Fig. 27. Definition of the GENERATE-AND-TEST-METHOD for achieving a SELECT GOAL whose SET is large.

ANTECEDENT-GOAL-METHOD

The ANTECEDENT-GOAL-METHOD is used to achieve any GOAL that has an antecedent goal.* It is an IPL method that selects the antecedent goal to be retried. The rationale is that the antecedent goal might produce a new result and the CURRENT-GOAL can be re-phrased in terms of the new result. In Fig. 10, for example, if G7 fails, its antecedent goal, G2, would be retried. If it produced the new result, A''', and if A''' were successfully transformed into B, G1 would be successful, which is the sole purpose of G7.

TRY-OLD-GOALS-METHOD

The TRY-OLD-GOALS-METHOD is an IPL method that is the last resort in finding a solution. When all else fails, it selects a goal.

---

* Antecedent GOAL is defined on pp. 50–51.

Basically, it selects the least difficult goal. This implies selecting a REDUCE goal, since difficulty is defined by means of the difference (see pp. 50–51). It will not select a goal if the methods for achieving it are EXHAUSTED. In addition it gives priority to REDUCE goals whose supergoals are TRANSFORM goals over those supergoals are APPLY goals. This reflects the fact that APPLY goals are themselves subgoals of TRANSFORM goals (or other APPLY goals) and hence their REDUCE goals seem to be more often irrelevant. The TRY-OLD-GOALS-METHOD may be applied repeatedly.

CHAPTER IV

THE REPRESENTATION OF TASKS

The purpose of this chapter is to describe how tasks are represented within GPS. As in the last chapter, no general issues will be discussed. In Chapter V, having completed the description of GPS, we shall take up the interaction of the representation of tasks with the problem-solving techniques of GPS.

The internal representation of a task consists of several different kinds of data structure:

objects	TABLE-OF-CONNECTIONS
operators	DIFF-ORDERING
goals	COMPARE-OBJECTS
differences	declarations

A section of this chapter is devoted to each of these. The discussion points out which of these data structures appear in the specification of a task and which are generated by the problem-solving process.

The whole of GPS consists of both data structures and programs. The data structures listed above are all those that vary with the task. The program represents a fixed structure, which does not vary with the task. There are two minor exceptions: the immediate operators, used in matching two objects; and the similarity tests, used in SELECT goals. These vary with the task, but only rarely. Hence, it did not seem worthwhile to create data structures to describe their variations.*

GPS is encoded in the list-processing language IPL-V, and the internal representation of all task structures consists of IPL symbols, lists, and list structures. For the most part, data structures are encoded in the description of IPL.† However, the internal representation will not be described in terms of IPL data structures, but rather in a language of tree structures, sets, and so on, in such a way that there is one-to-one correspondence to the IPL data structures.

To give GPS a task is to provide it, via some external representation, with information contained in the data structures listed above. In most previous reports on GPS, it has been useful to consider the notion of a *task environment*—that information common to tasks of a particular kind, e.g., to all integration tasks. In terms of our list, a task environment consists of operators, differences, TABLE-OF-CONNECTIONS, DIFF-ORDERING, COMPARE-OBJECTS, and the declarations. Given a task environment, a particular task consists of some objects and a goal. However, we will not need this distinction here since one or at most two tasks per task environment were given to GPS.

The last section of this chapter describes an external representation of tasks to aid the reader in understanding the task specification actually given to GPS (see Chapter VI). Since the external representation is very similar to the internal representation, only the semantics of the internal representation is described, and the description of external representation deals mainly with syntax. We note again that words printed in small capital letters (including hyphenated words) correspond, directly, to IPL symbols in GPS. These words, which comprise the basic vocabulary of GPS, are given in Appendix A.

To be concrete, the examples used in this chapter will be drawn from either the Missionaries and Cannibals task or the Integration task. Figures 28 and 29 show the heuristic search formulations of these tasks. Figures 30 and 31 show the specification of these tasks expressed in the external representation of GPS. Only a few integration operators are given in Figs. 29 and 31. These are typical and are sufficient for the expressions that GPS integrated.

---

* Each modification will be noted in connection with the specific task.

† An IPL description list is a sequence of pairs of IPL symbols. The first symbol in each pair is an attribute, the second is the value of the attribute. For example, the description list that represents the goal of transforming $X1$ into $X2$ is GOAL-TYPE TRANSFORM, FIRST-OBJECT $X1$, and SECOND-OBJECT $X2$. $X1$ and $X2$ are not atomic symbols but are list structures.

Generic form of objects:	The number of missionaries at each side of the river, the number of cannibals at each side of the river, and the position of the boat.
Initial situation:	Three missionaries, three cannibals, and the boat at the left bank of the river; nothing at the right bank of the river.
Desired situation:	Three missionaries, three cannibals, and the boat at the right bank of the river; nothing at the left bank of the river.
Operators:	Move x missionaries, y cannibals (x and y are variables), and the boat across the river provided that

(1) $1 \leqslant x + y \leqslant 2$ (the boat must not sink and someone must row);

(2) at both banks of the river in the resultant object, either the number of missionaries $\geqslant$ the number of cannibals, or the number of missionaries = 0 (no missionaries may be eaten).

Fig. 28. Heuristic-search formulation of the Missionaries and Cannibals task.

Generic form of objects:

Any expression.

Initial situation:

$\int te^t \, dt$

Desired situation:

An expression that does not contain $\int$.

Operators:

a. $\int u^n \, du = \dfrac{u^{n+1}}{n+1}$ g. $\int (f + g) \, du = \int f \, du + \int g \, du$

b. $\int u^{-1} \, du = \log u$ h. $\sin u \, du = -d(\cos u)$

c. $\int \sin u \, du = -\cos u$ i. $\cos u \, du = d(\sin u)$

d. $\int \cos u \, du = \sin u$ j. $u \, du = \frac{1}{2} \, d(u^2)$

e. $\int u \, du = \frac{1}{2} u^2$ k. $u^{-1} \, du = d(\log u)$

f. $\int e^u \, du = e^u$

Fig. 29. Heuristic-search formulation of the Integration task.

```
RENAME    (
    LEFT = FIRST
    RIGHT = SECOND
        )
DECLARE      (
    BOAT = ATTRIBUTE
    C = ATTRIBUTE
    B-L = FEATURE
    B-R = FEATURE
    C-L = FEATURE
    C-R = FEATURE
    DESIRED-OBJ = OBJECT-SCHEMA
    FROM-SIDE = LOC-PROG
    FROM-SIDE-TESTS = V-TESTS
    INITIAL-OBJ = OBJECT-SCHEMA
    M = ATTRIBUTE
    M-C-OPR = MOVE-OPERATOR
    M-L = FEATURE
    M-R = FEATURE
    SIDE-SET = SET
    TO-SIDE = LOC-PROG
    TO-SIDE-TESTS = V-TESTS
    X = CONSTANT
    X+Y = EXPRES
    Y = CONSTANT
    0,1,2-SET = SET
    1,2 = SET
```

Fig. 30. Specification for GPS of the Missionaries and Cannibals task.

```
              )
TASK-STRUCTURES      (
    TOP-GOAL = ( TRANSFORM THE INITIAL-OBJ INTO THE DESIRED-OBJ . )
    INITIAL-OBJ = ( LEFT ( M 3 C 3 BOAT YES )
                    RIGHT ( M 0 C 0 ) )
    DESIRED-OBJ = ( LEFT ( M 0 C 0 )
                    RIGHT ( M 3 C 3 BOAT YES ) )
    X+Y = ( X + Y )
    1,2 = ( 1 2 )
    0,1,2-SET = ( 0 1 2 )
    SIDE-SET = ( LEFT RIGHT )
    FROM-SIDE-TESTS = (    1. THE M OF THE FROM-SIDE IS NOT-LESS-THAN
                              THE C OF THE FROM-SIDE .
                           2. THE M OF THE FROM-SIDE EQUALS 0 . )
    TO-SIDE-TESTS = (   1. THE M OF THE TO-SIDE IS NOT-LESS-THAN
                           THE C OF THE TO-SIDE .
                        2. THE M OF THE TO-SIDE EQUALS 0 . )
    M-C-OPR = ( CREATION-OPERATOR
                $ MOVE X MISSIONARIES AND Y CANNIBALS FROM THE FROM-SIDE TO
                  THE TO-SIDE $
                VAR-DOMAIN
                1. Y IS A CONSTRAINED-MEMBER OF THE 0,1,2-SET ,
                   THE CONSTRAINT IS X+Y IS IN-THE-SET 1,2 .
                2. X IS A CONSTRAINED-MEMBER OF THE 0,1,2-SET ,
                   THE CONSTRAINT IS X+Y IS IN-THE-SET 1,2 .
                3. THE FROM-SIDE IS AN EXCLUSIVE-MEMBER OF THE SIDE-SET .
                4. THE TO-SIDE IS AN EXCLUSIVE-MEMBER OF THE SIDE-SET .
```

Fig. 30 (cont.).

```
         MOVES
             1. MOVE THE BOAT OF THE FROM-SIDE TO THE BOAT OF THE TO-SIDE
             2. DECREASE BY THE AMOUNT X THE M AT THE FROM-SIDE AND ADD
                IT TO THE M AT THE TO-SIDE .
             3. DECREASE BY THE AMOUNT Y THE C AT THE FROM-SIDE AND ADD
                IT TO THE C AT THE TO-SIDE .
         POST-TESTS
             1. ARE ANY OF THE FROM-SIDE-TESTS TRUE .
             2. ARE ANY OF THE TO-SIDE-TESTS TRUE . )
B-L = ( BOAT ON THE LEFT . )
B-R = ( BOAT ON THE RIGHT . )
C-L = ( C ON THE LEFT . )
C-R = ( C ON THE RIGHT . )
M-L = ( M ON THE LEFT . )
M-R = ( M ON THE RIGHT . )
DIFF-ORDERING = ( ( M-R M-L C-R C-L )
                  ( B-R B-L ) )
TABLE-OF-CONNECTIONS = ( ( COMMON-DIFFERENCE M-C-OPR ) )
COMPARE-OBJECTS = ( BASIC-MATCH )
BASIC-MATCH = ( COMP-FEAT-LIST ( M-L C-L B-L ) )
OBJ-ATTRIB = ( M C BOAT )
LIST-OF-VAR = ( FROM-SIDE TO-SIDE X Y )
    )     END
```

Fig. 30 (cont.).

```
RENAME    (

   LEFT = FIRST

   RIGHT = SECOND

      )

DECLARE    (

   COS = UNARY-CONNECTIVE

   D = UNARY-CONNECTIVE

   DESIRED-OBJ = DESCRIBED-OBJ

   EXP = N-ARY-CONNECTIVE

   INTEGRAL = UNARY-CONNECTIVE

   LOG = UNARY-CONNECTIVE

   SIN = UNARY-CONNECTIVE

   SYMBOL = ATTRIBUTE

   SYM-DIFF = FEATURE

   - = UNARY-CONNECTIVE

   * = N-ARY-CONNECTIVE

   + = N-ARY-CONNECTIVE

      )

LIST      (

   EXPRESSION-1 = ( THE INTEGRAL OF ( T * ( E EXP ( T EXP TWO ) ) * D T ) )

   INTEGRATE = ( 1. ( THE INTEGRAL OF ( ( U EXP N ) * D U ) YIELDS

                 ( ( U EXP ( N + ONE ) ) * ( ( N + ONE ) EXP - ONE ) ) ) ,

              2. ( THE INTEGRAL OF ( ( U EXP - ONE ) * D U ) YIELDS

                 LOG U ) ,

              3. ( THE INTEGRAL OF ( SIN U * D U ) YIELDS - COS U ) ,

              4. ( THE INTEGRAL OF ( COS U * D U ) YIELDS SIN U ) ,

              5. ( THE INTEGRAL OF ( U * D U ) YIELDS ( ( U EXP TWO ) *
```

Fig. 31. Specification for GPS of the task of integrating $\int te^{t^2} dt$.

```
                    ( TWO EXP - ONE ) ) ) ,

            5. ( THE INTEGRAL OF ( ( E EXP U ) * D U ) YIELDS

                ( E EXP U ) ) ,

            7. ' THE INTEGRAL OF ( ( F + G ) * D U ) YIELDS ( THE INTEGRAL

                OF ( F * D U ) + THE INTEGRAL OF ( G * D U ) ) ) )

DIFFERENTIATE = ( 1. ( ( SIN U * D U ) YIELDS - U COS U ) ,

            2. ( ( COS U * D U ) YIELDS U SIN U ) ,

            3. ( ( U * D U ) YIELDS ( ' TWO EXP - ONE ) *

                U ( U EXP TWO ) ) ) ,

            4. ( ( ( U EXP - ONE ) * D U ) YIELDS D LOG U ) )

EXPRESSION-2 = ( THE INTEGRAL OF ( ( ( ( SIN ( C * T ) EXP TWO ) *

            COS ( C * T ) ) + ( T EXP - ONE ) ) * D T ) )

    )

TASK-STRUCTURES  (

    TOP-GOAL = ' TRANSFORM EXPRESSION-1 INTO THE DESIRED-OBJ . )

    DESIRED-OBJ = ( SUBEXPRESSION-TESTS

                THE SYMBOL DOES NOT-EQUAL INTEGRAL . )

    SYM-DIFF = ( SYMBOL )

    TABLE-OF-CONNECTIONS = ( 1. ( SET-SIZE DIFFERENTIATE )

                2. ( SYM-DIFF INTEGRATE ) )

    DIFF-ORDERING = ( 1. SYM-DIFF

                2. SET-SIZE )

    LIST-OF-OPR = ( INTEGRATE DIFFERENTIATE )

    LIST-OF-VAR = ( F G U N )

    )

END
```

Fig. 31 (cont.).

OBJECTS

In GPS there are two basic representations for objects, which are described below.

OBJECT-SCHEMA

An OBJECT-SCHEMA is a tree structure, encoded in IPL description lists, which represents an object. Each node of the tree structure can have an arbitrary number of branches leading from it to other nodes. In addition to branches, each node can have a local description given by an arbitrary number of attribute–value pairs. The tree structure in Fig. 32a, for example, represents the initial situation in the Missionaries and Cannibals task. In Fig. 32a, the node to which the LEFT* branch leads represents the left bank of the river, and that to which the RIGHT branch leads represents the right bank. The local description at the node to which the LEFT branch leads indicates that there are three missionaries, three cannibals, and a boat at that bank of the river. The symbols M and C are attributes; the symbols 0 and 3 are values.

GPS knows† the generic form of OBJECT-SCHEMAs. In particular, it knows the names of the branches FIRST, SECOND, etc., and thus knows that all OBJECT-SCHEMAs have the form illustrated in Fig. 32b. GPS also knows the form of the local descriptions of the nodes and can generate the attribute–value pairs of a node, because such attributes are declared to be ATTRIBUTEs, and are thus a special class of symbols. For example, GPS knows that the M, C, and BOAT in Fig. 32a are ATTRIBUTEs because they are so declared in the task specification (Fig. 30).

LOC-PROGs (LOCation-PROGrams) are a special class of data structure used to refer to the nodes of an OBJECT-SCHEMA. They consist of an ordered list of the branches on the path between two nodes. LOC-PROGs designate one node of an OBJECT-SCHEMA *relative* to another node; i.e., they are functions of one argument—a node of an OBJECT-SCHEMA. For example, the LOC-PROG "SECOND-FIRST" (i.e., the branch SECOND followed by the branch FIRST) of the node containing a + in Fig. 32b designates the node containing a *. The name of a LOC-PROG that designates an immediate subnode of a node is the name of the branch that leads to the node. For example, the LOC-PROG "SECOND" of the node containing a + in Fig. 32b designates the node containing an X. TOP-NODE is the LOC-PROG that designates the given node of an OBJECT-SCHEMA—i.e., it is the null LOC-PROG. Internally, all branches are FIRST, SECOND, etc.; however, in the specifications other names are sometimes used (e.g., LEFT for FIRST in Fig. 30).

---

* LEFT is not part of the basic vocabulary of GPS; it is capitalized because it is defined in the task specification (Fig. 30) and is represented by an IPL symbol—in this case, an attribute.

† We say that GPS *knows* (*or understands*) something when the programmer assumes that knowledge in constructing the code that defined GPS. Hence, GPS knows the generic form of OBJECT-SCHEMAs, because details of their structure are assumed in the routines that process OBJECT-SCHEMAs. But GPS does not know (or understand) the details of a particular task. They are defined in the task specification in terms of the things that GPS does know, listed in Appendix A.

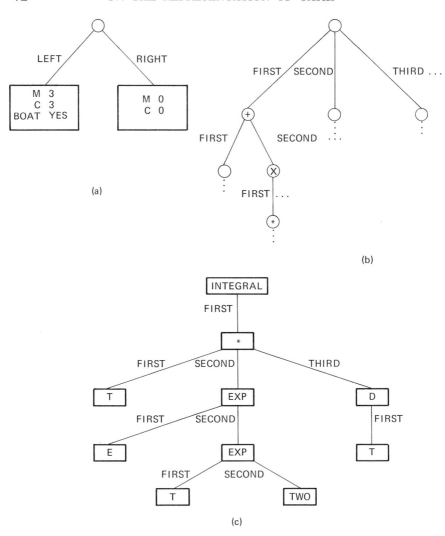

Fig. 32. Diagrams (a) and (c) are the tree-structure representations of the initial situations of the Missionaries and Cannibals task and an Integration task, respectively; (b) is the generic form of an OBJECT-SCHEMA.

The given object in the Integration task in Fig. 29 is represented by the tree structure in Fig. 32c. In this example, it is assumed that each node has two ATTRIBUTEs—SIGN and SYMBOL—but only their values are shown in Fig. 32c. The usual convention that a missing sign signifies a plus is adopted in this example. Since all of the signs are plus, none appear in Fig. 32c.

As mentioned in Chapter II, often there is more than one given object or one desired object in a problem. The use of variables in OBJECT-SCHEMAs allows a class of objects to be represented as a single structure. For example, the OBJECT-SCHEMA

$$\int e^u \, du,$$

where u is a free variable, represents a large class of objects. All members of the class have the same form but different values for u. Two objects that are members of the class are

$$\int e^{t^2} \, d(t^2)$$

and

$$\int e^{\sin t} \, d(\sin t).$$

GPS assumes that all OBJECT-SCHEMAS may contain variables and is prepared to process them as a class of objects. GPS can recognize the variables in OBJECT-SCHEMAs because the task specification indicates which symbols are variables.

OBJECT-SCHEMAS can represent only those classes of objects whose members all have the same form. One way to represent classes of objects whose forms are different is a list of OBJECT-SCHEMAs. In GPS the initial situation, but not the desired situation, can be a list of OBJECT-SCHEMAs.* But either the initial situation or the desired situation, both of which are given in the task specification, can be an OBJECT-SCHEMA. All of the objects generated during problem solving are OBJECT-SCHEMAS.

DESCRIBED-OBJs

A DESCRIBED-OBJ is a list of constraints that represents the class of objects, each of which satisfies all of the constraints. The desired object in the Integration task (Fig. 29) can be represented by a DESCRIBED-OBJ as the single constraint that must be satisfied at each node:

The SYMBOL does not equal $\int$.

Each constraint in a DESCRIBED-OBJ is a TEST that is a data structure consisting of a RELATION and several arguments (in most cases, two). A RELATION is a Boolean function of several arguments and is

---

* This restriction and several others arise because the methods of GPS cannot deal with the more general case. Sometimes (although not always) the restriction could be lifted by the addition of new methods. However, since we wish to keep the problem-solving character of GPS constant, we have not permitted the addition of new methods.

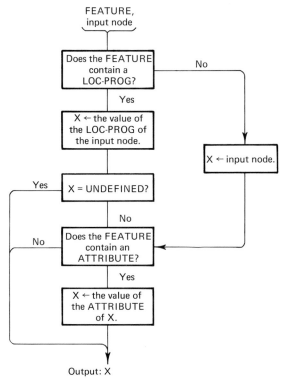

Fig. 33. Flow-chart for the evaluation of a FEATURE of a node of an OBJECT-SCHEMA.

a special type of symbol. In the previous example, the TEST is

> RELATION is NOT-EQUAL;
>
> first argument is SYMBOL;
>
> second argument is ∫.

GPS recognizes NOT-EQUAL as a RELATION and understands the semantics of all RELATIONs. (GPS currently knows fifteen RELATIONs, whose definitions are given in Appendix A; only these can be used, unless new ones are added.) On the other hand, ∫ is peculiar to the integration task and GPS treats it as a symbolic CONSTANT. SYMBOL is also peculiar to integration, but it is declared in the task specification to be an ATTRIBUTE. Thus, GPS treats SYMBOL in the Integration task in the same way as M (missionaries) in the Missionaries and Cannibals task.

An argument of a TEST is either a constant (i.e., not a function of objects, such as a CONSTANT or SET) or a FEATURE of an object. A FEATURE, which is a means of referring to a feature of an arbitrary object, is a function of one argument—a node of an object. A FEATURE is specified by an ATTRIBUTE and a LOC-PROG; the value of the FEATURE is the value of the ATTRIBUTE of the node designated by the LOC-PROG. (FEATUREs always have values, but a possible value is UNDEFINED.) For example, the FEATURE M LEFT of the OBJECT-SCHEMA in Fig. 32a has the value 3. LOC-PROGs and ATTRIBUTEs, like FEATUREs, are functions of one argument—a node of an object. Figure 33 shows how FEATUREs are evaluated.

Since a FEATURE is a function of an implied node of an object, a TEST is also a function of an implied node of an object because it may contain a FEATURE. In a DESCRIBED-OBJ, there are in general two kinds of TEST: (1) those whose implied node is the TOP-NODE of the implied OBJECT-SCHEMA; and (2) those whose implied node is every node of the implied OBJECT-SCHEMA. Each of the latter set of TESTs is evaluated for each node of the object as the implied node, and the TEST is true only if it is true for each evaluation.

Only the desired situation can be represented as a DESCRIBED-OBJ; the initial situation and the objects generated by the problem-solving process cannot be represented as DESCRIBED-OBJs.

OPERATORS

In GPS there are two different types of operator, which are discussed below.

FORM-OPERATORS

A simple way to express an operator is to state the form of its input object and the form of its resultant object. For example, the first operator in Fig. 29 can be expressed as follows, assuming u is a variable:

input object form: $\int u^n\, du$

resultant object form: $\dfrac{u^{n+1}}{n+1}.$

Such an expression will be called a FORM-OPERATOR. Both forms are OBJECT-SCHEMAs and thus represent classes of objects. The above FORM-OPERATOR can be applied to any object in the class of objects represented by the input OBJECT-SCHEMA. The resultant object is obtained by substituting for u in the resultant OBJECT-SCHEMA the value used for u in the input OBJECT-SCHEMA.

All of the operators in the integration task in Fig. 29 can be expressed as FORM-OPERATORs by expressing the left and right sides of the equation as the input OBJECT-SCHEMA and the resultant OBJECT-SCHEMA, respectively. However, FORM-OPERATORs are not an adequate means for expressing the operators of some tasks, e.g., the Missionaries and Cannibals task.

MOVE-OPERATORS

A MOVE-OPERATOR represents an operator by a group of TESTs and a group of TRANSFORMATIONs. The TRANSFORMATIONs describe how the resultant object differs from the input object, and the TESTs must be satisfied for the operator to be feasible. In the Missionaries and Cannibals task, for example, the operator in Fig. 28 can be stated as a MOVE-OPERATOR. The TESTs of the operator ensure that nothing chaotic happens, such as missionaries being eaten, and the TRANSFORMATIONs describe how the object changes when people cross the river in the boat. Before giving a complete statement of the MOVE-OPERATOR representation of the operator in Fig. 28, we define TRANSFORMATIONs.

A TRANSFORMATION is a data structure consisting of an OPERATION and several arguments. A typical TRANSFORMATION that might appear in the Missionaries and Cannibals task is:

> OPERATION is MOVE;
>
> first argument is BOAT LEFT;
>
> second argument is BOAT RIGHT.

The meaning of this TRANSFORMATION is:

> Find the value of the BOAT at the LEFT;
>
> Make the value of the BOAT at the RIGHT
> equal to the result of the preceding step;
>
> Remove the BOAT at the LEFT.

If the result of the first step is UNDEFINED, the TRANSFORMATION is not applicable to the object, and the operator is infeasible.

GPS knows the meaning of MOVE and all other OPERATIONs in the same way that it understands the RELATIONs. (There are six different OPERATIONs, which are defined in Appendix A.) GPS also recognizes

1. MOVE (BOAT FROM-SIDE , BOAT TO-SIDE)
2. DECREASE (M FROM-SIDE , M TO-SIDE , X)
3. DECREASE (C FROM-SIDE , C TO-SIDE , Y)

(a)

1. One is TRUE :
  NOT-GREATER-THAN (C LEFT , M LEFT)
  EQUALS (M LEFT , O)
2. One is TRUE :
  NOT-GREATER-THAN (C RIGHT , M RIGHT)
  EQUALS (M RIGHT , O)

(b)

1. EXCLUSIVE-MEMBER (FROM-SIDE , [LEFT , RIGHT])
2. EXCLUSIVE-MEMBER (TO-SIDE , [LEFT , RIGHT])
3. CONSTRAINED-MEMBER (X , [0 , 1 , 2] ,
       IN-THE-SET (X + Y , [1 , 2]))
4. CONSTRAINED-MEMBER (Y , [0 , 1 , 2] ,
       IN-THE-SET (X + Y , [1 , 2]))

(c)

Fig. 34. The operator that moves X missionaries (M), Y cannibals (C) and the BOAT from the FROM-SIDE to the TO-SIDE: (a) the TRANSFORMATIONS of the operator; (b) the TESTS that the resultant object of the operator must satisfy; (c) the TESTS that constrain the legitimate values of the variables.

that the two arguments of the above TRANSFORMATION are FEATURES. Although both arguments of MOVE must be FEATUREs, in general, only the second argument of an OPERATION must be a FEATURE.

The TRANSFORMATIONs in Fig. 34a describe how an object is modified when X missionaries (M) and Y cannibals (C) go from the FROM-SIDE of the river to the TO-SIDE of the river. X, Y, FROM-SIDE, and TO-SIDE are all variables. Thus, these three TRANSFORMATIONs represent all possible ways that missionaries and cannibals can cross the river. The first TRANSFORMATION is the example we have just discussed, except that the two location programs are variables. The second TRANSFORMATION in Fig. 34a means[*]

> Decrement the number of missionaries at the FROM-SIDE by X.

> Increment the number of missionaries at the TO-SIDE by X.

[*] It would seem that "move" would be a better name than DECREASE. But MOVE is a different OPERATION and DECREASE results in a readable statement in the task specification. See the MOVES in the M-C-OPR in Fig. 30.

If the number of missionaries at the FROM-SIDE is less than X, the TRANSFORMATION is not applicable and the operator is infeasible.

TRANSFORMATIONs are functions of nodes of objects because they contain FEATUREs, which are functions of objects. But unlike a TEST, each TRANSFORMATION is a function of two object nodes—a node of the input object and the corresponding node of the resultant object. The input-object node is used to designate the inputs to the TRANSFORMATIONs, and the TRANSFORMATIONs are performed relative to the resultant-object node. In the first TRANSFORMATION in Fig. 34a, for example, the value of the BOAT at the FROM-SIDE of the input object is found. Then this value is placed in the resultant object as the value of the BOAT at the TO-SIDE. Finally, the ATTRIBUTE "BOAT" and its value are removed from the FROM-SIDE of the resultant object. In this particular example, the value has no significance— i.e., the ATTRIBUTE "BOAT" always has the value "YES"—but, in general, an ATTRIBUTE may have many different values and the value that is "moved" is its value in the input object.

The constraints in Fig. 34b represent the class of objects in which no missionaries can be eaten. The form of these constraints is the conjunction of two disjunctive sets of TESTs. Normally in a set of TESTs the logical connective of the tests is a conjunction. That is, objects that satisfy *all* of the TESTs are members of the class. But a set of TESTs can be divided into disjunctive subsets by using TRUE* which GPS recognizes and understands. TRUE is a RELATION on one argument—a set of TESTs. It is the only RELATION that has a set of TESTs as an argument and is processed somewhat differently than other RELATIONs.

All legal Missionaries and Cannibals objects must satisfy the constraints in Fig. 34b; else missionaries would be eaten. Consequently, both the input object and the resultant object of the operator must satisfy the constraints in Fig. 34b. But, if all objects produced by the application of the operator satisfy these constraints, all of the input objects to the operator will also satisfy the constraints, because the input object is either the initial situation or a result of a previous operator application. Thus, the constraints in Fig. 34b need only be satisfied by the resultant object. This fact is indicated by a syntactic device described in the last section of this chapter.

The variables in MOVE-OPERATORs are not universally quantified but can only take on certain values. The TESTs in Fig. 34c must be

---

* Although TRUE is a strange name for this RELATION ("or" would be more suggestive), it results in a readable statement. See POST-TESTs of the M-C-OPR in Fig. 30.

satisfied if the variables in the TRANSFORMATIONS in Fig. 34a are to have legitimate values. The first two TESTS in Fig. 34c ensure that both TO-SIDE and FROM-SIDE are either LEFT or RIGHT but that they are different. A TEST whose RELATION is EXCLUSIVE-MEMBER is true if the first argument is in the set designated by the second argument and if no other "exclusive member" of the set has the same value as the first argument. Thus, the concept of an exclusive member is an alternate way to state that α, β, and γ are in a set and that $\alpha \neq \beta$, $\alpha \neq \gamma$, and $\beta \neq \gamma$.

The third and fourth TESTS in Fig. 34c ensure that the number of people in the boat is legitimate. A TEST whose RELATION is CON-STRAINED-MEMBER is true if the third argument, which must be a TEST, is true and if the first argument is in the set designated by the second argument. CONSTRAINED-MEMBER and its negation are the only RELATIONS that have a TEST as an argument. Figure 34 is the MOVE-OPERATOR representation of the operator in Fig. 28 without the syntax of the external representation.

In general, a MOVE-OPERATOR is a set of TRANSFORMATIONS and three sets of TESTS. The operator is feasible if all of the TESTS (with the exception of some in a disjunctive subset) are satisfied and the TRANSFORMATIONS are applicable. Two of the sets of TESTS are stated relative to the node of the input object to which the operator is applied. One of these (indicated syntactically by VAR-DOMAIN) must be satisfied in order for the variables in the operator to have legitimate values. The other (indicated syntactically by PRE-TESTS) constrains the class of input objects for which the operator is feasible. The third set of TESTS (POST-TESTS) must be satisfied by the resultant object. Any of these sets may be empty, in which case it is, by convention, satisfied.

GOALS

A goal is a data structure consisting of the information necessary for a problem-solving context. For example, a goal has as the values of attributes the names of its supergoals, the names of subgoals, its type, its objects, its operator, its difference, and so on. The only goal that appears in the specification of a task is the TOP-GOAL—the statement of the problem. The type and the objects of the TOP-GOAL are given in the task specification; all of the other information is generated internally by GPS. The TOP-GOAL of all of the tasks in Chapter VI has the same form: TRANSFORM one object into another. The TOP-

GOAL could be a different type of goal, e.g., REDUCE, although this situation has not arisen here.

DIFFERENCES

A difference, which GPS detects in matching two objects, is a data structure consisting of a difference type, the value of the difference, and the name of the node where the difference was detected. For example, in matching the given situation to the desired situation in the Missionaries and Cannibals task, GPS would find the following differences:

> difference type is M, LEFT;
>
> difference value is −3;
>
> difference location is TOP-NODE.

Difference types are task dependent and must be defined for each task. But differences are not given in the task specification; they are generated during problem solving.

Currently, all difference types are FEATUREs. Although a richer representation for difference types would be desirable, FEATUREs are adequate for the tasks discussed in Chapter VI.*

TABLE-OF-CONNECTIONS

TABLE-OF-CONNECTIONS is a data structure that associates with each difference type a list of operators. Each operator on a list has the capability of reducing the difference type with which the list is associated. The operators in the TABLE-OF-CONNECTIONS can be either FORM-OPERATORS or MOVE-OPERATORS. Thus, the TABLE-OF-CONNECTIONS is a way to give GPS, exogenously, information about the properties of operators. However, as we shall see later, it need not be used for MOVE-OPERATORS in some cases.

---

* The logic task that was given to previous versions of GPS (see p. 25) required more complex differences, such as a decrease in the number of occurrences of a term. This issue is discussed in Chapter V.

DIFF-ORDERING

DIFF-ORDERING is a list of difference types and/or groups of difference types that are ordered according to difficulty. GPS considers the difference types at the top of the list to be the most difficult to alleviate and those at the bottom the easiest. All difference types within a group on the list are considered equally difficult. DIFF-ORDERING is a means to give GPS information about the nature of the difference types.

COMPARE-OBJECTS

The MATCH-DIFF-METHOD (Fig. 18) subdivides a data structure into parts and detects differences (if any exist) between corresponding parts. COMPARE-OBJECTS is a data structure that specifies for the MATCH-DIFF-METHOD how two OBJECT-SCHEMAS should be matched. There are two options for subdividing OBJECT-SCHEMAS into parts: match each pair of corresponding nodes or match the two OBJECT-SCHEMAS *in toto* (i.e., match only the top nodes). COMPARE-OBJECTS specifies which of these options is to hold. It also specifies the types of differences to be detected. Since these are all FEATURES, a simple list is adequate to provide this information. The MATCH-DIFF-METHOD also requires that the immediate operators be provided for each task. Since these are specified by IPL routines, they do not appear in Fig. 30. In general they do not vary with task, since they are used primarily to mechanize substitution.

If the desired situation is a DESCRIBED-OBJ, COMPARE-OBJECTS is not required in the representation of a task because the information is contained implicitly in the process that compares a DESCRIBED-OBJ to an OBJECT-SCHEMA.

DECLARATIONS

Besides the foregoing structures, GPS must be given the types of the symbols with which it deals. Some of the basic types are part of GPS's basic knowledge, e.g., LOC-PROGS and RELATIONS. Others are declared individually or by listing them; e.g., LIST-OF-VAR is a list of the symbols that should be interpreted as variables; LIST-OF-OPR is a list of the FORM-OPERATORs; BOAT is declared an ATTRIBUTE; the initial situation is declared an OBJECT-SCHEMA; and so on. No attempt has been made to minimize the number of declarations needed, although with some assumptions about the structure of the external environment and the communication situation a good many of the declarations could be inferred.

EXTERNAL REPRESENTATION OF A GPS TASK

As we noted at the beginning of the chapter, a moderately readable external representation was designed in which to specify a new task to GPS. Although of little substantive interest in itself, we give here enough description of the external language to ease the reading of the task specifications.

A task description in the external representation is a string of words, and the final word in the string is END. Space is used to delimit words. A word, then, is any string of characters that does not contain a space but is preceded and followed by a space.

Comments, which are ignored, can be inserted in the string of words at any occurrence of a space. $ is used to denote comments. A comment is a $ followed by any string of characters not containing a $, followed by a $. All comments must be preceded and followed by a space.

A task description contains meta-words and text-words. The meta-words are instructions to the translator on how to interpret the text-words. All of the meta-words are listed in Appendix A, Section 1, along with their function.

The most commonly used meta-words are left and right parentheses, "(" and ")." They serve their usual function of delimiting a group of words. Throughout the translating process ")" is matched to the corresponding "(" so that they can be nested. Although the use of parentheses is a very powerful punctuation device, extensive use of them makes the text unreadable. An attempt was made to give the text a syntactic structure that limited the occurrences of parentheses. In addition to parentheses, periods and commas are used to delimit groups of words.

All of the remaining meta-words determine the *mode of translation*. Text-words are translated under the current mode of translation, and the current mode can be changed only by the occurrence of certain meta-words, each of which is discussed below.

RENAME

The text-words in the basic vocabulary of GPS, which are given in Appendix A, appear in task specifications and are replaced by their corresponding IPL symbols in translation. For convenience, these words can be assigned new names in the RENAME mode of translation. The format of such assignment statements is

$$W1 = W2.$$

The word W1 becomes associated with the IPL symbol that was previously associated with W2. W2 is free to be used for a different purpose. For example, in the Missionaries and Cannibals task specification, FIRST is assigned the new name LEFT.

SKIP-WORDS

The basic strategy of the translator is to process key words and ignore all others. All of the text-words translated in the SKIP-WORDS mode are designated as words that should be ignored. The words that are normally ignored are listed in Appendix A, Section 3.

DECLARE

All text-words that (1) are not assigned an internal symbol, (2) are not to be ignored, or (3) are not in the basic vocabulary (e.g., AT-TRIBUTE, OBJECT-SCHEMA, etc.) are assigned a *type*. In the DECLARE mode of translation a word is assigned a type by a statement of the form

$$W1 = W2.$$

This means that the word W2 is assigned to be the type of the word W1. For example, in the Missionaries and Cannibals task, BOAT is assigned the type ATTRIBUTE. By convention, if a word is not explicitly assigned a type in the DECLARE mode, it is assigned the type CONSTANT.

TASK-STRUCTURES

All of the data structures of a task, e.g., FEATUREs, OBJECT-SCHEMAs, etc., are translated in the TASK-STRUCTURES mode after the words have been assigned types. The format for data structures is

$$W1 = (W2\,W3 \cdot \cdot \cdot WN).$$

The data structure's name is $W1$, and $W2 \cdot \cdot \cdot WN$ are the substructures that comprise the structure. They may be either words or parenthesized expressions.

The name of any structure must be assigned a type prior to translating it as a data structure. Associated with certain types are the forms of their data structures, and the structures are translated according to these forms. For example, the Missionaries and Cannibals task (Fig. 30) contains the data structure

M-L = (THE M AT THE LEFT.).

Prior to the occurrence of this structure, M-L was assigned the type FEATURE. The form of a FEATURE has two "slots": one is for an ATTRIBUTE and the other is for a LOC-PROG. Neither "slot" need be filled. In constructing M-L, the translator copies the form of a FEATURE and fills the "ATTRIBUTE slot" with M, since it was declared to be an ATTRIBUTE, and the "LOC-PROG slot" with LEFT, since it is the new name of FIRST which is a LOC-PROG. (AT and THE are ignored). It then assigns this data structure to the M-L. Thus, the language interprets expressions largely according to their semantics (i.e., their types). Order is used only when the semantics is ambiguous, as in two subexpressions of the same type.

Most data structures are quite similar to OBJECT-SCHEMAs in that they are tree structures. Figure 35 shows a MOVE-OPERATOR in the internal tree-structure form. The tree representation is used for MOVE-OPERATORs in order to keep the internal representation of data homogeneous. However, it seems more natural to consider MOVE-OPERATORs as groups of TESTs and TRANSFORMATIONs, rather than as a tree.

The main work of the translator is to convert the linear text into the hierarchal structures of the internal representation. This conversion is done by filling slots in the forms, because the forms have the hierarchal structure built into them. There is a provision for adding new forms without modifying the translator.

The formal syntax of the language will not be given since it is rather complicated. An informal description of the syntax will be given by describing the standard forms of the data structures. However, most of these standard forms must be modified slightly in certain cases: for example, TEST usually has two arguments, but when the RELATION is CONSTRAINED-MEMBER it has a third argument. Thus, there are some syntactic devices for modifying forms, such as a means for in-

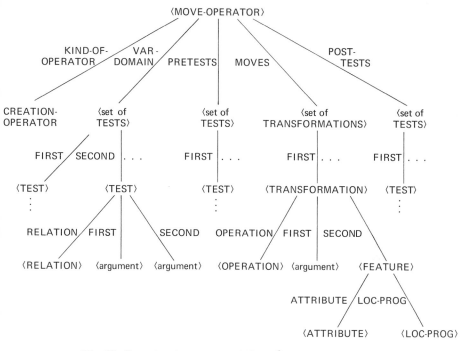

Fig. 35. Tree-structure representation of a MOVE-OPERATOR.

serting symbols in standard forms and for inserting punctuation; e.g., the period for terminating structures. Any exceptions to the standard forms will be noted in Appendix A, Section 2, under the words that are responsible for the modification of the forms; e.g., the definition of CONSTRAINED-MEMBER designates the fact that it is a RELATION on three arguments.

The notation used for a form is a list of items. Each member of the list will be assigned a label such as *a*, *b*, and so on. If the order of the list is important, it will be designated as an *ordered form;* otherwise, it is an *unordered form.* Certain items in the forms may be *optional;* i.e., they may occur but are not required. Unless otherwise stated, items are not optional. The meta symbols "<" and ">" are used to denote classes; e.g., <ATTRIBUTE> means any word that has been assigned the type ATTRIBUTE. Lists and sets are represented externally by sequences of expressions enclosed in parentheses.*

* Internally, lists become IPL lists and sets become attribute-value structures using FIRST, SECOND, . . . , as in Fig. 35.

TOP-GOAL.   TOP-GOAL has the ordered form

    a.   TRANSFORM;

    b.   <OBJECT-SCHEMA or list of OBJECT-SCHEMAS>;

    c.   <OBJECT-SCHEMA or DESCRIBED-OBJ>.

As noted above, if a list of OBJECT-SCHEMAs is given in *b*, then the name of a sequence of OBJECT-SCHEMAs is required, not just a sequence of names.

FEATURES.   A FEATURE has the unordered form

        a.   <ATTRIBUTE>;

        b.   <LOC-PROG>.

Both *a* and *b* are optional. M-L in Fig. 30 is an example of a FEATURE. LEFT is *b* and M is *a*. The other words are ignored.

SETS.   A SET is an ordered list of words. Although SETs are ordered, the order is usually unimportant. For example, IN-THE-SET does not depend on the order of the elements of a SET. SIDES in Fig. 30 is the set of two elements, LEFT and RIGHT.

EXPRES.   An EXPRES (EXPRESsion) is a list of numbers or variables that stand for numbers separated by +. This elementary form of an arithmetic expression could easily be generalized, but it is sufficient for the tasks encountered.

TESTS.   A TEST has the ordered form

        a.   <argument>;

        b.   <RELATION>;

        c.   <argument>.

Each argument is either a FEATURE, a CONSTANT, a SET, an EXPRES, or a variable. In the first TEST following VAR-DOMAIN in Fig. 30, *a* is FROM-SIDE, *b* is EXCLUSIVE-MEMBER, and *c* is SIDE-SET. The other words are ignored.

TRANSFORMATIONS.   The ordered form of a TRANSFORMATION is

        a.   <OPERATION>;

        b.   <argument>;

        c.   <FEATURE>.

In general, the argument can be of the same type as the argument of a TEST, but certain OPERATIONs require that the argument must be a FEATURE. In the first TRANSFORMATION following MOVES in Fig. 30, *a* is MOVE, *b* is the FEATURE "FROM-SIDE BOAT," and *c* is the FEATURE "TO-SIDE BOAT."

MOVE-OPERATORS. MOVE-OPERATOR has the unordered form

    a.   <kind of operator>;

    b.   VAR-DOMAIN   <list of TESTs>;

    c.   PRETESTS   <list of TESTs>;

    d.   MOVES   <list of TRANSFORMATIONs>;

    e.   POST-TESTS   <list of TESTs>.

In all of the examples in Chapter VI, *a* is a CREATION-OPERATOR because the resultant object is always to be a new object. An alternative value for *a* is MODIFICATION-OPERATOR, which would indicate that the resultant object is the input object, modified. MODIFICATION-OPERATORs never occur with this version of GPS, because it assumes that after an object is generated it is not destroyed. Only *a* and *d* must exist; *b*, *c*, and *e* are optional.

The first argument of each TEST associated with VAR-DOMAIN is assumed to be a variable that stands for itself. Often such a variable could be a FEATURE as well. For example, in Fig. 30 the first argument of the third TEST of VAR-DOMAIN is FROM-SIDE. The intent is that the *value* of this argument is either LEFT or RIGHT and not a node that represents the bank of the river in an object.

The TESTs following POST-TESTS are stated relative to the resultant object; the others are stated relative to the input object. Any of three kinds of tests (*b*, *c*, *e*) may be missing. In M-C-OPR in Fig. 30, for example, *c* is missing.

DESCRIBED-OBJS. A DESCRIBED-OBJ has the unordered form

    a.   TEX-DESCRIPTION   <set of TESTs>;

    b.   SUBEXPRESSION-TESTS   <set of TESTs>.

Both *a* and *b* are optional. DESIRED-OBJ in Fig. 31 is an example of a DESCRIBED-OBJ. Since there are no TESTs peculiar to the TOP-NODE in it, *a* is missing. The TESTs in *b* must be true of every node of the objects represented by the DESCRIBED-OBJ.

OBJECT-SCHEMA. An OBJECT-SCHEMA has the recursive unordered form

    a. <LOC-PROG> (<OBJECT-SCHEMA>)

    b. ATTRIBUTE <word>.

There may be any number of items of the form *a* or of the form *b*, including none. INITIAL-OBJ in Fig. 30 is an example of an OBJECT-SCHEMA.

DIFF-ORDERING. DIFF-ORDERING is a list of FEATUREs and groups of FEATUREs. The FEATUREs of the same group are enclosed in parentheses (see Fig. 30).

TABLE-OF-CONNECTIONS. TABLE-OF-CONNECTIONS is a list of items of the form.

    a. <FEATURE> (<list of operators>).

COMMON-DIFFERENCE stands for all FEATUREs (see Fig. 30).

COMPARE-OBJECTS. COMPARE-OBJECTS has the form

    a. (BASIC-MATCH),

where BASIC-MATCH has the ordered form

    b. COMP-FEAT-LIST <list of FEATUREs>;

    c. SUBEXPRESSIONS.

Item *c* is optional. In Fig. 30, *c* is missing, which indicates that differences are observed only at the TOP-NODE of objects. The FEATUREs following COMP-FEAT-LIST are the type of differences for which the match looks.

ADDITIONAL FACILITIES

Any TEST can be universally quantified over one variable. Such a TEST is treated as an arbitrary number of TESTs—one TEST for each value of the variable. The test is true only if it is true for all values of the variable. Quantification is syntactically indicated by the occurrence, in a TEST, of FOR-ALL followed by a variable followed by an argument that designates a SET. In such a TEST, the variable is quantified over all members of the SET. (The Tower of Hanoi task specification uses this facility.) (See pp. 150–156.)

A FEATURE can be used to designate a feature of any type of data structure and not only features of OBJECT-SCHEMAs. However, unless stated explicitly, a FEATURE takes as its argument the object that is implicitly designated—e.g., the object being operated upon. Whenever PARTICULAR, followed by the name of a data structure, occurs in a FEATURE, the FEATURE refers to that data structure rather than to the implicit object. (An example occurs in the Tower of Hanoi task specification.) (See pp. 150–156.)

The syntax of OBJECT-SCHEMA in the external language is clumsy for expressing the objects of some tasks. For example,

$$\int t \, dt$$

expressed as an OBJECT-SCHEMA is

(SYMBOL INTEGRAL LEFT (SYMBOL * LEFT (SYMBOL T)
    RIGHT (SYMBOL D LEFT (SYMBOL T)))).

To alleviate this clumsiness, there are some conversion routines that allow OBJECT-SCHEMA to be expressed in a language with a different syntax.

In the LIST mode of translation, a string of symbols enclosed by matching parentheses are loaded as a linear list. In this mode, the translator does not consider "(" and ")" as meta-words, even though it does match the "(" to ")." Objects and operators whose statements contain parentheses can be translated in the LIST mode and converted to internal form after translation. For example, the operators and initial situation of integration (Fig. 31) are translated in the LIST mode.

EXAMPLE

The translation of the Missionaries and Cannibals task in Fig. 30 illustrates the way in which the text is processed. Starting at the top of Fig. 30, RENAME designates the mode of translation and the translator assigns LEFT and RIGHT to be the new names of FIRST and SECOND, respectively. The ")" signifies the end of the scope of RENAME, and DECLARE changes the mode of translation. BOAT is then assigned the type ATTRIBUTE, and the other declaration statements are processed similarly. The next ")" indicates the end of the scope of DECLARE, and TASK-STRUCTURES becomes the mode of translation.

TOP-GOAL, whose form happens to be identical in all tasks, is the first data structure to be translated. TOP-GOAL is defined by the text (enclosed in parentheses) that follows it. The word that follows the next ")," INITIAL-OBJ, is the name of the next data structure to be translated. INITIAL-OBJ does not correspond to an IPL symbol in the basic vocabulary of GPS and is assigned a new IPL symbol for this task. (The same IPL symbol is also used for the occurrence of INITIAL-OBJ in TOP-GOAL.) INITIAL-OBJ is translated according to the form of an OBJECT-SCHEMA because it has been so declared. The ")" that matches the "(" following INITIAL-OBJ indicates the end of its definition.

After translating DESCRIBED-OBJ in the same way, the EXPRES "x+y" is translated. x+y and the three SETs that follow are used in the definition of the M-C-OPR.

FROM-SIDE-TESTS is translated as V-TESTS whose form is a disjunctive set of TESTs. FROM-SIDE-TESTS consists of the two TESTs enclosed in the parentheses that follow it. TO-SIDE-TESTS are used in similarly. Both FROM-SIDE-TESTS and TO-SIDE-TESTS are used in the definition of the M-C-OPR.

The M-C-OPR, which is translated as a MOVE-OPERATOR, consists of the text enclosed in the parentheses that follow it. VAR-DOMAIN indicates that the four TESTs that follow specify the legitimate values of the variables in the M-C-OPR. MOVES indicates the end of the scope of VAR-DOMAIN and that the TRANSFORMATIONs of the operator follow. POST-TESTS signifies that the third TRANSFORMATION is the last and that the following constraints must be satisfied by any object produced by the M-C-OPR in order for it to be feasible. The POST-TESTS consists of two disjunctive sets of TESTs, which is indicated by the occurrences of TRUE.

After translating the M-C-OPR, the types of difference B-L through M-R are translated. Each of these data structures is translated as a FEATURE. They are used during problem solving as difference types rather than the arguments of TESTs only because their names occur in DIFF-ORDERING and BASIC-MATCH instead of in TESTs.

DIFF-ORDERING divides the types of differences into two groups (each enclosed in parentheses). The types of difference in the first group are considered more difficult than those in the second group; within each group there is no ordering.

TABLE-OF-CONNECTIONS consists of a single type of difference (COMMON-DIFFERENCE, which stands for any type of difference) with which a list of one operator is associated.

After translating the next four data structures, the translator recognizes the ")" matching the "(" following TASK-STRUCTURES, which indicates the end of its scope. The meta-word END terminates translation and control is transferred to the PROBLEM-SOLVING-EXECUTIVE of GPS.

CHAPTER V

REPRESENTATION AND GENERALITY

The interdependence of the power and generality of a problem solver was discussed in Chapter II. In the construction of a general problem solver, employing a fixed set of problem-solving techniques, the internal representation is critical; that is, it must be general so that tasks can be expressed in it; yet its structure must be simple enough for the problem-solving techniques to be applicable. Since the techniques require that certain information be abstracted from the internal representation, they are applicable only if processes that abstract the necessary information from the internal representation are feasible. Thus, the difficulty of constructing a general problem solver is determined primarily by the variety and complexity of its problem-solving techniques.

Chapter III described the problem-solving techniques of GPS, and Chapter IV described the internal representation of GPS. This chapter can now discuss the impact that the problem-solving techniques had on the way in which the internal representation of GPS-2-5 was generalized. To simplify the following discussion, the demands of the problem-solving techniques of GPS are summarized in Fig. 36. This is a list of processes that GPS must perform regardless of what internal representation is used. These processes are given in a simpli-

Object comparison	Test whether two objects represent the same situation.
Object difference	Find a difference between two objects if they do not represent the same situation.
Operator application	Produce the result of applying an operator to an object if the operator is feasible.
Operator difference	Find a difference between an object and the class of objects to which an operator can be applied, if the operator is not applicable to the object.
Desirability selection	Select from a set of operators those operators that are desirable.
Feasibility selection	Select from a set of operators those operators that are feasible.
Canonization	Find the canonical name of an uncanonized data structure (might depend on type of structure).

Fig. 36. Processes required by the problem-solving methods of GPS.

fied form. For example, in some cases objects are not represented individually, but are represented as classes of objects. In such cases, *object comparison* (Fig. 36) must test whether two classes of objects have any common members.

The first section of this chapter describes the properties of several different modes of representation and illustrates their correspondence to the types of objects and operators described in Chapter IV. The remainder of the chapter can then illustrate the interaction between the problem-solving techniques of GPS and its internal representation. Each section discusses some aspect of proposed tasks that prevented them from being expressed in the internal representation of the version of GPS available at the initiation of this work (GPS-2-5). The attempts to alleviate the deficiency in the internal representation are related. Some of these attempts have been successful while others could not be adequately carried out within the existing program.

MODES OF REPRESENTATION

We have asserted that a key role of a representation is the extent to which it allows the required processes to extract the information necessary to their operation. Thus, the appropriate way to represent alternative representations would be according to this ability. Our understanding of representation is hardly at such a stage. However, we have tried to develop a common framework such that all the representations used in GPS can be described in its terms and thus in some sense compared. However, we have not been concerned with extending this framework beyond the several types of representations used in GPS.

The basis of this framework is the processing required to answer questions of identity and instance; i.e., is X equal to Y, if both X and Y represent objects; and is X an instance of Y, if X represents an object and Y represents a class of objects? Such identity processes seem to be basic to most of the processes of Fig. 36 (all except possibly *desirability selection* and *feasibility selection*). The amount of work involved in answering the questions—that is, the amount of search— seems to agree with feelings about how directly information can be extracted.*

The framework provides a scheme for representing objects. Once this is in hand, extension to the representation of operators is immediate, as well as extension to differences at the level at which they occur in GPS.

FRAMEWORK FOR THE REPRESENTATION OF OBJECTS

The representation of an object is given by a set of *information units*. Each information unit has the same generic form: a *Boolean function* of several arguments (in most cases two). The arguments can be *atomic constants*—either symbolic or numeric. An argument can also be a *feature* of an object, which is a function whose domain is objects and whose range is values. (A FEATURE is a special kind of feature.) An example of an information unit is

the number of missionaries at the left bank of the river equals 3.

In this information unit,

the Boolean function is "equals";

the feature is "the number of missionaries at the left";

the atomic constant is "3."

This information unit represents the fact that there are three missionaries at the left bank of the river in the object.

* Our choice of this basis is also closely related to our assessment that much of the power of heuristic programs arises from the process of matching (Newell and Ernst, 1965).

A *subexpression* of an object is a subset of the information units that represent the total object. A *subexpression name* is a function whose domain is objects and whose range is subexpressions. An example of a subexpression name is "left," and its value in the initial situation of the Missionaries and Cannibals task is the subexpression consisting of the following three information units:

> missionaries at left = 3;
>
> cannibals at left = 3;
>
> boat at left = yes.

MODELS

One mode of representation, which will be called a *model*, is a set of information units all of which have the same form:

> Boolean function is = ;
>
> first argument is a feature;
>
> second argument is an atomic constant.

The set of information units that comprise a *model* must be consistent and complete. That is, each feature of the represented object must be contained in one and only one information unit.

For example, a *model* of the object $\int t \, dt$ is given in Fig. 37a, assuming that t is not a free variable and t and dt are ordered. Figure 37a uses the terminology of the formulation of integration in Fig. 31. Many features do not appear in Fig. 37a, e.g.,

LEFT-LEFT-LEFT   SYMBOL.

Nevertheless, Fig. 37a is complete because, by convention, all of those features that do not appear explicitly equal the special atomic constant "UNDEFINED."

The key property of *models* is that their identity test is a simple matching process, provided that the *models* use the same set of features. That is, two *models* are identical if and only if the atomic constants in each pair of information units that contain the same feature are identical. The match must place information units with the same features into correspondence. This will require search, if the information units do not occur in some canonical order. But this search is not open ended, since there is one and only one correspondence.

(a) SYMBOL = INTEGRAL   (b)   INTEGRAL
     LEFT SYMBOL = *
     LEFT-LEFT SYMBOL = T
     LEFT-RIGHT SYMBOL = D
     LEFT-RIGHT-LEFT SYMBOL = T

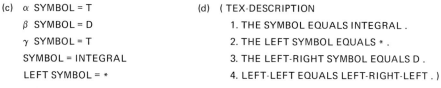

(c) α SYMBOL = T   (d) (TEX-DESCRIPTION
     β SYMBOL = D   1. THE SYMBOL EQUALS INTEGRAL .
     γ SYMBOL = T   2. THE LEFT SYMBOL EQUALS * .
       SYMBOL = INTEGRAL   3. THE LEFT-RIGHT SYMBOL EQUALS D .
       LEFT SYMBOL = *   4. LEFT-LEFT EQUALS LEFT-RIGHT-LEFT .)

Fig. 37. Different representations of the integral ∫*t dt:* (a) a model; (b) an OBJECT-SCHEMA tree structure; (c) an *unordered schema;* (d) a DESCRIBED-OBJ.

In GPS the tree structures generally provide a unique ordering, but unordered *models* will occur in the integration task.

SCHEMAS

There are two different kinds of *schemas,* which for present purposes can be considered as a single mode of representation. The simplest kind of *schema* has the same definition as a *model,* with the exception that the atomic constant in an information unit may be (but is not necessarily replaced by a variable whose domain is atomic constants. We shall not distinguish between those variables that are universally quantified and those variables whose domain is restricted, even though any restriction on the domain of variables must be given either explicitly in the encoding of the objects or by some uniform convention. The interpretation of *schemas* is that they represent a class of *models* each of which can be obtained by the substitution for variables. Hence, a *model* is the special kind of *schema* in which no variables appear.

The second kind of *schema* is the same as the one just described, with the exception that some of the information units may have the form

Boolean function is = ;

first argument is a subexpression name;

second argument is a variable whose domain is subexpressions.

For example, Fig. 37a is a schema representation of $\int t\,dt$, assuming t and dt are ordered. OBJECT-SCHEMAS are *schemas*, and if an OBJECT-SCHEMA contains no variables, it is a *model* as well as a *schema*.

Figure 37b is the tree-structure representation of the OBJECT-SCHEMA represented as a *schema* in Fig. 37a. Any variables in OBJECT-SCHEMAS stand for subexpressions. Hence, if T is a free variable, Fig. 37b represents the class of *models* whose LEFT-LEFT and LEFT-RIGHT-LEFT subexpressions can be any subexpression.

The key property of a *schema* is similar to that of a *model:* the identity test for two schemas is a match that incorporates the substitution for variables. It takes very little additional effort over the match for a *model*.

UNORDERED SCHEMAS

The *unordered-schema* mode of representation is the generalization of *schemas* in which the features or subexpression names in the information units may (or may not) be replaced by variables whose domains are features or subexpression names, respectively. Figure 37c is $\int t\,dt$ represented as an *unordered schema*, assuming that t and dt are unordered. α, β, and γ are variable features. If α is LEFT-LEFT SYMBOL, then β must be LEFT-RIGHT SYMBOL and γ must be LEFT-RIGHT-LEFT SYMBOL. On the other hand, if α is LEFT-RIGHT SYMBOL, then β must be LEFT-LEFT SYMBOL and γ must be LEFT-LEFT-LEFT SYMBOL. The variable features in Fig. 37c are not independent and are not universally quantified, but nevertheless they are variables.

Considerable complexity is introduced by using variable features and subexpression names because there is no unique way to place information units in correspondence as there was in *schemas*. However, the key property of *unordered schemas* is that the identity test is still a match that incorporates substitution of variables, provided that it substitutes values for variable features.

CHARACTERISTIC LISTS

In the modes or representation described so far, the only Boolean function used is equality. The match can be used for an identity test only because equality is both transitive and reflexive. That is, two information units that contain the same feature are identical only if their atomic constants are identical. When Boolean functions that are intransitive or irreflexive are used, the identity test is more complicated. For example, the two information units

$$\alpha \text{ is not less than } \beta \quad \text{and} \quad \alpha \neq \beta$$

are equivalent to the single information unit

$$\alpha > \beta$$

(α is a feature and β is a number).

A *characteristic list,* a mode of representation, consists of a set of information units, each of which has the generic form $R(\alpha, \beta)$, where

> R is in a given set of Boolean functions;
>
> α is a feature or a subexpression-name;
>
> β is a feature, subexpression-name, subexpression, or atomic constant.

A *characteristic list* is not neccessarily complete in the sense that a *model* must be complete. If none of the information units in a *characteristic list* contain a particular feature, by convention its value is irrelevant; whereas in a *model* its value was assumed to be UNDE-FINED. Two information units may contain the same feature and still be consistent because some of the Boolean functions may be intransitive or irreflexive and because an information unit may be a Boolean function of two features. For example, the two information units

$$\alpha > \beta \quad \text{and} \quad \beta < 5,$$

where α and β are features, are certainly not inconsistent.

DESCRIBED-OBJs in GPS are *characteristic lists.* Figure 37d is a DESCRIBED-OBJ that represents $\int t \, dt$.

Characteristic lists have the interesting property that all *schemas* can be represented as *characteristic lists,* even though the latter contain no explicit variables. (Since unmentioned features in *characteristic lists* can have any value, they have the flavor of a set of independent, universally quantified variables.) We shall not show that *characteristic lists* are as general as *schemas.* However, in Appendix B the operators of the logic task* are expressed both as

---

* Experiments with previous versions of GPS used extensively the formulation of the task of proving a theorem in the propositional calculus that is described on pp. 25–26. These are the operators from this specification of logic.

FORM-OPERATORs (which are *schemas*) and MOVE-OPERATORs without variables (which are *characteristic lists*). Note that some of the MOVE-OPERATORs in Appendix B can only be expressed as two FORM-OPERATORs.

CHARACTERISTIC-LIST SCHEMAS

The *characteristic-list schema* mode of representation is a generalization of the *characteristic list* that is obtained by allowing the use of variables for either argument of information units. Thus, *characteristic lists* are those *characteristic-list schemas* that do not contain variables. None of the data structures that represent objects in GPS are *characteristic-list schemas* which contain variables. DESCRIBED-OBJs do not contain any explicit variables, except for those variables associated with FOR-ALL. However, there are operators, i.e., MOVE-OPERATORs, that contain variables and hence are *characteristic-list schemas*.

TEST PROCESS

Another way to represent an object is as a program that takes a single object as its input and provides "yes" or "no" as its output. Such a program represents the object A if its execution, when A is the input, results in "yes" and if its execution on all other inputs results in "no." We shall call such a program a *test process*. A *test process* can also be used to represent a class of objects. In this case, the result of the program will be "yes" whenever its input is a member of the class and "no" for all other inputs. For example, the desired situation in checkers is represented as a *test process* in Samuel's program (1959).

In terms of our framework a *test process* is the mode of representation consisting of a single information unit of the form

$$R \text{ (total object)}.$$

R is the Boolean function defined by the *test process* program. Total object is the subexpression name that designates the entire object. For example, a *test process* representation of $\int t \, dt$ is a program that checks whether the input contains the information units in Fig. 37a. This implies that the *test process* must understand how information units are encoded.

One advantage of a *test process* is its generality. Any object represented in one of the other modes of representation can be represented as a *test process* if the *test process* is expressed in a general program-

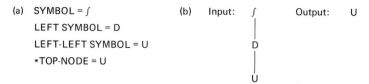

Fig. 38. (a) A *schema* encoded as a tree structure in (b).

ming language, e.g., IPL. Another advantage of a test process, of course, is that its identity test is the *test process* itself. The disadvantage of *test processes* is that they are unanalyzable processes as far as GPS is concerned.[*] Thus, *test processes* cannot be operated upon to produce new objects; nor can differences be extracted from a *test process* that produces a negative result.

MODES OF REPRESENTATION OF OPERATORS

In the following, we shall consider only operators that have one object (or one class of objects) as an input and one object (or one class of objects) as an output. This case can be generalized easily to the several-input, several-output case.

Operators involve statements about two objects: one is the input object, the other is the output object. For the purpose of this discussion, features and subexpression names preceded by an asterisk (*) will refer to the output object; other features and subexpression names will refer to the input object. (This syntactic device is not used in GPS.) Quite generally, then, the modes of representation for operators are obtained from the modes of representation of objects by allowing any of the features or subexpression names to be preceded by an asterisk. That is, an operator is a union of a set of information units that make assertions about the input expression (i.e., that represent it), with a set of information units that make assertions about the output expression, usually in terms of the input expression. Therefore, given an input expression, one can derive a set of information units that refer solely to the output expression; i.e., one can apply the operator.

FORM-OPERATORS are the union of the two sets of information units that represent the input and output *schemas*, respectively. The features and subexpression name in the latter are preceded by asterisks. Figure 38a is the operator *schema* of the FORM-OPERATOR in Fig. 38b.

---

[*] That processes described in programming languages such as IPL might be analyzable is not denied; however, from the viewpoint of the current GPS they are inscrutable.

The TRANSFORMATIONs of MOVE-OPERATORs are *characteristic-list schemas*. For example, TRANSFORMATIONs of the form

MOVE F1 TO F2,

where F1 and F2 are features, are equivalent to the three information units that incorporate the asterisk convention:

DEFINED (F1)

EQUALS (F1, * F2)

UNDEFINED (*F1).

Since all TRANSFORMATIONs can be restated as several information units, MOVE-OPERATORs are *characteristic-list schemas*. Figure 39a is the set of information units of the MOVE-OPERATOR in Fig. 39b. In Fig. 39a, *sum* is a Boolean function that is true if the sum of the first two arguments equals the third.

The modes of representation are summarized in Fig. 40. The attempts to make GPS general can be viewed almost entirely as the discovery of inadequacies in the modes of representation used in GPS-2-5 and the introduction of new modes to alleviate these inadequacies. The remainder of the chapter discusses five examples: inadequacies in representing the desired situation, in representing operators, in representing unordered objects, in representing large objects, and in representing differences. The first three of these cover the modifications made in developing GPS out of GPS-2-5. These can be seen in Fig. 41, which shows the modes of representation used in GPS-2-5 and the current GPS. The last two inadequacies were not overcome. In fact, one of them resulted from the success-

(a) sum (M FROM-SIDE , −X , *(M FROM-SIDE))

sum (M TO-SIDE , X , *(M TO-SIDE))

M FROM-SIDE NOT-LESS-THAN X

*(C LEFT) NOT-LESS-THAN *(M LEFT)

(b) (MOVES

DECREASE BY THE AMOUNT X THE M AT THE FROM-SIDE AND ADD IT TO THE M AT THE TO-SIDE .

POST-TESTS

THE C AT THE LEFT IS NOT-LESS-THAN THE M AT THE LEFT .)

Fig. 39. (a) A characteristic-list schema encoded as a MOVE-OPERATOR in (b).

Model A complete and consistent set of information units of the form "feature equals atomic constant." A match is an identity test for two models.

Schema A model in which the atomic constants may be replaced by variables and some of the information units may be of the form "subexpression name equals variable." A match with substitution for variables is an identity test for two schemas.

Unordered schema A schema in which the features and subexpression names may be replaced by variables. A match that pairs elements and substitutes for variables is an identity test for two unordered schemas.

Characteristic list A set of information units of the form "Boolean function (α, β)," where α is a feature or subexpression name and β is a feature, subexpression name, subexpression, or atomic constant. An identity test for two characteristic lists is more complex than a match.

Characteristic-list schema A characteristic list in which features, subexpression names, subexpressions, and atomic constants may be replaced by variables. An identity test for two characteristic-list schemas is more complex than a match.

Test process A complex Boolean function defined in a programming language. A test process is its own identity test.

Fig. 40. Summary of several modes of representation.

Modes of representation of GPS-2-5

    Objects: schemas
    Initial situation: schema, list of schemas
    Desired situation: schema
    Operators: schemas

Modes of representation of GPS (current version)

    Objects: schemas (unordered schema in Integration)
    Initial situation: schema, list of schemas (unordered schema)
    Desired situation: schema, characteristic list
    Operators: schemas, characteristic-list schemas

Types of objects and operators

    OBJECT-SCHEMA: schema, (unordered-schema in Integration)
    DESCRIBED-OBJ: characteristic list
    FORM-OPERATOR: schema
    MOVE-OPERATOR: characteristic-list schema

Fig. 41. Summary of the representations used in GPS-2-5 and current GPS.

ful modifications that were made. However, discussion of these two examples is still instructive.

DESIRED SITUATION

In many tasks, the desired situation is not a single object, but a large class of objects. In GPS-2-5, *schemas* and lists of *schemas* were the only means of expressing classes of objects, and they are not an adequate representation for many classes of objects. In integration, for example, the desired situation is an expression that does not contain an $\int$, and there are an infinite number of such expressions. A *schema* cannot represent this class of objects because a *schema* implies identity of form. Similarly, no finite list of *schemas* is adequate.

A *test process* can be used to represent the desired situation in integration. An example would be a program that generates the symbols of an object and tests that none is $\int$. If so, the program signals that the object is a member of the class of objects not requiring integration.

If we consider how to accomplish the requirements in Fig. 36 when the desired situation is represented as a *test process*, we find that some are easy—*object comparison*,* which is the *test process* itself—while others are formidable—*object difference*. The *object-difference* process could be imbedded in a *test process* by having it produce a difference whenever the input object was not represented by the *test process*. Such a solution seems inherently unsatisfactory, since it implies that some of the problem-solving processes proper to GPS are to be encoded into one of the task objects. If there were to be but one desired situation, as in chess or checkers, one might code it in and forget it; but if one has to specify desired situations repeatedly, the situation would be intolerable. The only other way to obtain the difference is for the *object difference* process to analyse the *test process* to discover the conditions that give rise to the negative signal. However, such an analysis requires an understanding of the programming language and is not feasible.

A *characteristic list*—in particular, a DESCRIBED-OBJ—can be used to represent the desired situation in integration. In GPS the desired situation can be represented as a DESCRIBED-OBJ. However, a DESCRIBED-OBJ cannot be used to represent the initial situation or objects derived from it, since GPS cannot apply an operator to a DESCRIBED-

---

* Throughout this chapter we use the short names of the demands of the problem-solving techniques of GPS introduced in Fig. 36.

OBJ *(operator application)* and cannot produce a DESCRIBED-OBJ as the result of an application of an operator. Thus, for *object-comparison* and *object difference,* GPS need only compare an OBJECT-SCHEMA and a DESCRIBED-OBJ, because the necessity for comparing two DESCRIBED-OBJs never arises.

In comparing two data structures whose modes of representation are different, e.g., OBJECT-SCHEMA versus DESCRIBED-OBJ, a match cannot be used for the comparison process, because there is no general way to place the two structures into correspondence. An OBJECT-SCHEMA and a DESCRIBED-OBJ are compared by an interpreter that understands the semantics of the RELATIONs and the format of a DESCRIBED-OBJ. The interpreter evaluates the arguments of the TESTs in the DESCRIBED-OBJ relative to the OBJECT-SCHEMA, and if it finds all of the TESTs to be true, it signals that the OBJECT-SCHEMA and the DESCRIBED-OBJ represent the same situation. For example, in Fig. 42 the OBJECT-SCHEMA (a) and the DESCRIBED-OBJ (b) represent the same class of objects, if U is a variable. The MATCH-DIFF-METHOD can recognize this fact. (In (a), "INTEGRAL," "D," and "U" are values of the ATTRIBUTE "SYMBOL"; and the LOC-PROG "LEFT" refers to the leftmost branch of the TOP-NODE.) In comparing (a) to (b), the MATCH-DIFF-METHOD recognizes EQUALS and TEX-DESCRIPTION as words it understands, and recognizes that

THE SYMBOL AT THE LEFT

in (b) refers to the D in (a), and so on.

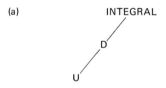

(a)　　　INTEGRAL

D

U

(b)　(TEX-DESCRIPTION
　　　　1. THE SYMBOL EQUALS INTEGRAL .
　　　　2. THE SYMBOL AT THE LEFT EQUALS D .)

(c)　(SUBEXPRESSION-TESTS
　　　　1. THE SYMBOL DOES NOT-EQUAL INTEGRAL .)

Fig. 42. (a) The tree-structure representation of an object in the Integration task; (b) the representation of (a) as a DESCRIBED-OBJ; (c) the representation of the desired situation of the Integration task as a DESCRIBED-OBJ. In this figure, U is a variable, SYMBOL is an ATTRIBUTE, and LEFT is a LOC-PROG.

When an OBJECT-SCHEMA and a DESCRIBED-OBJ do not represent
the same situation, an *object-difference* process analyzes the TESTs
in the DESCRIBED-OBJ that are not satisfied in order to produce a
difference. For example, in matching the OBJECT-SCHEMA in (a) (Fig.
42) to the DESCRIBED-OBJ in (c), GPS would detect a difference
because the TEST in (c) is not true of the TOP-NODE. Only one difference would be detected because the TEST is true at the other two
nodes. Hence, in analyzing this GPS would construct the following
difference:

> type of difference = SYMBOL
>
> location of difference = TOP-NODE
>
> value of difference = a symbol other than INTEGRAL.

In general, GPS produces one difference for each TEST that is not
satisfied. The type of the difference is a FEATURE that is an argument
of the TEST; the location of the difference is the LOC-PROG that names
the node to which the TEST was applied; and the value of the difference is the value the FEATURE should have in order for the difference to be alleviated.

In order for GPS to determine the value of the difference, it must
understand the RELATION of the TEST. For example, GPS must understand the semantics of NOT-EQUAL in order to determine the value
of the difference in the previous example. GPS understands the
semantics of the RELATIONS only because they are task invariant.
On the other hand, GPS cannot understand the semantics of the types
of difference, because they vary from task to task. GPS knows only
that SYMBOL in the integration task is an ATTRIBUTE (this fact is given
in the task description) and knows that it is to process it in the same
way that it processes, for example, BOAT in the Missionaries and
Cannibals task.

Earlier, we dismissed *test processes* as a candidate for generalizing
the desired situation, because of the impossibility of analyzing a
test process. In the present generalization we can see exactly how
restriction of the generality to a *characteristic list* (from the full
generality of an IPL program in *test process*) permits enough analysis
to be carried out so that differences can be produced.

Allowing the desired situation to be a DESCRIBED-OBJ does not
affect the existing processes for *operator application, operator difference, feasibility selection,* and *desirability selection* because
operators are never applied to DESCRIBED-OBJs. A DESCRIBED-OBJ

never needs to be canonized because new ones are not generated during problem solving. However, in any difference detected between an OBJECT-SCHEMA and a DESCRIBED-OBJ, the type of difference does not have a canonical name. In the example the difference type "SYMBOL," being a single symbol, already has a unique name. However, if a more general FEATURE occurred—e.g., LEFT SYMBOL—it would require a canonical name. *Canonization* of difference types is accomplished by the same process that canonizes OBJECT-SCHEMAs, because they are all FEATUREs and can be matched by the IDENTITY-MATCH-METHOD. If the types of differences were structures, such as IPL programs, separate *canonization* processes would be required.

OPERATORS

In GPS-2-5, all operators were expressed as *schemas*. This is a convenient representation for some operators, particulary those found in mathematical calculi. However, the operators of the other tasks—e.g., the operators of the Missionaries and Cannibals task—cannot be expressed conveniently, if at all, as FORM-OPERATORs. To alleviate this difficulty, the internal representation of operators was extended to include MOVE-OPERATORs (*characteristic-list schemas*).

The addition of MOVE-OPERATORs to the internal representation does not affect *object comparison* or *object difference* because they are concerned only with objects. However, the other existing processes listed in Fig. 36 were not adequate for MOVE-OPERATORs. The modification of each will be discussed below.

OPERATOR APPLICATION

A new *operator-application* process had to be added so that a MOVE-OPERATOR could be applied to an OBJECT-SCHEMA. MOVE-OPERATORs always have one OBJECT-SCHEMA as input and produce, if successful, a single OBJECT-SCHEMA as the result. No attempt was made to apply a MOVE-OPERATOR to a DESCRIBED-OBJ.

The *operator-application* process for MOVE-OPERATORs tests an operator's feasibility (PRETESTS are satisfied, etc.) and, if feasible, produces the result. This process interprets the semantics of the TRANSFORMATIONS, which involves understanding the semantics of the OPERATIONS. But GPS does not understand the semantics of task-dependent symbols; e.g., all ATTRIBUTEs are processed similarly. The *operator-application* process for MOVE-OPERATOR also interprets the semantics of the TESTS in a MOVE-OPERATOR, which is accomplished by the same apparatus used in the *object-comparison* process for an OBJECT-SCHEMA and a DESCRIBED-OBJ described in the previous section.

OPERATOR DIFFERENCE

The *operator-difference* process for a MOVE-OPERATOR is quite similar to the *object-difference* process for an OBJECT-SCHEMA and a DESCRIBED-OBJ. In fact, for the TESTS in PRETESTS the two processes are identical.

The failure of a TEST in the set of TESTS in VAR-DOMAIN causes the operator to fail unconditionally, and no difference is produced. This condition indicates that one of the variables has an illegitimate value and thus the operator is infeasible, independent of the object to which it is applied; e.g., move two missionaries and two cannibals to the right.

The inapplicability of a TRANSFORMATION will result in a difference. To produce such a difference GPS must understand the semantics of the OPERATIONS. For example, the TRANSFORMATION

MOVE THE BOAT AT THE FROM-SIDE TO THE BOAT AT TO-SIDE,

with FROM-SIDE equal to LEFT and TO-SIDE equal to RIGHT, is not applicable to an OBJECT-SCHEMA in which the boat is at the RIGHT. An attempt to apply this TRANSFORMATION will result in the type of difference

LEFT BOAT,

because MOVE requires the first argument of the TRANSFORMATION to be DEFINED. This type of difference is obtained by substituting LEFT for FROM-SIDE in the first argument of the TRANSFORMATION.

This example illustrates the important fact that types of difference are not atomic symbols, but rather, data structures (FEATURES) whose generic form is known by GPS. Since some of the FEATURES in the TRANSFORMATIONS of MOVE-OPERATORS contain variables, it is not possible to preassign each individual type of difference to be an atomic symbol (as was true in GPS-2-5). In a particular application, a FEATURE that contains specified variables may be produced as a type of difference. If the variables were specified differently, the FEATURE would be equivalent to another type of difference. For example, the application of the TRANSFORMATION above with FROM-

SIDE equal to RIGHT and TO-SIDE equal to LEFT might result in the difference

RIGHT BOAT.

In the previous example, the same argument of the same TRANS-FORMATION resulted in a different type of difference because the value of FROM-SIDE was different.

The current *operator-difference* process does not produce a difference upon the failure of a TEST in POST-TESTS. Instead, this condition results in unconditional infeasibility. POST-TESTS are stated relative to the resultant object instead of the input object. Hence, the FEATURE that is incorrect and causes the failure probably was modified in applying the TRANSFORMATIONs. The current process for producing a difference is not sophisticated enough to state the difference relative to the input object. Such a restatement is required because GPS assumes that all differences are stated relative to the input object.

DESIRABILITY SELECTION

The REDUCE-METHOD does not select operators randomly but selects desirable operators—those that modify in a desirable way that feature of an object to which the difference of the REDUCE goal pertains. TABLE-OF-CONNECTIONS is a means of providing information about the desirability of operators. Associated with each type of difference is a list of the operators that have the capability of reducing the type of difference. Although the information in TABLE-OF-CONNECTIONS should be discovered by GPS, GPS-2-5 was normally given the TABLE-OF-CONNECTIONS exogenously. However, an attempt was made in earlier work with GPS-2-5 to construct the TABLE-OF-CONNECTIONS for a set of FORM-OPERATORs (Newell, 1962b). To determine the differences for which a FORM-OPERATOR was relevant, its input form was matched to its output form. This was possible, since both were OBJECT-SCHEMAs. The differences that were produced as a result of the match were those the FORM-OPERATOR had the capability of reducing.

For example, one of the FORM-OPERATORs used in the logic task is

$$(A \supset B) \text{ YIELDS } (\sim A \vee B)$$

where A and B are variables. Matching the left-hand expression to the right-hand expression results in the types of difference logical connective;

sign of the first operand.

Thus, this operator was considered desirable for changing either the logical connective or the sign of the first operand.* This example is interesting because it demonstrates the dependence of processing on the representation. For example, it is not feasible to construct the TABLE-OF-CONNECTIONS if the operators are represented as *test processes*.

Although the TABLE-OF-CONNECTIONS is adequate for expressing the desirability of *schema* operators, it is not adequate for *characteristic-list schemas*. Even after selection, *characteristic-list schema* operators may contain variables whose values may determine the desirability of the operator. In the extreme case, illustrated by Missionaries and Cannibals, only one operator appears in the TABLE-OF-CONNECTIONS. Consequently, no selectivity is possible. Since MOVE-OPERATORs are not *schemas*, the technique used to discover the desirability of FORM-OPERATORs in GPS-2-5 is not applicable. Thus, a new *desirability-selection* mechanism had to be added to GPS to determine the desirability of MOVE-OPERATORs. The essential part of this is to determine the desirable values for the pertinent variables in MOVE-OPERATORs.

The desirability-selection process for MOVE-OPERATORs can best be described by an example. Suppose that in attempting the Missionaries and Cannibals task, an operator was wanted for reducing the difference

the BOAT at the LEFT is UNDEFINED.

This could have arisen, for instance, by trying to move from left to right when the boat was on the right side. After the M-C-OPR is selected from the TABLE-OF-CONNECTIONS (see Fig. 30), the *desirability-selection* process attempts to make the functions of the TRANSFORMA-TIONs desirable by substitution for variables. The functions of the second and third TRANSFORMATIONs are not relevant to reducing the above difference, because they do not affect the value of the BOAT at the LEFT. But the first TRANSFORMATION, since its OPERATION is MOVE, is desirable provided that its second argument is identical

---

* The actual process described in Newell (1962b) is somewhat more complex but the basic idea is the same. A method in a predecessor of GPS-2-5 used a similar process, dynamically, to determine desirability (Newell and Simon, 1961b).

to the type of difference

the BOAT at the LEFT.

The desirability of this TRANSFORMATION is determined by matching its second argument to the type of difference (both are FEATUREs). Since they are identical when TO-SIDE equals LEFT, the *desirability-selection* process reports that the M-C-OPR with TO-SIDE equal to LEFT is a desirable operator.

Although there is a special match routine for FEATUREs in the *desirability-selection* process, ideally the MATCH-DIFF-METHOD would be used by the *desirability-selection* process to match two FEATUREs. The special match was used because of two peculiarities. First, variables are bound only if the two FEATUREs can be made identical, whereas, in matching two OBJECT-SCHEMAs, variables are bound regardless of whether they can be made identical. Second, only those values are substituted for the variables that satisfy VAR-DOMAIN.

The *desirability-selection* process depends on the homogeneous representation of types of difference and the arguments of TRANS-FORMATIONs. In matching them, the task-dependent detail of the FEATUREs cancels out. In the previous example, the match recognizes that the ATTRIBUTE in both FEATUREs is the same symbol and thus does not need to understand the semantics of BOAT (except that it is an ATTRIBUTE). If their modes of representation were different, the comparison process would be more complex than a match.

Desirability selection is, in some respects, similar to *operator difference*. In both cases, GPS must understand the semantics of the OPERATIONs, which are the task-invariant symbols in TRANSFORMA-TIONs. Note that GPS understands only the generic form of the arguments of the TRANSFORMATIONS; i.e., GPS knows that they are FEATUREs, CONSTANTS, etc., but does not attach any further significance to the task-variant symbols in the TRANSFORMATIONs. A crucial property on which both *desirability selection* and *operator difference* depend is that FEATUREs are not atomic symbols but data structures in which variables may occur (see pp. 74–75).

The use of variables in MOVE-OPERATORs allows many operators to be represented as single data structures that are only marginally larger than the representation of any one of the operators. Not only does this make the representation more concise, but it allows many operators to be simultaneously analyzed in order to determine their desirability.

FEASIBILITY SELECTION

Because of the way an operator is processed in GPS, it has been defined as a function represented as a single entity whose domain and range are both sets of objects. An operator with *models* for its input and output is a degenerate case because both its domain and range are single objects. However, it is still an operator according to the definition. Although *model* operators are unparsimonious in both their memory and processing requirements, they will be used below to illustrate some properties of better modes of representation.

SCHEMAS. A *schema* operator represents a class of *model* operators as a single entity. Before a *schema* operator can be applied to an object, the variables in the *schema* must be specified. Since a *schema* that contains no variables is a *model*, the specification of variables in a *schema* operator is equivalent to selecting a member from the class of *model* operators represented by the *schema*. *Feasibility selection* requires that a feasible *model* operator be selected (variable specification), if one exists. If an infeasible *model* operator were selected, GPS might still try to apply it by attempting to reduce a difference on the object. This would be a waste of effort if the *schema* contained a feasible *model* operator.

Feasibility selection for FORM-OPERATORS is accomplished by matching the input form of the operator to the object to which the operator is being applied and by making the necessary substitutions for variables (MATCH-DIFF-METHOD). However, the match can be used only because the modes of representation of the input form and the object are the same (both are always OBJECT-SCHEMAS).

CHARACTERISTIC LISTS. *Characteristic-list* operators like *schema* operators, represent a class of *model* operators as a single entity. In fact, every *schema* operator can be represented by a *characteristic-list* operator, as illustrated in Appendix B. *Characteristic-list* operators in GPS are MOVE-OPERATORS that do not contain variables. Since these operators are applied to OBJECT-SCHEMAS, the match cannot be used for *feasibility selection* because their modes of representation are different. Moreover, since there are no variables in *characteristic lists, feasibility selection* for *characteristic-list* operators is of a different nature than that for *schemas*.

MOVE-OPERATORS describe how the output object of the operator differs from its input. By convention, any FEATURES of the output object that are not specified explicitly by the TRANSFORMATIONS have the same values as their correspondents in the input object. Hence, a MOVE-OPERATOR applies to a class of input objects via nonspecification of TRANSFORMATIONS, just as does the FORM-OPERATOR via variables. Although the *feasibility selection* so performed seems to be free (no substitution of variables is required), there is a corresponding expense in the generally increased complexity of the MOVE-OPERATOR compared with the FORM-OPERATOR.

One advantage of MOVE-OPERATORs that do not contain variables is their ability to express classes of operators as a single entity that can only be expressed as several FORM-OPERATORs. An example is the MOVE-OPERATOR R1: a, b in Appendix B.* In applying this MOVE-OPERATOR, the feasible *model* operator, if one exists, will be selected. But, if it is represented by the two corresponding FORM-OPERATORs, the REDUCE-METHOD must select one to be applied. If the wrong one is selected (i.e., the other one contains a feasible *model* operator) GPS may waste considerable effort by attempting to reduce differences between the object and the operator selected.

CHARACTERISTIC-LIST SCHEMAS. The use of variables in MOVE-OPERATORs allows many MOVE-OPERATORs that do not contain variables to be expressed as a single MOVE-OPERATOR. From the previous example, it would appear that the use of MOVE-OPERATORs that contain variables would lead to more efficient problem-solving because *feasibility selection* can be applied to larger classes of *model* operators. Unfortunately, the current *feasibility-selection* process does not capitalize on the compactness of MOVE-OPERATORs that contain variables. GPS applies a MOVE-OPERATOR by first generating legal variable specifications (those for which the set of TESTs in VAR-DOMAIN of the MOVE-OPERATOR is satisfied) until it finds a set of values for which the operator is feasible or for which the difference between the operator and the object is not too difficult. This method for applying a MOVE-OPERATOR has two major disadvantages. First, the operator selected may not be the easiest operator. An infeasible *model* operator may be selected even though a different variable specification might have led to the selection of a feasible *model* operator. Since all variable specifications seem to be equally desirable (else further selection for desirability would have been made by *desirability selection*), a better strategy would be to apply the easiest operator first.

The second disadvantage is that the number of different variable specifications may be large. However, any specification of variables

---

* From this example, it might seem that the use of variables with restricted domains in FORM-OPERATORs would yeild the generality of MOVE-OPERATORs (i.e., $A \alpha B \rightarrow B \alpha A$ where $\alpha \in \{v, .\}$). However, this generalization of FORM-OPERATORs would not help in the statement of the distributive law in Appendix B (R7, of form $A \alpha (B \beta C) \rightarrow (A \beta B) \alpha (A \beta C))$ where the two connectives are not independent.

by the REDUCE-METHOD to ensure the desirability of the operator, considerably decreases the number of legitimate variable specifications that can be generated in attempting to apply the operator. In the tasks discussed in the next chapter, no case was encountered that had more than five different legitimate variable specifications; in most cases, only one or two legitimate variable specifications could be generated. However, the number of variable specifications conceivably could be much larger for other tasks.

In the best of all worlds, the variables in a MOVE-OPERATOR would be assigned feasible values one at a time as their specification was required in applying the MOVE-OPERATOR. This is the main advantage of the match routine in applying a FORM-OPERATOR. But considerable complexity is introduced by unspecified variables in MOVE-OPERATORS. It is difficult to determine which values of the variables in MOVE-OPERATORS make the operator feasible. In the M-C-OPR in Fig. 30, for example, the POST-TESTS constrain the feasible value of X and Y, even though X and Y do not appear explicitly in the POST-TESTS. In addition, a single TEST, such as

THE M AT THE LEFT IS NOT-LESS THAN THE C AT THE LEFT,

constrains the feasible values of both X and Y simultaneously.

Another difficulty with specifying the variables in MOVE-OPERATORS as they turn up is the possibility of several feasible values. When variables do not have unique values that make the operator feasible, the application of the operator will have different results depending on which value is selected. That is, the resultant class of objects cannot be represented by a single OBJECT-SCHEMA. In such cases, GPS must decide which member it will work with, since it can do only one thing at a time. In the Missionaries and Cannibals task, for example, when GPS attempts the goal of applying the M-C-OPR in Fig. 30 with TO-SIDE equal to LEFT, several different results can be produced, depending on the values assigned to the variables X and Y. When applied to the object

(LEFT (M 1 C 1) RIGHT (M 2 C 2 BOAT YES))

the result can be either

(LEFT (M 3 C 1 BOAT YES) RIGHT (M 0 C 2))

or

(LEFT (M 2 C 2 BOAT YES) RIGHT (M 1 C 1)).

If the only reason for applying the operator was to move the BOAT to the LEFT bank of the river, both results would seem equally desirable, and X and Y would have two equally desirable and feasible values.

CANONIZATION

MOVE-OPERATORs never need to be *canonized* because new MOVE-OPERATORs are never created. But, if *desirability selection* specifies several variables in a MOVE-OPERATOR, then the goal of applying a partially specified MOVE-OPERATOR is created. A partially specified MOVE-OPERATOR is represented by a data structure consisting of a variable specification and the name of a MOVE-OPERATOR. Since new partially specified MOVE-OPERATORs are generated during problem solving, their *canonization* is required. All partially specified MOVE-OPERATORs are represented homogeneously, and the IDENTITY-MATCH-METHOD can match them by testing whether the MOVE-OPERATOR and the values assigned to the variables are the same. Thus, the *canonization* process for OBJECT-SCHEMAs can be used.

The only other data structures that must be *canonized* as a result of the addition of MOVE-OPERTAORs are differences generated when a MOVE-OPERATOR is inapplicable. These differences are *canonized* in precisely the same way that the differences produced as a result of comparing an OBJECT-SCHEMA and a DESCRIBED-OBJ are *canonized*.

In summary, MOVE-OPERATORs generalize the GPS operators by extension from *schemas* to *characteristic-list schemas*. To do so requires substantial modification in almost all the processes of Fig. 36 that have to do with operators: *operator application, operator difference, desirability selection,* and *feasibility selection. Object comparison* and *object difference,* which have nothing to do with operators, did not have to be modified. *Canonization* did not require modification either. Even though it is used in connection with MOVE-OPERATORs, it deals only with the form of data structures, and not with their use or interpretation.

UNORDERED SCHEMAS

An example of a task that can use *unordered schemas* beneficially is integration. If multiplication and addition are represented as ordered binary functions, their associativity and commutativity must be expressed as operators. On the other hand, multiplication and addition can be represented as functions of an unordered set of argu-

---

V. REPRESENTATION AND GENERALITY

ments. Then the commutativity and associativity of multiplication and addition are expressed implicitly in the representation (provided that none of the arguments of multiplication was the multiplication of a set of arguments and none of the arguments of addition was the addition of a set of arguments). This representation has problem-solving implications. For example,

$$\int t e^{t^2} \, dt \quad \text{and} \quad \int e^{t^2} t \, dt$$

would appear identical if the arguments of multiplication were un-ordered. But to make

$$\int t * (e^{t^2} * dt) \quad \text{and} \quad \int e^{t^2} * (t * dt)$$

identical would require the application of three operators.

To illustrate the problem-solving efficiency that can be obtained by using *unordered schemas* to represent unordered sets, consider an alternate representation of an unordered set as an ordered set, represented as a *schema*, and a permutation operator that permutes any two elements. To test the identity of two unordered sets so represented, the permutation operator must be applied in an attempt to make the two *schemas* identical (to within a substitution for variables). Successive application of the permutation operator corresponds to searching the tree in Fig. 43. This search is unnecessary

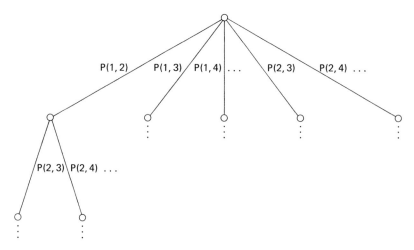

Fig. 43. The tree defined by a set and a permutation operator $P(\alpha,\beta)$ that permutes the elements α and β.

if *unordered schemas* are used instead of *schemas*, provided that the match routine can take into consideration their unordered property. Such a match routine will have to do some search in comparing two *unordered schemas*, but since it can search the entire set of candidates directly for the matching possibilities, it is only moderately more expensive than a match for *schemas*. Thus, the savings over the use of permutation operators will be substantial, since the tree defined by the initial situation and the operators (i.e., the main problem-solving tree) will be compressed.

Testing the identity of two *unordered schemas* would be rather straightforward if they contained no variables. However, incorporating the substitution for variables in a process for matching two *unordered schemas* introduces considerable complexity. To demonstrate this, consider matching the two unordered sets

$$\{e^u, u, v\} \qquad \text{and} \qquad \{b, c, e^c\},$$

in which u and v are variables.* Substituting b for u might seem desirable, since it makes a pair of elements of the sets identical. But this substitution would make the two sets different. The match must be sophisticated enough to substitute c for u (and b for v) in order to recognize that the two sets can be made identical.

Object difference and *operator difference* for *unordered schemas* are difficult because there may be several pairings of the elements of the two sets that seem equally good. Consider the example of applying the operator

$$\int e^u \, du = e^u, \tag{1}$$

in which u is a variable, to the object

$$\int t e^{t^2} \, dt \tag{2}$$

The operator is applied by matching the left-hand side of the equation to the object and, if identical, using the right-hand side of the equation as the result. Obviously, the two sets of factors cannot be made identical because they have a different number of elements. But either the substitution of t for u or the substitution of t^2 for u will make one pair of elements identical. The latter is the correct substitution, but only because the operator

$$t \, dt = \tfrac{1}{2} d(t^2)$$

* This example also shows that (with variables permitted) there is no way of canonically ordering the sets so as to make the match again into an ordered one.

can be applied to (2) in order to make (1) applicable. This cannot be easily known at the time of matching the left-hand side of (1) to (2).

Before GPS was given the integration task, the MATCH-DIFF-METHOD and the IDENTITY-MATCH-METHOD were modified so that they could match unordered sets. The modification consisted of first putting the elements of an unordered set into correspondence according to several rules (given below) and then matching each pair of components.

First, an attempt is made to match elements that do not contain variables. An error in correspondence cannot be made pairing identical elements that do not contain variables, and such a pairing might prevent an unnecessary substitution for a variable. This modified match requires a list of properties that is used to rank elements according to their respective importance. This information, which is task dependent, is given to GPS exogenously as an IPL structure because it cannot be expressed in the external representation. After matching constant elements, other elements are selected in the order of their importance, and are matched allowing substitution for variables. However, if two elements in the same set are equally important (have the same property), these elements will be matched later. The strategy is to find a correspondence between unique, important elements of the two sets so that the substitution for variables is made correctly.

Finally, the remaining elements of the two sets are matched. The differences between the two sets are the unmatched elements. The match works strictly forward and cannot try two different substitutions for the same variable. Consequently, in some cases, the match will not recognize that two *unordered schemas* can be made to be identical; but for the integration task, this match appears to be sufficient.

In applying the operator (1) to the object (2), for example, first the two exponential elements are matched because they are considered the most important. Upon substitution of t^2 for u they become identical. None of the other elements can be matched, and the difference reported is that the number of elements in the set $\{t, dt\}$ is too large (SET-SIZE).

Object comparison, operator application, feasibility selection, and *canonization* for *unordered schemas* are all satisfied by this generalization of the match, because the match is incorporated in all of them. With the list of properties for ranking elements according to their importance, the generalized match can draw good correspondences between the elements of two sets even if the two sets are not identical. This, together with the addition of a few set differences (e.g., set is too small, set is too large), satisfies *object difference* and *operator difference*. The existing *desirability selection* process is applicable for *unordered schema*.

LARGE OBJECTS

The result of an application of an operator in GPS is always a new data structure, provided that it is not identical to some data structure created previously. GPS is designed to handle only simple problems (i.e., problems that require a limited amount of search), because it is not prepared to erase these data structures. Hence, the size of the data structures that represent objects is important; if too large, memory will be exhausted before even simple problems can be solved. For many tasks, this difficulty is critical because in GPS objects represent total situations and the total situations of some tasks are large. (There is no facility for processing object fragments as independent data structures.)

Examples of tasks in which the representation of objects is too large are those that use boards, such as the Block puzzle shown in Fig. 44, or tasks on a chess board, such as the Eight Queens problem, in which eight queens are to be placed on the board such that no

Generic form of objects: A configuration of the nine blocks in the box.

Initial situation:

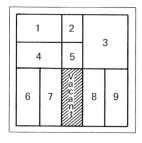

Desired situation: A configuration in which block 3 is in the lower left corner.

Operator: Move any block into an adjacent vacancy; e.g., move block 8 into the vacancy at its left.

Fig. 44. Block puzzle.

queen can capture another queen. For instance, by generalizing slightly the tree-structure representation of OBJECT-SCHEMAs to allow any node to have more than one super node, a chess board could be represented as an OBJECT-SCHEMA. The TOP-NODE of an OBJECT-SCHEMA that represents a chess board has sixty-four branches; the nodes to which these branches lead represent the sixty four squares of the chess board. For example, the branch labeled S1 in Fig. 45a leads to the node that represents the square S1 in Fig. 45b. Each square has eight branches (except for border squares, which have fewer) leading from it to the eight neighboring squares. For example, in Fig. 45a, the branch labeled FORWARD leading from the node

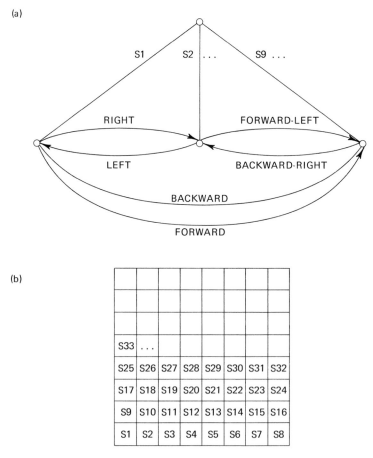

Fig. 45. (a) The OBJECT-SCHEMA that represents the chess board whose squares are named in (b).

representing S1 to the node representing S9 indicates that the square S9 is in the FORWARD direction from the square S1 in Fig. 45b. The position of the pieces on the chess board would be given by the local description of the squares (nodes) along with any other information peculiar to a square, such as its color.

Although the representation in Fig. 45a is convenient for processing,* a single chess position is very large because of the elaborate system of branches between nodes. There are 484 branches between the nodes of Fig. 45a. Since the internal representation of each branch requires at least two IPL-V words, the internal representation of a single chess position would require more than a thousand IPL words.

Obviously, the information represented by the system of branches in Fig. 45a must be expressed to the problem solver somewhere in the specification of the task of playing chess. But since this information does not vary from chess position to chess position, it should be represented *only once* and not in the representation of every chess position generated during problem solving. One way to avoid this duplication of information is to represent chess positions independently of the chess board, e.g., as a list of pairs in which one member of a pair is a square and the other member is a piece on the square. This representation contains no information about which pieces are on adjacent squares, etc. Before considering a particular position, GPS would put the pieces on a board such as the one in Fig. 45a and, after it had finished processing the position, it would remove the pieces from the board. Such a scheme would require adding mechanisms for "setting up" and "tearing down" chess positions. (In fact, all existing chess programs operate in this fashion.)

An alternate representation for chess positions is that of expressing the relationships between the squares of the chess board implicitly in the names of the squares instead of explicitly in the structure of each object. For example, the name S1 in Fig. 45a could contain the information that the square at the RIGHT was S2 and the square in the FORWARD direction was S8, and so on. That is, S1 would be a data structure as well as the name of a square, and information peculiar to S1—e.g., S2 is at the RIGHT of S1—would be encoded in the data structure S1 in some convenient form.† This representation cannot be used in the current version of GPS because LOC-PROGs operate on

---

* This representation is almost identical to the one used in Baylor and Simon (1966).

† This is essentially what is involved in using a matrix board representation, where $S[i,j]$ is the square at the ith row and the jth column. The internal addresses (i.e., names) representing each square encode relative positions that can be extracted by suitable arithmetic processes.

the structure of objects. Since RIGHT, FORWARD, etc., are LOC-PROGS—
i.e., they correspond to the branches of tree structures—they must be
in the structure of objects, whether or not the relationships among
squares are expressed in the names of squares.

DIFFERENCES

In GPS, all types of differences are FEATUREs, and a particular
difference indicates that the value of the FEATURE is incorrect. If
the value of the FEATURE is a number, the difference designates the
amount by which the number should be increased or decreased in
order to alleviate the difference; if the value of the FEATURE is a
symbolic constant, the difference designates the correct value of the
FEATURE. These elementary differences are not an adequate representation for the differences of some tasks. That is, for some tasks GPS's
problem solving would appear aimless, since these elementary
differences are not sufficient to guide the search.

We can illustrate the inadequacies of the types of differences that
are represented as FEATUREs by a detailed example of how GPS
should solve simultaneous equations. Figure 46 is an informal
formulation for GPS of the task of solving two simultaneous equations.
The initial situation is the set of the two OBJECT-SCHEMAS in Fig.
46a. The desired situation, expressed as the DESCRIBED-OBJ in Fig.
46c, represents an expression of the form Y *equals an expression that
does not contain a* Z. (Y and Z are considered the independent
variables of the equations.)

The operators, given in Fig. 46b, are all represented as FORM-
OPERATORs, even though the last would really have to be a MOVE-
OPERATOR. It is a version of the rule of replacement, whereby a subexpression can be replaced by any expression equal to it. The ↔
indicates that the form on either side can be used as the input form;
the → indicates that the form to the left is the input form; and the
comma in the input form indicates two separate objects for input.
We assume that GPS can do elementary algebraic simplification
implicitly and that it understands that multiplication and addition
are commutative and associative. Thus, GPS does not need to create
goals to simplify expressions or to commute two factors. These are
the same assumptions used in the Integration task.

Since the initial situation is a set of objects, GPS would select one
and attempt to transform it into the desired situation. Suppose that
the first equation in Fig. 46a were selected. The current version of

(a) Initial situation:

    1. $A * Y + B * Z = Y + E$

    2. $C * Z + Y = D * Z$

(b) Operators:

    1. $(U + V = W) \longleftrightarrow (U = W - V)$

    2. $(U - V = W) \longleftrightarrow (U = W + V)$

    3. $(U - V = O) \longleftrightarrow (U = V)$

    4. $(O = U - V) \longleftrightarrow (U = V)$

    5. $(U * V = W) \longleftrightarrow (U = W / V)$

    6. $(U / V = W) \longleftrightarrow (U = W * V)$

    7. $(U * (V + W)) \longleftrightarrow (U * V + U * W)$

    8. $(EX(U), U = V) \rightarrow EX(V)$

(c) Desired situation:

    (TEX-DESCRIPTION

       1.   THE SYMBOL AT THE LEFT EQUALS Y .

       2.   THE SYMBOL EQUALS = .

       3.   THE SYMBOL AT X DOES NOT-EQUAL Y , FOR-ALL
          X IN THE RIGHT-SUBEXPRESSION .

    SUBEXPRESSION-TESTS

    THE SYMBOL DOES NOT-EQUAL Z .)

Fig. 46. An informal formulation of solving two simultaneous equations.

GPS would detect that the Y's and the Z in the object should be re-placed by different SYMBOLs; e.g., one of the differences detected would be

    RIGHT-RIGHT SYMBOL should not be a Y.

According to such differences, all of the operators would appear desirable, because they all replace SYMBOLs with other SYMBOLs. Thus, for this task, GPS must detect types of difference that are more global than the elementary types of difference that can be represented as FEATURES. Suppose that GPS could detect differences that sum-marize what is wrong with the entire object or a subexpression of the object. GPS might recognize the difference that the first equation in Fig. 46a contains one Z instead of none. The only operator cap-able of reducing this difference is the last operator in Fig. 46b where V must stand for a subexpression that does not contain a Z if the oper-ator is to reduce the difference.

GPS would attempt to apply this operator by setting U equal to Z in order to supply the first input and would look for the second input to the operator—an OBJECT-SCHEMA of the form

$$Z = V,$$

where V stands for some expression that does not contain a Z. To modify the second equation in Fig. 46a so that it could be used as the second input to the operator, GPS would attempt to reduce the difference that the expression to the right of $=$ contains a Z.

The third and sixth operators are both applicable and relevant. Assuming the third operator is selected, GPS would produce the new object

$$(C * Z) + Y - (D * Z) = 0.$$

Since this object has two Z's to the left of $=$ instead of one, the seventh operator would be applied to it to produce

$$Z * (C - D) + Y = 0,$$

which is still not of the form

$$Z = V.$$

The difference that the subexpression to the left of $=$ is too large is not an adequate summary of this state of affairs, because the first operator would seem very desirable since it can be applied to produce

$$Y = -Z * (C - D).$$

A better difference is that the Z is in the wrong position; it should be higher in the subexpression to the left of $=$. Using this difference, GPS would select and apply the first operator to produce

$$Z * (C - D) = -Y$$

Detecting the same difference again, GPS would select and apply the fifth operator to produce

$$Z = -Y/(C - D).$$

The Z in the first equation can now be replaced yielding

$$A * Y - B * Y/(C - D) = Y + E.$$

From this expression GPS can go on to solve the problem.

The point of this example is that GPS must have a good set of differences to guide its search. Two types of differences were introduced that cannot be represented in the current version of GPS, i.e., by

FEATUREs. *Tree-structure* types of differences refer to the global properties of tree structures; e.g., a tree structure contains too many occurrences of a particular symbol. The *position* type of difference refers to the position of a particular symbol in the tree. Such a difference denotes where a symbol should be, relative to where it is.

In GPS-2-5, the match could detect tree-structure differences between two OBJECT-SCHEMAs; e.g.,

> the number of Z's occurring in a tree structure
> should be decreased by one.

This facility could easily be added to GPS. However, to detect these types of differences between an OBJECT-SCHEMA and a DESCRIBED-OBJ is considerably more complex, because their modes of representation are different, and the *desirability-selection* process for MOVE-OPERATORs assumes that the types of differences are FEATUREs. By making some of the routines in GPS more sophisticated, tree-structure types of differences could be added to GPS, although there probably exist some unforeseen difficulties.

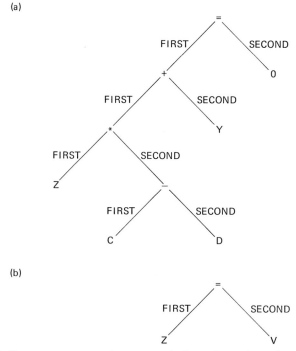

Fig. 47. Two tree structures that are matched in solving the task in Fig. 46.

On the other hand, position types of differences cannot be added to GPS without extensive modifications. The match places the nodes of the tree structures of the two OBJECT-SCHEMAs in correspondence. The resulting differences that are detected are all of the form:

> At a particular position in the tree structure,
> certain features should have certain values.

In order to find position differences, the match would have to place symbols in correspondence and compare their positions in the tree structures. For example, in the two tree structures in Fig. 47, the match should place the Z's in correspondence to detect that the Z in Fig. 47a is to the LEFT of the Z in Fig. 45b. Thus, both tree-structure differences and position differences cannot be used because of short-comings in *object difference, operator difference* and *desirability selection.*

SUMMARY

We have discussed five representational issues that arose in trying to extend GPS to do a wider domain of tasks. In the first three of these we made successful adaptations. In the last two we either did not make the extension (to large objects), or accepted a more restricted domain for GPS (in the differences) as the price of generality elsewhere (the MOVE-OPERATORs). Throughout we have used a simple characterization of the different modes of representation, based on the difficulty of making an identity test. Hopefully, this has made the underlying representational issues more apparent than would a completely idiosyncratic treatment. With this analysis at hand it should now be possible to look at the actual tasks given to GPS with a moderately discerning eye.

CHAPTER VI

TASKS GIVEN TO GPS

This chapter discusses eleven different tasks that were given to GPS. The discussion of each task consists of four parts: a description of the task; a description of the specification of the task for GPS; a description of the way in which GPS attempts to find a solution for the task; and a discussion of the important aspects of giving the task to GPS.

All of the tasks in this chapter were run on the CDC G21 computer at Carnegie–Mellon University. The IPL-V system on this machine has an "available space" of about 20,000 IPL locations. On the average, 76,000 IPL instructions were spent on processing a goal. This amounts to approximately 76 seconds per goal on the G21. In more common terms, since the G21 is a rare machine, this is about 17 seconds per goal on an IBM 7090.

MISSIONARIES AND CANNIBALS TASK

The Missionaries and Cannibals task (stated on p. 3) had already been solved by GPS-2-2.*

* See Newell (1963, pp. 92–96).

GPS FORMULATION

The Missionaries and Cannibals task has already been discussed extensively,* and only the details are given here. The task is formulated for GPS in Fig. 48. TOP-GOAL is a statement of the problem. INITIAL-OBJ, shown in tree structure form in Fig. 49, represents the situation when all of the missionaries, all of the cannibals, and the BOAT are on the LEFT bank of the river. M is the ATTRIBUTE whose value is the number of missionaries, and C is the ATTRIBUTE whose value is the number of cannibals. The value "YES" of the ATTRIBUTE "BOAT" signifies the presence of the BOAT, while the absence of the BOAT is indicated by the absence of a value of BOAT. DESIRED-OBJ is the OBJECT-SCHEMA that represents the situation when all of the missionaries, all of the cannibals, and the BOAT are at the RIGHT bank of the river.

The only operator in this formulation is the M-C-OPR, whose application has the affect of moving X missionaries, Y cannibals, and the BOAT from the FROM-SIDE to the TO-SIDE. The first two TESTS in VAR-DOMAIN require that both X and Y be either 0, 1, or 2 and that their sum be either 1 or 2. The sum of X and Y, which represents the number of people in the BOAT, cannot be less than 1 because there must be someone operating the BOAT. Since the capacity of the BOAT is two, the sum of $X+Y$ must be no greater than two.

The third and fourth TESTS in VAR-DOMAIN constrain FROM-SIDE and TO-SIDE to stand for different banks of the river. The three TRANSFORMATIONS have the effect of moving across the river the BOAT, X missionaries, and Y cannibals, respectively.

The formulation assumes that in all existing objects no missionaries are eaten and checks this constraint before producing a new object. If POST-TESTS are satisfied, no missionaries will be eaten in the resultant OBJECT-SCHEMA, because they cannot be eaten in the BOAT, because of its limited capacity. Since GPS does not understand the concept of "eating," it must be told explicitly that a missionary must be present before he can be eaten (the second TEST in both FROM-SIDE-TESTS and TO-SIDE-TESTS).

COMPARE-OBJECTS and BASIC-MATCH indicate that all differences are observed at the TOP-NODE, and that only the ATTRIBUTES of the node at the LEFT are matched. Since the formulation prevents the missionaries from being eaten, everything that is not at LEFT must be at RIGHT. If the values of corresponding ATTRIBUTES of the RIGHT

---

* The formulation of the M-C-OPR is described on pp. 76–78; the translation of Fig. 1 is described on pp. 89–90.

```
RENAME    (

   LEFT = FIRST

   RIGHT = SECOND

      )

DECLARE       (

   BOAT = ATTRIBUTE

   C = ATTRIBUTE

   B-L = FEATURE

   B-R = FEATURE

   C-L = FEATURE

   C-R = FEATURE

   DESIRED-OBJ = OBJECT-SCHEMA

   FROM-SIDE = LOC-PROG

   FROM-SIDE-TESTS = V-TESTS

   INITIAL-OBJ = OBJECT-SCHEMA

   M = ATTRIBUTE

   M-C-OPR = MOVE-OPERATOR

   M-L = FEATURE

   M-R = FEATURE

   SIDE-SET = SET

   TO-SIDE = LOC-PROG

   TO-SIDE-TESTS = V-TESTS

   X = CONSTANT

   X+Y = EXPRES

   Y = CONSTANT

   0,1,2-SET = SET

   1,2 = SET
```

Fig. 48. Specification for GPS of the Missionaries and Cannibals task.

```
                    )
TASK-STRUCTURES        (
   TOP-GOAL = ( TRANSFORM THE INITIAL-OBJ INTO THE DESIRED-OBJ ˉ )
   INITIAL-OBJ = ( LEFT ( M 3 C 3 BOAT YES )
                      RIGHT ( M 0 C 0 ) )
   DESIRED-OBJ = ( LEFT ( M 0 C 0 )
                      RIGHT ( M 3 C 3 BOAT YES ) )
   X+Y = ( X + Y )
   1,2 = ( 1 2 )
   0,1,2-SET = ( 0 1 2 )
   SIDE-SET = ( LEFT RIGHT )
   FROM-SIDE-TESTS = (    1. THE M OF THE FROM-SIDE IS NOT-LESS-THAN
                             THE C OF THE FROM-SIDE .
                          2. THE M OF THE FROM-SIDE EQUALS 0 . )
   TO-SIDE-TESTS = (  1. THE M OF THE TO-SIDE IS NOT-LESS-THAN
                          THE C OF THE TO-SIDE .
                          2. THE M OF THE TO-SIDE EQUALS 0 . )
   M-C-OPR = ( CREATION-OPERATOR
                    $ MOVE X MISSIONARIES AND Y CANNIBALS FROM THE FROM-SIDE TO
                      THE TO-SIDE $
                    VAR-DOMAIN
                    1. Y IS A CONSTRAINED-MEMBER OF THE 0,1,2-SET ,
                       THE CONSTRAINT IS X+Y IS IN-THE-SET 1,2 .
                    2. X IS A CONSTRAINED-MEMBER OF THE 0,1,2-SET ,
                       THE CONSTRAINT IS X+Y IS IN-THE-SET 1,2 .
                    3. THE FROM-SIDE IS AN EXCLUSIVE-MEMBER OF THE SIDE-SET .
                    4. THE TO-SIDE IS AN EXCLUSIVE-MEMBER OF THE SIDE-SET .
```

Fig. 48 (cont.).

```
            MOVES
               1. MOVE THE BOAT OF THE FROM-SIDE TO THE BOAT OF THE TO-SIDE
               2. DECREASE BY THE AMOUNT X THE M AT THE FROM-SIDE AND ADD
                  IT TO THE M AT THE TO-SIDE .
               3. DECREASE BY THE AMOUNT Y THE C AT THE FROM-SIDE AND ADD
                  IT TO THE C AT THE TO-SIDE .
            POST-TESTS
               1. ARE ANY OF THE FROM-SIDE-TESTS TRUE .
               2. ARE ANY OF THE TO-SIDE-TESTS TRUE . )
B-L = ( BOAT ON THE LEFT . )
B-R = ( BOAT ON THE RIGHT . )
C-L = ( C ON THE LEFT . )
C-R = ( C ON THE RIGHT . )
M-L = ( M ON THE LEFT . )
M-R = ( M ON THE RIGHT . )
DIFF-ORDERING = ( ( M-R M-L C-R C-L )
                  ( B-R B-L ) )
TABLE-OF-CONNECTIONS = ( ( COMMON-DIFFERENCE M-C-OPR ) )
COMPARE-OBJECTS = ( BASIC-MATCH )
BASIC-MATCH = ( COMP-FEAT-LIST ( M-L C-L B-L ) )
OBJ-ATTRIB = ( M C BOAT )
LIST-OF-VAR = ( FROM-SIDE TO-SIDE X Y )
    )     END
```

Fig. 48 (cont.).

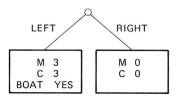

Fig. 49. Tree-structure representation of INITIAL-OBJ.

are also matched, the differences detected would cause the same operators to be selected.

DIFF-ORDERING designates that types of differences pertaining to the BOAT are easier than those pertaining to the missionaries or cannibals. TABLE-OF-CONNECTIONS signifies that the M-C-OPR is relevant to reducing all differences. It does not contain any information about the desirability of operators to reducing particular types of differences. OBJ-ATTRIB lists the ATTRIBUTEs of this task and LIST-OF-VAR lists the variables that appear in Fig. 49.

NEW-OBJ is a criterion for selecting OBJECT-SCHEMAs from a SET of OBJECT-SCHEMAs and does not appear in Fig. 48, because it was given to GPS as an IPL-V structure. Any OBJECT-SCHEMA that has never appeared in the statement of a TRANSFORM GOAL fulfills the NEW-OBJ criterion. This criterion is used in conjunction with the TRANSFORM-SET-METHOD (see Fig. 24). Its first submethod is a SELECT GOAL-SCHEMA, whose selection criterion is NEW-OBJ for this task. It is used in two other tasks (Water Jug task, Father and Sons task) as well. However, a different criterion may be used. For example the Predicate Calculus task uses SMALLEST (see p. 172) as the criterion.

GPS attempts to generate new goals (EXPANDED-TRANSFORM-METHOD) whenever it runs into trouble; e.g., enters a loop by generating a goal equivalent to an old goal. Transforming an OBJECT-SCHEMA that fulfills NEW-OBJ into the desired object is a new goal, and attempting it might yield new results. Such a goal is equivalent to the initial problem (TOP-GOAL), because all objects generated during problem solving (hence NEW-OBJ) are derived from TOP-GOAL.

The TRANSFORM-METHOD has been slightly generalized for this task (and this generalized version is used also in the Bridges of Konigsberg). Whenever the MATCH-DIFF-METHOD detects more than one difference with the same difficulty according to DIFF-ORDERING, GPS has the capability of generating more than one REDUCE goal. The rationale is that since GPS has no reason for selecting any one difference in particular, it considers all of them if necessary. The TRANSFORM-METHOD (shown in Fig. 15) terminates on the FAILURE of the first REDUCE subgoal (fifth submethod). In the generalized version of this method, FAILURE of a REDUCE subgoal causes GPS to attempt to construct another REDUCE goal. This generalization is, of course, not really task dependent, and could well have been introduced for all tasks.

BEHAVIOR OF GPS

Figure 50 shows the behavior of GPS in solving the task in Fig. 48. In attempting TOP-GOAL, GPS detects that there are too many missionaries and cannibals at the LEFT and that the BOAT should not be at the LEFT. GOAL 2 is created in an attempt to reduce the number of cannibals at the LEFT, and the M-C-OPR with Y equal to 2 and FROM-SIDE equal to LEFT is considered relevant to reducing this difference. GOAL 3 results in OBJECT 5, and GPS attempts to transform the new object into the DESIRED-OBJ (GOAL 4).

Since there are still too many cannibals at the LEFT (GOAL 5), GPS attempts to move the remaining cannibal to the RIGHT (GOAL 6). However, it realizes that it needs the boat to do so (GOAL 7). In an attempt to bring the BOAT back to the LEFT (GOAL 7), GPS applies the M-C-OPR with the TO-SIDE equal to LEFT (GOAL 8) and OBJECT 6 is produced. GPS moves one cannibal across the river (GOAL 9); it does not realize that bringing the BOAT back to the LEFT also brought a cannibal with it. Since transforming the result of GOAL 9, which is an old object, into the DESIRED-OBJ is an old goal, GPS does not attempt it but looks for something else to do.

GOAL 11 is created in an attempt to transform all of the OBJECT-SCHEMAS derived from the INITIAL-OBJ into the DESIRED-OBJ. (OBJECT 4, the SET of all OBJECT-SCHEMAS derived from the INITIAL-OBJ, is generated internally by GPS.) GOAL 13 is created because OBJECT 6 has never appeared in a TRANSFORM GOAL. Since there are too many cannibals at the LEFT in OBJECT 6 (GOAL 14), two are moved across the river (GOAL 15, OBJECT 7).

Everything goes smoothly until GOAL 27, which results in an old object. At this point GPS generates a goal identical to GOAL 22. GPS does not reattempt GOAL 22 but generates a new goal (GOAL 29) by selecting a NEW-OBJ (OBJECT 8). Attempting GOAL 29 quickly leads to the old object OBJECT 7 (GOAL 31) and the old goal GOAL 16. GOAL 33 is generated by selecting another NEW-OBJ and GPS does not run into trouble until GOAL 49, which results in an old object. Again a new goal is generated by selecting a NEW-OBJ. GOAL 52 is abandoned because attempting it creates a goal identical to GOAL 43. The generation of GOAL 54 quickly leads to success.

Fig. 50. Performance of GPS on the Missionaries and Cannibals task.

```
1 TOP-GOAL TRANSFORM INITIAL-OBJ INTO DESIRED-OBJ        (SUBGOAL OF NONE)

2 GOAL 2 REDUCE C-L ON INITIAL-OBJ        (SUBGOAL OF TOP-GOAL)

3 GOAL 3 APPLY M-C-OPR WITH Y = 2, FROM-SIDE = LEFT, TO INITIAL-OBJ        (SUBGOAL OF 2)
        SET: X = 0, TO-SIDE = RIGHT
        OBJECT 5: (LEFT(M 3 C 1) RIGHT(M 0 C 2 BOAT YES))

2 GOAL 4 TRANSFORM 5 INTO DESIRED-OBJ        (SUBGOAL OF TOP-GOAL)

3 GOAL 5 REDUCE C-L ON 5        (SUBGOAL OF 4)

4 GOAL 6 APPLY M-C-OPR WITH Y = 1, FROM-SIDE = LEFT, TO 5        (SUBGOAL OF 5)
        SET: X = 0, TO-SIDE = RIGHT

5 GOAL 7 REDUCE B-L ON 5        (SUBGOAL OF 6)

6 GOAL 8 APPLY M-C-OPR WITH TO-SIDE = LEFT, TO 5        (SUBGOAL OF 7)
        SET: Y = 1, X = 0, FROM-SIDE = RIGHT
        OBJECT 6: (LEFT(M 3 C 2 BOAT YES) RIGHT(M 0 C 1))

6 GOAL 9 APPLY M-C-OPR WITH Y = 1, FROM-SIDE = LEFT, TO 6        (SUBGOAL OF 6)
        SET: X = 0, TO-SIDE = RIGHT
        OBJECT 5: (LEFT(M 3 C 1) RIGHT(M 0 C 2 BOAT YES))

2 GOAL 11 TRANSFORM 4 INTO DESIRED-OBJ        (SUBGOAL OF TOP-GOAL)

3 GOAL 12 SELECT FROM 4 A/C NEW-OBJ OF DESIRED-OBJ        (SUBGOAL OF 11)
        4 SELECTED

3 GOAL 13 TRANSFORM 4 INTO DESIRED-OBJ        (SUBGOAL OF 11)
```

Fig. 50 (cont.).

```
4 GOAL 14 REDUCE C-L ON 6          (SUBGOAL OF 13)

5 GOAL 15 APPLY M-C-OPR WITH Y = 2, FROM-SIDE = LEFT, TO 6      (SUBGOAL OF 14)
         SET: X = 0, TO-SIDE = RIGHT
         OBJECT 7: (LEFT(M 3 C 0) RIGHT(M 0 C 3 BOAT YES))

4 GOAL 16 TRANSFORM 7 INTO DESIRED-OBJ        (SUBGOAL OF 13)

5 GOAL 17 REDUCE M-L ON 7          (SUBGOAL OF 16)

5 GOAL 18 APPLY M-C-OPR WITH X = 2, FROM-SIDE = LEFT, TO 7      (SUBGOAL OF 17)
         SET: Y = 0, TO-SIDE = RIGHT

7 GOAL 19 REDUCE B-L ON 7          (SUBGOAL OF 18)

8 GOAL 20 APPLY M-C-OPR WITH TO-SIDE = LEFT, TO 7       (SUBGOAL OF 19)
         SET: Y = 1, X = 0, FROM-SIDE = RIGHT
         OBJECT 8: (LEFT(M 3 C 1 BOAT YES) RIGHT(M 0 C 2))

7 GOAL 21 APPLY M-C-OPR WITH X = 2, FROM-SIDE = LEFT, TO 8      (SUBGOAL OF 18)
         SET: Y = 0, TO-SIDE = RIGHT
         OBJECT 9: (LEFT(M 1 C 1) RIGHT(M 2 C 2 BOAT YES))

5 GOAL 22 TRANSFORM 9 INTO DESIRED-OBJ         (SUBGOAL OF 16)

5 GOAL 23 REDUCE C-L ON 9          (SUBGOAL OF 22)

7 GOAL 24 APPLY M-C-OPR WITH Y = 1, FROM-SIDE = LEFT, TO 9      (SUBGOAL OF 23)
         SET: X = 0, TO-SIDE = RIGHT

8 GOAL 25 REDUCE B-L ON 9          (SUBGOAL OF 24)
```

```
9 GOAL 26 APPLY M-C-OPR WITH TO-SIDE = LEFT; TO 9        (SUBGOAL OF 25)
   SET: Y = 1, X = 1, FROM-SIDE = RIGHT
   OBJECT 10: (LEFT(M 2 C 2 BOAT YES) RIGHT(M 1 C 1))

8 GOAL 27 APPLY M-C-OPR WITH Y = 1, FROM-SIDE = LEFT, TO 10        (SUBGOAL OF 24)
   SET: X = 1, TO-SIDE = RIGHT
   OBJECT 9: (LEFT(M 1 C 1) RIGHT(M 2 C 2 BOAT YES))

3 GOAL 12 SELECT FROM 4 A/C NEW-OBJ OF DESIRED-OBJ        (SUBGOAL OF 11)
   10 SELECTED

3 GOA  29 TRANSFORM 3 INTO DESIRED-OBJ        (SUBGOAL OF 29)

4 GOAL 30 REDUCE C-L ON 8        (SUBGOAL OF 29)

5 GOAL 31 APPLY M-C-OPR WITH Y = 1, FROM-SIDE = LEFT, TO 8        (SUBGOAL OF 30)
   SET: X = 0, TO-SIDE = RIGHT
   OBJECT 7: (LEFT(M 3 C 0) RIGHT(M 0 C 3 BOAT YES))

3 GOAL 12 SELECT FROM 4 A/C NEW-OBJ OF DESIRED-OBJ        (SUBGOAL OF 11)
   10 SELECTED

3 GOA  37 TRANSFORM 10 INTO DESIRED-OBJ        (SUBGOAL OF 11)

4 GOAL 34 REDUCE C-L ON 10        (SUBGOAL OF 33)

5 GOAL 35 APPLY M-C-OPR WITH Y = 2, FROM-SIDE = LEFT, TO 10        (SUBGOAL OF 34)
   SET: X = 2, TO-SIDE = RIGHT

4 GOAL 36 REDUCE M-L ON 10        (SUBGOAL OF 33)

5 GOAL 37 APPLY M-C-OPR WITH X = 2, FROM-SIDE = LEFT, TO 10        (SUBGOAL OF 36)
   SET: Y = 0, TO-SIDE = RIGHT
   OBJECT 11: (LEFT(M 0 C 2) RIGHT(M 3 C 1 BOAT YES))
```

Fig. 50 (cont.).

Fig. 50 (cont.).

```
4  GOAL  38 TRANSFORM 11 INTO DESIRED-OBJ        (SUBGOAL OF 33)

5  GOAL  39 REDUCE C-L ON 11        (SUBGOAL OF 38)

6  GOAL  40 APPLY M-C-OPR WITH Y = 2, FROM-SIDE = LEFT, TO 11        (SUBGOAL OF 39)
      SET:  X = 0, TO-SIDE = RIGHT

7  GOAL  41 REDUCE B-L ON 11        (SUBGOAL OF 40)

8  GOAL  42 APPLY M-C-OPR WITH TO-SIDE = LEFT, TO 11        (SUBGOAL OF 41)
      SET:  Y = 1, X = 0, FROM-SIDE = RIGHT
      OBJECT 12: (LEFT(M 0 C 3 BOAT YES) RIGHT(M 3 C 0))

7  GOAL  43 APPLY M-C-OPR WITH Y = 2, FROM-SIDE = LEFT, TO 12        (SUBGOAL OF 40)
      SET:  X = 0, TO-SIDE = RIGHT
      OBJECT 13: (LEFT(M 0 C 1) RIGHT(M 3 C 2 BOAT YES))

5  GOAL  44 TRANSFORM 13 INTO DESIRED-OBJ        (SUBGOAL OF 38)

6  GOAL  45 REDUCE C-L ON 13        (SUBGOAL OF 44)

7  GOAL  46 APPLY M-C-OPR WITH Y = 1, FROM-SIDE = LEFT, TO 13        (SUBGOAL OF 45)
      SET:  X = 0, TO-SIDE = RIGHT

8  GOAL  47 REDUCE B-L ON 13        (SUBGOAL OF 46)

9  GOAL  48 APPLY M-C-OPR WITH TO-SIDE = LEFT, TO 13        (SUBGOAL OF 47)
      SET:  Y = 1, X = 0, FROM-SIDE = RIGHT
      OBJECT 14: (LEFT(M 0 C 2 BOAT YES) RIGHT(M 3 C 1))

8  GOAL  49 APPLY M-C-OPR WITH Y = 1, FROM-SIDE = LEFT, TO 14        (SUBGOAL OF 46)
```

Fig. 50 (cont.).

```
               SET: X = 0, TO-SIDE = RIGHT
               OBJECT 13: (LEFT(M 0 C 1) RIGHT(M 3 C 2 BOAT YES))

3   GOAL 12  SELECT FROM 4 A/C NEW-OBJ OF DESIRED-OBJ        (SUBGOAL OF 11)
               14 SELECTED

3   GOAL 51  TRANSFORM 12 INTO DESIRED-OBJ        (SUBGOAL OF 11)

4   GOAL 52  REDUCE C-L ON 12        (SUBGOAL OF 51)

3   GOAL 12  SELECT FROM 4 A/C NEW-OBJ OF DESIRED-OBJ        (SUBGOAL OF 11)
               14 SELECTED

3   GOAL 54  TRANSFORM 14 INTO DESIRED-OBJ        (SUBGOAL OF 11)

4   GOAL 55  REDUCE C-L ON 14        (SUBGOAL OF 54)

5   GOAL 56  APPLY M-C-OPR WITH Y = 2, FROM-SIDE = LEFT, TO 14        (SUBGOAL OF 55)
               SET: X = 0, TO-SIDE = RIGHT
               OBJECT 15: (LEFT(M 0 C 0) RIGHT(M 3 C 3 BOAT YES))

4   GOAL 57  TRANSFORM 15 INTO DESIRED-OBJ        (SUBGOAL OF 54)

SUCCESS
```

DISCUSSION

It is instructive to compare the specification of the Missionaries and Cannibals task in Fig. 48 with its specification for GPS-2-2.* The latter contains information about the nature of operators that the current GPS discovers for itself. GPS-2-2 was given ten operators: move one missionary from left to right; move two missionaries from left to right; move one missionary and one cannibal from left to right; etc. The desirability of these operators for reducing the various types of difference was given to GPS-2-2 exogenously in the TABLE-OF-CON-NECTIONS. In Fig. 48 there is only a single operator. In applying this operator, GPS specifies the variables so that the operator performs a desirable function.

GPS-2-2 was given a desirability filter for operators. This filter prevented GPS-2-2 from attempting to move more missionaries and cannibals across the river than there were on the side from which they were being moved. Such a separate filter is unnecessary in GPS because GPS never considers applying such an operator. Each operator in the GPS-2-2 formulation consisted of an IPL routine with its parameters (described on p. 26). The operator filter was also encoded in IPL. Not only is it tedious to construct IPL routines but, more important, the construction of these routines requires some knowledge of the internal structure of GPS. The M-C-OPR in Fig. 48 contains no information about the internal structure of GPS.†

INTEGRATION

The Integration task is analogous to that faced by an engineer who wants to integrate an expression symbolically. If the expression is at all complex, the engineer will probably use an integration table; otherwise, he will use an elementary integral form that he has memorized. Although all of these forms can be derived either by limiting procedures or from previously derived forms, it is impractical for the engineer or GPS to do so.

GPS FORMULATION

Only the details of the Integration task are described here because it has already been discovered extensively in the preceding chapter. Figure 51 is the GPS formulation of the task of integrating EXPRES-

---

* See Newell (1963, pp. 92–96).

† Note added in proof: An extensive discussion of different representations of the Missionaries and Cannibals task has recently appeared in Amarel (1968).

```
RENAME    (

    LEFT = FIRST

    RIGHT = SECOND

        )

DECLARE    (

    COS = UNARY-CONNECTIVE

    D = UNARY-CONNECTIVE

    DESIRED-OBJ = DESCRIBED-OBJ

    EXP = N-ARY-CONNECTIVE

    INTEGRAL = UNARY-CONNECTIVE

    LOG = UNARY-CONNECTIVE

    SIN = UNARY-CONNECTIVE

    SYMBOL = ATTRIBUTE

    SYM-DIFF = FEATURE

    - = UNARY-CONNECTIVE

    * = N-ARY-CONNECTIVE

    + = N-ARY-CONNECTIVE

        )

LIST    (

    EXPRESSION-1 = ( THE INTEGRAL OF ( T * ( E EXP ( T EXP TWO ) ) * D T ) )

    INTEGRATE = ( 1. ( THE INTEGRAL OF ( ( U EXP N ) * D U ) YIELDS

                        ( ( U EXP ( N + ONE ) ) * ( ( N + ONE ) EXP - ONE ) ) ) ,

                  2. ( THE INTEGRAL OF ( ( U EXP - ONE ) * D U ) YIELDS

                        LOG U ) ,

                  3. ( THE INTEGRAL OF ( SIN U * D U ) YIELDS - COS U ) ,

                  4. ( THE INTEGRAL OF ( COS U * D U ) YIELDS SIN U ) ,

                  5. ( THE INTEGRAL OF ( U * D U ) YIELDS ( ( U EXP TWO ) *
```

Fig. 51. Specification for GPS of the task of integrating $\int t e^{t^2} dt$.

```
                      ( TWO EXP - ONE ) ) ) ,

            6.  ( THE INTEGRAL OF ( ( E EXP U ) * D U ) YIELDS

                ( E EXP U ) ) ,

            7.  ( THE INTEGRAL OF ( ( F + G ) * D U ) YIELDS ( THE INTEGRAL

                OF ( F * D U ) + THE INTEGRAL OF ( G * D U ) ) ) ) )

  DIFFERENTIATE = ( 1.  ( ( SIN U * D U ) YIELDS - U COS U ) ,

                    2.  ( ( COS U * D U ) YIELDS U SIN U ) ,

                    3.  ( ( U * D U ) YIELDS ( ( TWO EXP - ONE ) *

                        U ( U EXP TWO ) ) ) ,

                    4.  ( ( ( U EXP - ONE ) * D U ) YIELDS U LOG U ) )

  EXPRESSION-2 = ( THE INTEGRAL OF ( ( ( ( SIN ( C * T ) EXP TWO ) *

                   COS ( C * T ) ) + ( T EXP - ONE ) ) * D T ) )

        )

TASK-STRUCTURES    (

  TOP-GOAL = ( TRANSFORM EXPRESSION-1 INTO THE DESIRED-OBJ . )

  DESIRED-OBJ = ( SUBEXPRESSION-TESTS

                  THE SYMBOL DOES NOT-EQUAL INTEGRAL . )

  SYM-DIFF = ( SYMBOL )

  TABLE-OF-CONNECTIONS = ( 1.  ( SET-SIZE DIFFERENTIATE )

                           2.  ( SYM-DIFF INTEGRATE ) )

  DIFF-ORDERING = ( 1.  SYM-DIFF

                    2.  SET-SIZE )

  LIST-OF-OPR = ( INTEGRATE DIFFERENTIATE )

  LIST-OF-VAR = ( F G U N )

        )

  END
```

Fig. 51 (cont.).

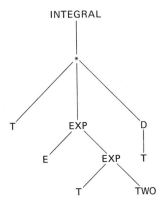

Fig. 52. Tree-structure representation of EXPRESSION-1. The symbols at the nodes are values of the ATTRIBUTE "SYMBOL" of the node.

SION-1, shown in tree-structure form in Fig. 52, which represents the integral

$$\int t e^{t^2}\, dt.$$

"TWO" is used instead of "2" because TWO is a symbolic CONSTANT, not a number (IPL data term), and by convention the value of SYMBOL cannot be a number. The only numbers used are integers. Fractions are represented by the use of EXP. For instance, $\frac{2}{3}$ is represented as TWO * (THREE EXP − ONE). EXPRESSION-1 and the operators of this task are translated into tree structures (LIST mode). The DESIRED-OBJ represents an expression that does not contain an $\int$; i.e., at every node the value of the ATTRIBUTE "SYMBOL" is not INTEGRAL. TOP-GOAL is the statement that the problem is to remove all occurrences of INTEGRAL from EXPRESSION-1.

In this task there are only two operators—INTEGRATE and DIF-FERENTIATE—both of which are a SET of FORM-OPERATORs separated by commas. INTEGRATE represents an integral table, since each of the FORM-OPERATORs it contains is a standard integral form. For example, the first FORM-OPERATOR in INTEGRATE represents the integral form

$$\int u^n\, du = \frac{u^{n+1}}{n+1}.$$

Similarly, DIFFERENTIATE represents a table of standard derivatives.

In addition to these two explicit operators, there are several oper-ators given to GPS as IPL structures which will be discussed in detail later. These operators, listed below, can be applied implicitly, i.e., without creating special goals to apply them:

commutativity and associativity of addition;

commutativity and associativity of multiplication;

$\int cf(u)\,du = c\int f(u)\,du;$

$d(cf(u)) = c\,d(f(u));$

$d(c + f(u)) = d(f(u));$

$u = v$ implies that $wu = wv;$

numeric simplification: $u * 0 = 0$, $u * 1 = u$, $u + 0 = u$, u EXP $0 = 1$, and integer arithmetic.

There are two types of differences in this task—SYM-DIFF and SET-SIZE. SYM-DIFF indicates that the value of SYMBOL of the node where the difference was detected is incorrect. Since this type of difference is detected when an OBJECT-SCHEMA containing the SYMBOL "INTE-GRAL" is compared to DESIRED-OBJ, the TABLE-OF-CONNECTIONS indicates that INTEGRATE should be used to reduce SYM-DIFF. In general, of course, SYM-DIFF could arise in situations in which INTEGRATE would not be a good operator to apply; however, this formulation is sufficient for the integration tasks considered.

The other type of difference, SET-SIZE, is not a FEATURE, and its role will be discussed later. For the tasks considered, DIFFERENTIATE should be applied when SET-SIZE is detected. DIFF-ORDERING designates that SYM-DIFF is the more difficult type of difference, because the main goal of integration is to remove all occurrences of INTEGRAL in an OBJECT-SCHEMA.

LIST-OF-OPR is a list of those operators that must be converted into their internal representation after translation. This conversion process assigns print names to each FORM-OPERATOR in INTEGRATE and DIFFERENTIATE. Figure 53 gives names that were assigned; e.g., the topmost integral form in Fig. 53 was assigned the name 1.

SIMILARITY, which was given to GPS as an IPL structure, is a selection criterion used in SELECT type of goals and is a definition of the similarity of two OBJECT-SCHEMAS. It is a list of properties, ranked in order of their importance, that an OBJECT-SCHEMA might contain. All of the properties are properties of a SET of factors that contain a differential, e.g., D T. In the order of their importance the properties are as follows:

contains a factor whose SYMBOL IS +;

contains a factor whose SYMBOL is LOG;

```
15 DERIVATION LIST OF (EXPRESSION-1 )

1  (INTEGRAL((U EXP N)  *  D U)  YIELDS  ((U EXP (N + ONE))  *  ((N + ONE) EXP -ONE)))

2  (INTEGRAL((U EXP -ONE)  *  D U)  YIELDS  LOG U)

3  (INTEGRAL(SIN U  *  D U)  YIELDS  -COS U)

4  (INTEGRAL(COS U  *  D U)  YIELDS  SIN U)

5  (INTEGRAL(U  *  D U)  YIELDS  ((U EXP TWO)  *  (TWO EXP -ONE)))

6  (INTEGRAL((E EXP U)  *  D U)  YIELDS  (E EXP U))

7  (INTEGRAL((F + G)  *  D U)  YIELDS  (INTEGRAL(F  *  D U)  +  INTEGRAL(G  *  D U)))

9  ((SIN U  *  D U)  YIELDS  -D COS U)

10  ((COS U  *  D U)  YIELDS  D SIN U)

11  ((U  *  D U)  YIELDS  ((TWO EXP -ONE)  *  D(U EXP TWO)))

12  (((U EXP -ONE)  *  D U)  YIELDS  D LOG U)
```

Fig. 53. Print-name assignments for the FORM-OPERATORS in DIFFERENTIATE and INTEGRATE.

contains a factor whose SYMBOL is EXP,
whose first argument is the same as its
correspondent in the criterion OBJECT-SCHEMA,
and whose second argument is a function of
the variable of integration;

contains a factor whose SYMBOL is SIN;

contains a factor whose SYMBOL is COS;

contains none of the preceding properties.

Although this definition of similarity might seem rather strange,[*] its usefulness is clarified by Figs. 54 and 55.

---

[*] Analogous to SIMILARITY is the classification of integral forms in an integral table, e.g., logarithmic forms, exponential forms, etc.

```
1 TOP-GOAL TRANSFORM EXPRESSION-1 INTO DESIRED-OBJ        (SUBGOAL OF NONE)

2 GOAL 2 REDUCE SYM-DIFF ON EXPRESSION-1        (SUBGOAL OF TOP-GOAL)

3 GOAL 3 APPLY INTEGRATE TO EXPRESSION-1        (SUBGOAL OF 2)

4 GOAL 4 SELECT FROM INTEGRATE A/C SIMILARITY OF EXPRESSION-1        (SUBGOAL OF 3)
      5 SELECTED

4 GOAL 5 APPLY 6 TO EXPRESSION-1        (SUBGOAL OF 3)

5 GOAL 6 REDUCE SET-SIZE ON LEFT EXPRESSION-1        (SUBGOAL OF 5)
      OBJECT 17: (T * D T)

6 GOAL 7 APPLY DIFFERENTIATE TO 17        (SUBGOAL OF 6)

7 GOAL 8 SELECT FROM DIFFERENTIATE A/C SIMILARITY OF 17        (SUBGOAL OF 7)
      11 SELECTED

7 GOAL 9 APPLY 11 TO 17        (SUBGOAL OF 7)
      OBJECT 19: ((TWO EXP -ONE) * D(T EXP TWO))
      OBJECT 20: INTEGRAL((E EXP (T EXP TWO)) * D(T EXP TWO))

5 GOAL 10 APPLY 6 TO 20        (SUBGOAL OF 5)
      OBJECT 21: ((E EXP (T EXP TWO)) * (TWO EXP -ONE))

2 GOAL 11 TRANSFORM 21 INTO DESIRED-OBJ        (SUBGOAL OF TOP-GOAL)

SUCCESS
```

Fig. 54. Performance of GPS on the task of integrating $\int t e^{t^2} dt$.

```
TOP-GOAL TRANSFORM EXPRESSION-2 INTO DESIRED-OBJ        (SUBGOAL OF NONE)

2 GOAL 3 REDUCE SYM-DIFF ON EXPRESSION-2       (SUBGOAL OF TOP-GOAL)

3 GOAL 4 APPLY INTEGRATE TO EXPRESSION-2       (SUBGOAL OF 3)

4 GOAL 5 SELECT FROM INTEGRATE A/C SIMILARITY OF EXPRESSION-2       (SUBGOAL OF 4)
        7 SELECTED

4 GOAL 6 APPLY 7 TO EXPRESSION-2       (SUBGOAL OF 4)
        OBJECT 20: (INTEGRAL((SIN(C * T) EXP TWO) * D T * COS(C * T)) + INTEGRAL((T EXP
        -ONE) * D T))

2 GOAL 7 TRANSFORM 20 INTO DESIRED-OBJ       (SUBGOAL OF TOP-GOAL)

3 GOAL 8 REDUCE SYM-DIFF ON LEFT 20       (SUBGOAL OF 7)

4 GOAL 9 APPLY INTEGRATE TO LEFT 20       (SUBGOAL OF 8)

5 GOAL 10 SELECT FROM INTEGRATE A/C SIMILARITY OF LEFT 20       (SUBGOAL OF 9)
        7 SELECTED

5 GOAL 11 APPLY 1 TO LEFT 20       (SUBGOAL OF 9)

6 GOAL 12 REDUCE SET-SIZE ON LEFT LEFT 20       (SUBGOAL OF 11)
        OBJECT 21: (COS(C * T) * D T)
```

7 GOAL 13 APPLY DIFFERENTIATE TO 21   (SUBGOAL OF 12)

3 GOAL 14 SELECT FROM DIFFERENTIATE A/C SIMILARITY OF 21   (SUBGOAL OF 13)
          10 SELECTED

3 GOAL 15 APPLY 10 TO 21   (SUBGOAL OF 13)
          OBJECT 23: (D SIN(C * T) * (C EXP -ONE))
          OBJECT 24: (INTEGRAL((SIN(C * T) EXP TWO) * D SIN(C * T) * (C EXP -ONE)) + INTEGRAL
                     ((T EXP -ONE) * D T))

6 GOAL 16 APPLY 1 TO LEFT 24   (SUBGOAL OF 11)
          OBJECT 25: (INTEGRAL((T EXP -ONE) * D T) + ((SIN(C * T) EXP THREE) * (THREE EXP
                     -ONE) * (C EXP -ONE)))

3 GOAL 17 TRANSFORM 25 INTO DESIRED-OBJ   (SUBGOAL OF 7)

4 GOAL 18 REDUCE SYM-DIFF ON LEFT 25   (SUBGOAL OF 17)

5 GOAL 19 APPLY INTEGRATE TO LEFT 25   (SUBGOAL OF 18)

6 GOAL 20 SELECT FROM INTEGRATE A/C SIMILARITY OF LEFT 25   (SUBGOAL OF 19)
          2 SELECTED

6 GOAL 21 APPLY 2 TO LEFT 25   (SUBGOAL OF 19)
          OBJECT 26: (LOG T + ((SIN(C * T) EXP THREE) * (THREE EXP -ONE) * (C EXP -ONE))
)

4 GOAL 22 TRANSFORM 26 INTO DESIRED-OBJ   (SUBGOAL OF 17)

SUCCESS

Fig. 55. Performance of GPS on the task of integrating $\int (\sin^2(ct)\cos(ct) + t^{-1})\,dt$.

Behavior of GPS

Figure 54 shows the behavior exhibited by GPS in integrating EXPRESSION-1 as formulated in Fig. 51. In attempting TOP-GOAL, GPS notices that the SYMBOL at the TOP-NODE of EXPRESSION-1 is INTEGRAL, and it creates GOAL 2 to change the value of SYMBOL. According to TABLE-OF-CONNECTIONS, INTEGRATE is a desirable operator and GOAL 3 is created.

Since INTEGRATE is a SET of FORM-OPERATORs, GOAL 4 is created to select one whose input form is similar to EXPRESSION-1. GPS selected OPERATOR 6 (see Fig. 53) because it, like EXPRESSION-1, contains an E raised to a power that is a function of the variable of integration. In applying OPERATOR 6 (GOAL 5) GPS substitutes T EXP TWO for U, which changes OPERATOR 6 to

$$\int e^{t^2} d(t^2) = e^{t^2}.$$

This operator cannot be applied directly to EXPRESSION-1 because there are too many factors in the SET of factors that is the argument of INTEGRAL in EXPRESSION-1. Since T and DT are the unmatched factors (have no correspondents in OPERATOR 6), GPS creates OBJECT 17 and attempts to reduce the number of factors in OBJECT 17.

Since DIFFERENTIATE has the capability of reducing the number of factors in a SET of factors GOAL 7 is created. GPS does not attempt to reduce the number of factors in EXPRESSION-1, because the exponential factor might be eliminated. The result of GOAL 8 is OPERATOR 11 (see Fig. 53), because the input forms of each of the other FORM-OPERATORs in DIFFERENTIATE are more complex than OBJECT 17. That is, they contain a factor that is a function of the variable of integration—e.g., cos u in OPERATOR 10 or u^{-1} in OPERATOR 12. OPERATOR 11 is successfully applied to OBJECT 17 (GOAL 11), which results in OBJECT 19. OBJECT 19 is substituted for T * D T in EXPRESSION-1 (OBJECT 20) because OBJECT 19 is derived from OBJECT 17.

In reattempting GOAL 5, OBJECT 21 is produced by applying 6 to OBJECT 20 (GOAL 10). GOAL 11 and thus TOP-GOAL are successful because there is no INTEGRAL in OBJECT 21.

Figure 55 is the behavior of GPS when given the task of integrating EXPRESSION-2:

$$\int (\sin^2(ct)\cos(ct) + t^{-1})\, dt.$$

Figure 51 is the formulation of the task for GPS except that EXPRESSION-1 is replaced by EXPRESSION-2 in TOP-GOAL. The assignment of names in Fig. 53 is the same for this task.

DISCUSSION

It might seem that most of the problem solving in this task is done by implicit application of the operators listed on p. 141, rather than by the explicit application of DIFFERENTIATE and INTEGRATE. Indeed, to integrate

$$\int 4 * (\cos(2 * t) * dt)$$

requires the implicit application of at least five operators in addition to the explicit application of

$$\int \cos(u) * du = \sin u$$

in order to produce the expression

$$2 * \sin(2 * t).$$

If all of the operators were used explicitly, a tree would have to be searched to a depth of 6 in order to find the solution to this simple problem.

GPS's formulation of integration is quite similar to the one used by SAINT (Slagle, 1963), a program that is rather proficient at symbolic integration.[*] SAINT can apply "algorithmlike transformations" whenever necessary without creating special goals for applying them. These "algorithmlike transformations" include all of the operators used implicitly by GPS plus many others such as OPERATOR 9 in Fig. 53. Hence, both SAINT and GPS would integrate

$$\int 4 * (\cos(2 * T) * dt)$$

in a single step by recognizing that it is a substitution instance of

$$\int \cos(u) * du = \sin u.$$

In addition to the "algorithmlike transformations," SAINT can apply "heuristic transformations," which it uses in much the same way that GPS uses the operators DIFFERENTIATE and INTEGRATE. Consider the example of integrating EXPRESSION-1 in Fig. 51. SAINT notices that the integral is not of "standard form" and selects a "heuristic transformation" relevant to reducing this difficulty. The

---

[*] Recently another study of integration has been completed (Moses, 1967), which is much improved over SAINT. However, it goes at the task somewhat differently than either SAINT or GPS, so that detailed comparisons are not worthwhile here. Likewise, it is not appropriate here to take up the more fundamental discussion of heuristic search versus a collection of highly specific mechanisms (the approach of Moses' program).

particular "heuristic transformation" selected is: Let u equal a nonconstant, nonlinear subexpression of the integrand. Although Slagle thought that, using this "heuristic transformation," SAINT would substitute $u = t^2$, SAINT actually makes the substitution

$$u = e^{t^2}.$$

Either of these substitutions reduce the integral to "standard form" and the task is solved.

The substitution $u = t^2$ performs the same function performed by applying OPERATOR 11 in Fig. 53, since both reduce EXPRESSION-1 to the standard integral form $\int e^u \, du$. However, the "heuristic transformations" of SAINT are more general than the operators of GPS because each "heuristic transformation" corresponds to many GPS operators. This is a nontrivial difference in the two formulations.

The operators that GPS uses implicitly have two outstanding qualities: they are relatively simple compared with the operators in Fig. 53; and it is obvious when they should be applied. For example, in GOAL 15 in Fig. 55, it is obvious that

$$d(c * t) = c \, dt$$

must be used after C * T has been substituted for U.

The associativity and commutativity of addition and multiplication is implicit in the representation (see pp. 113–117 of Chapter V). Multiplication and addition are represented as a function of an unordered set of arguments. In matching two unordered sets GPS pairs the elements so that the difference between the two sets will be small. Even though in Figs. 54 and 55 the elements in unordered sets always appear in the correct order, GPS pairs the elements without any consideration of their order.*

The commutative match, used in this task, pairs elements according to their "importance" (see pp. 141–142). The most important element is the one that best fulfills the criterion "SIMILARITY" (see pp. 141–142). However, a SELECT goal is not constructed to select the most important element; the commutative match uses this criterion in a special way.

All newly generated OBJECT-SCHEMAs are processed by an IPL-V routine that does numeric simplification and removes unnecessary parentheses. Figure 56a is an example of an OBJECT-SCHEMA with unnecessary parentheses, which are removed in the equivalent OBJECT-SCHEMA in Fig. 56b.

---

* In listing the elements of a set, they must be listed in some order. But the set can be considered unordered if no significance is attached to the order in which the elements are listed.

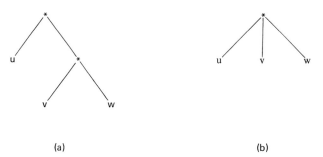

(a)   (b)

Fig. 56. (a) Tree-structure representation of $(u * (v * w))$; (b) tree-structure representation of $(u * v * w)$.

In some cases, two SETs that contain a different number of elements are matched. This fact is recognized by the match, and a difference whose type is SET-SIZE is reported. (This is the only type of difference that is not a FEATURE, and it is task independent.) The value of the difference is the unmatched elements of the SETs. Hence, it is necessary to consider only a subset of a SET. An example is GOAL 6 in Fig. 54. Consequently, the REDUCE-METHOD was generalized so that it could create a new object that consisted of a subset of a SET. When a difference is reduced on such an object, the REDUCE-METHOD substitutes the result for the subset in the SET. For example, in Fig. 54 OBJECT 17 is a subset of the set of factors in EXPRESSION-1. OBJECT 19 is derived from OBJECT 17 in an attempt to achieve GOAL 6 and is substituted into EXPRESSION-1, which results in OBJECT 20.

All of the other operators that are applied implicitly are given to GPS as immediate operators and are applied by the MATCH-DIFF-METHOD. Each of these is an IPL-V routine.

An alternative way of representing the operators of this task is to represent them individually, instead of grouping them into two SETs of operators. Using such a representation, GPS would not select one whose input form is similar to an object, but would try them in the order in which they appeared in the TABLE-OF-CONNECTIONS. This, of course, gives GPS less selectivity than the formulation in Fig. 51, particularly if the number of operators were to be increased.

It seems reasonable to group all integral forms together, since they have the common function of removing an $\int$. Since there are a considerable number of integral forms and many more could be added, it seems reasonable to attempt to apply them in the order in which they are most likely to be applicable. Selecting the operators whose input forms are most similar to the object to which they are applied is synonymous with selecting the operator that seems to be the most feasible to apply. Currently, the REDUCE-METHOD selects only desirable operators and does not evaluate them according to their feasibility. Perhaps the reduce method should also select operators that seem to be feasible as well as desirable.*

Certain algebraic operators, such as $u * u = u^2$, are not included in this formulation of integration. These would certainly be included in a more complete formulation. Some of the operators in Fig. 53 are equivalent. For example, OPERATOR 3 is the integral form of OPER-ATOR 8. Some operators are special cases of others; e.g., OPERATOR 5 is a special case of OPERATOR 1. A more complete formulation of this task would certainly involve an analysis of whether such redundancies were appropriate.

TOWER OF HANOI

In the Tower of Hanoi, a classical puzzle, there are three pegs and a number of disks, each of whose diameter is different from all of the others. Initially, all of the disks are stacked on the first peg in order of descending size as illustrated in Fig. 57. The problem is to dis-

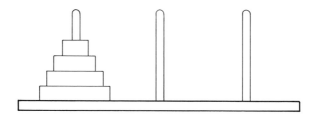

Fig. 57. Front view of the initial situation of the Tower of Hanoi.

cover a sequence of moves that will transfer all of the disks (as originally ordered) to the third peg. Each move consists of removing the top disk on any peg and placing it on top of the disks on another peg, but never placing a disk on top of one smaller than itself.

GPS FORMULATION

A representation of the four-disk version of the Tower of Hanoi to GPS is given in Fig. 58. TOP-GOAL is the statement that the problem is to produce the DESIRED-OBJ from the INITIAL-OBJ, which represents the situation when all of the disks are on the first peg (PEG-1). (The

---

* This is proposed also in Newell *et al.* (1960b, p. 81).

dashes in parentheses are ignored by the translator.) INITIAL-OBJ is an OBJECT-SCHEMA and is illustrated as a tree structure in Fig. 59. The only node with a local description is PEG-1. (All of the ATTRIBUTEs of the other nodes are UNDEFINED.) The presence of a disk on a peg is indicated by the value YES of the disk (which is an ATTRIBUTE) at the node that represents the peg. The absence of a disk on a peg is indicated by the ATTRIBUTE corresponding to the disk being UNDEFINED at the node that represents the peg. Disks are the only ATTRIBUTEs in this task (OBJ-ATTRIB). The DESIRED-OBJ is an OBJECT-SCHEMA that represents the situation when all of the disks are on PEG-3.

The only operator in this task is MOVE-DISK, which moves a disk from one peg to another peg provided the move is legitimate. The operator MOVE-DISK contains four free variables:

FROM-PEG is the peg from which the disk is moved;

TO-PEG is the peg to which the disk is moved;

OTHER-PEG is neither the FROM-PEG nor the TO-PEG;

DISK is the disk that is moved.

The first three TESTs following VAR-DOMAIN ensure that FROM-PEG, TO-PEG, and OTHER-PEG all stand for pegs and that no two of them stand for the same peg. The fourth TEST following VAR-DOMAIN is the statement that DISK stands for one of the four disks.

The formulation of MOVE-DISK is based on the fact that the top disk on a peg is also the smallest disk on the peg. Since this is true of the INITIAL-OBJ, it is true of all other objects because a disk is never placed on a smaller disk. Thus, in order to move the DISK, it must be the smallest disk on the FROM-PEG as well as smaller than any disk on TO-PEG. Because of the conversation of disks, these two constraints can be restated as follows: all of the disks that are smaller than DISK must be on the OTHER-PEG. This is the meaning of the TEST following PRETESTs. If the disk X at the node OTHER-PEG is DEFINED (i.e., X is an ATTRIBUTE of the node that OTHER-PEG stands for), X is on the OTHER-PEG. The TEST following PRETESTS is true only of any disk X that is smaller than DISK is on the OTHER-PEG.

FOR-ALL is used as a replicator. That is, the TEST following PRE-TESTS is actually the conjunction of several TESTs. Each of these TESTs has the form

X ON THE OTHER PEG IS DEFINED,

```
RENAME    (

    PEG-1  =  FIRST

    PEG-2  =  SECOND

    PEG-3  =  THIRD

      )

DECLARE (

    DISK  =  ATTRIBUTE

    DISKS  =  SET

    DISK-1  =  ATTRIBUTE

    DISK-2  =  ATTRIBUTE

    DISK-3  =  ATTRIBUTE

    DISK-4  =  ATTRIBUTE

    D1.1  =  FEATURE

    D1.2  =  FEATURE

    D1.3  =  FEATURE

    D2.1  =  FEATURE

    D2.2  =  FEATURE

    D2.3  =  FEATURE

    D3.1  =  FEATURE

    D3.2  =  FEATURE

    D3.3  =  FEATURE

    D4.1  =  FEATURE

    D4.2  =  FEATURE

    D4.3  =  FEATURE

    DESIRED-OBJ  =  OBJECT-SCHEMA

    FROM-PEG  =  LOC-PROG

    INITIAL-OBJ  =  OBJECT-SCHEMA
```

Fig. 58. Specification for GPS of the four-disk Tower of Hanoi task.

```
MOVE-DISK = MOVE-OPERATOR

NONE = SET

OTHER-PEG = LOC-PROG

PEGS = SET

SMALLER = ATTRIBUTE

THE-FIRST = SET

THE-FIRST-2 = SET

THE-FIRST-3 = SET

TO-PEG = LOC-PROG

X = ATTRIBUTE

    )

TASK-STRUCTURES (

    TOP-GOAL = ( TRANSFORM THE INITIAL-OBJ INTO THE DESIRED-OBJ )

    INITIAL-OBJ = ( PEG-1 ( DISK-1 YES DISK-2 YES DISK-3 YES DISK-4 YES )

                    PEG-2 ( ----- )

                    PEG-3 ( ----- )      )

    OBJ-ATTRIB = ( DISK-1 DISK-2 DISK-3 DISK-4 )

    DESIRED-OBJ = ( PEG-1 ( ----- )

                    PEG-2 ( ----- )

                    PEG-3 ( DISK-1 YES DISK-2 YES DISK-3 YES DISK-4 YES ) )

    MOVE-DISK = ( CREATION-OPERATOR

                  VAR-DOMAIN

                  1. THE TO-PEG IS AN EXCLUSIVE-MEMBER OF THE PEGS .

                  2. THE FROM-PEG IS AN EXCLUSIVE-MEMBER OF THE PEGS .

                  3. THE OTHER-PEG IS AN EXCLUSIVE-MEMBER OF THE PEGS .

                  4. THE DISK IS IN-THE-SET OF DISKS .

                  PRETESTS
```

Fig. 58 (cont.).

```
                    1.  X ON THE OTHER-PEG IS DEFINED FOR-ALL X SMALLER
                        THAN THE PARTICULAR DISK .
                MOVES
                    1.  MOVE THE DISK ON THE FROM-PEG TO THE DISK ON THE TO-PEG .
        )
DISKS = ( DISK-1 DISK-2 DISK-3 DISK-4 )
PEGS = ( PEG-1 PEG-2 PEG-3 )
DISK-1 = ( THE SMALLER ONES ARE NONE )
DISK-2 = ( THE SMALLER ONE IS THE-FIRST )
DISK-3 = ( THE SMALLER ONES ARE THE-FIRST-2 )
DISK-4 = ( THE SMALLER ONES ARE THE-FIRST-3 )
NONE = ( ----- )
THE-FIRST = ( DISK-1 )
THE-FIRST-2 = ( DISK-1 DISK-2 )
THE-FIRST-3 = ( DISK-1 DISK-2 DISK-3 )
D1.1 = ( DISK-1 ON PEG-1 . )
D1.2 = ( DISK-1 ON PEG-2 . )
D1.3 = ( DISK-1 ON PEG-3 . )
D2.1 = ( DISK-2 ON PEG-1 . )
D2.2 = ( DISK-2 ON PEG-2 . )
D2.3 = ( DISK-2 ON PEG-3 . )
D3.1 = ( DISK-3 ON PEG-1 . )
D3.2 = ( DISK-3 ON PEG-2 . )
D3.3 = ( DISK-3 ON PEG-3 . )
D4.1 = ( DISK-4 ON PEG-1 . )
D4.2 = ( DISK-4 ON PEG-2 . )
D4.3 = ( DISK-4 ON PEG-3 . )
COMPARE-OBJECTS = ( BASIC-MATCH )
```

Fig. 58 (cont.).

```
BASIC-MATCH = ( COMP-FEAT-LIST ( D1.1 D1.2 D1.3 D2.1 D2.2 D2.3 D3.1 D3.2

                                 D3.3 D4.1 D4.2 D4.3 ) )

DIFF-ORDERING = ( 1. ( D4.1 D4.2 D4.3 )

                  2. ( D3.1 D3.2 D3.3 )

                  3. ( D2.1 D2.2 D2.3 )

                  4. ( D1.1 D1.2 D1.3 ) )

TABLE-OF-CONNECTIONS = ( ( COMMON-DIFFERENCE MOVE-DISK ) )

LIST-OF-VAR = ( DISK FROM-PEG OTHER-PEG TO-PEG X )

  )

END
```

Fig. 58 (cont.).

and each has a different value for x, which is indicated syntactically by the fact that x follows FOR-ALL. The domain of x is the SET designated by the phrase (whose semantics are discussed below)

SMALLER THAN THE PARTICULAR DISK.

Under MOVES there is only one TRANSFORMATION, which has the effect of moving the DISK (which must be on the FROM-PEG) from the FROM-PEG to the TO-PEG.

DISKS is the SET of disks and PEGS is the SET of pegs, both of which are used in the stating of the TESTs in VAR-DOMAIN in MOVE-DISK. Each disk is not only an ATTRIBUTE (e.g., DISK-3), but is also a data structure. With each disk is associated one attribute–value pair: SMALLER is the ATTRIBUTE and its value is the SET of those disks that are smaller than the disk. For example, for DISK-3, the value of

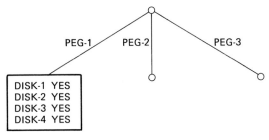

Fig. 59. Tree-structure representation of the INITIAL-OBJ in the Tower of Hanoi.

SMALLER is THE-FIRST-2 which is the set of two disks DISK-1, DISK-2. This information defines the size of a disk relative to the other disks, and is used in the TEST following PRETESTS in MOVE-DISK. When DISK has the value DISK-3, the phrase

SMALLER THAN THE PARTICULAR DISK

designates the value of SMALLER of DISK-3, which is THE-FIRST-2. SMALLER in this example is a FEATURE. PARTICULAR DISK indicates that this FEATURE does not refer to the input object of the operator, but to the data structure whose name is the value of the variable DISK.

D1.1 through D4.3 in Fig. 58 are the types of differences in this task. Each is a FEATURE. COMPARE-OBJECTS indicates that the match should check for the type of differences listed after COMP-FEAT-LIST in BASIC-MATCH. The match checks for differences only at the TOP-NODE of objects.

DIFF-ORDERING is the statement that the larger the disk, the more difficult the difference. In DIFF-ORDERING, the difference types are divided into four categories. All of the difference types in a category pertain to a particular disk and are considered equally difficult. The categories are arranged according to the difficulty of their difference types, which is determined by the size of the disk to which they pertain.

The TABLE-OF-CONNECTIONS indicates that MOVE-DISK is to be used to reduce any type of difference. This means that no selection power comes directly from the TABLE-OF-CONNECTIONS; instead it must come from the *desirability-selection* process for MOVE-OPER-ATORS.

LIST-OF-VAR is a list of symbols in Fig. 58 that are variables.

BEHAVIOR OF GPS

The way GPS arrives at the solution to the Tower of Hanoi is shown in Fig. 60. In attempting TOP-GOAL, GPS notices that DISK-4 should be on PEG-3 (i.e., the ATTRIBUTE "DISK-4" of the node named PEG-3 should have the value YES), and creates GOAL 2 to reduce this difference. GPS also notices that the other three disks should be on PEG-3, but selects the difference of type D4.3, because it is the most difficult difference detected.

By referring to TABLE-OF-CONNECTIONS, GPS selects MOVE-DISK to be applied to INITIAL-OBJ. The *desirability-selection* process finds

Fig. 60. Performance of GPS on the Tower of Hanoi.

```
1 TOP-GOAL TRANSFORM INITIAL-OBJ INTO DESIRED-OBJ     (SUBGOAL OF NONE)

2 GOAL 2 REDUCE D4.3 ON INITIAL-OBJ     (SUBGOAL OF TOP-GOAL)

3 GOAL 3 APPLY MOVE-DISK WITH TO-PEG = PEG-3, DISK = DISK-4, TO INITIAL-OBJ     (SUBGOAL OF 2)
        SET: FROM-PEG = PEG-1, OTHER-PEG = PEG-2

4 GOAL 4 REDUCE D3.2 ON INITIAL-OBJ     (SUBGOAL OF 3)

5 GOAL 5 APPLY MOVE-DISK WITH TO-PEG = PEG-2, DISK = DISK-3, TO INITIAL-OBJ     (SUBGOAL OF 4)
        SET: FROM-PEG = PEG-1, OTHER-PEG = PEG-3

6 GOAL 6 REDUCE D2.3 ON INITIAL-OBJ     (SUBGOAL OF 5)

7 GOAL 7 APPLY MOVE-DISK WITH TO-PEG = PEG-3, DISK = DISK-2, TO INITIAL-OBJ     (SUBGOAL OF 6)
        SET: FROM-PEG = PEG-1, OTHER-PEG = PEG-2

8 GOAL 8 REDUCE D1.2 ON INITIAL-OBJ     (SUBGOAL OF 7)

9 GOAL 9 APPLY MOVE-DISK WITH TO-PEG = PEG-2, DISK = DISK-1, TO INITIAL-OBJ     (SUBGOAL OF 8)
        SET: FROM-PEG = PEG-1, OTHER-PEG = PEG-3
        OBJECT 5: (PEG-1(DISK-2 YES DISK-3 YES DISK-4 YES) PEG-2(DISK-1 YES) PEG-3(-----
        ))

8 GOAL 10 APPLY MOVE-DISK WITH TO-PEG = PEG-3, DISK = DISK-2, TO 5     (SUBGOAL OF 7)
        SET: FROM-PEG = PEG-1, OTHER-PEG = PEG-2
        OBJECT 6: (PEG-1(DISK-3 YES DISK-4 YES) PEG-2(DISK-1 YES) PEG-3(DISK-2 YES))

6 GOAL 11 APPLY MOVE-DISK WITH TO-PEG = PEG-2, DISK = DISK-3, TO 6     (SUBGOAL OF 5)
        SET: FROM-PEG = PEG-1, OTHER-PEG = PEG-3
```

Fig. 60 (cont.).

```
7 GOAL 12 REDUCE D1.3 ON 6         (SUBGOAL OF 11)


8 GOAL 13 APPLY MOVE-DISK WITH TO-PEG = PEG-3, DISK = DISK-1, TO 6     (SUBGOAL OF 12)
         SET: FROM-PEG = PEG-2, OTHER-PEG = PEG-1
         OBJECT 7: (PEG-1(DISK-3 YES DISK-4 YES) PEG-2(-----) PEG-3(DISK-1 YES DISK-2 YES
              ) )

7 GOAL 14 APPLY MOVE-DISK WITH TO-PEG = PEG-2, DISK = DISK-3, TO 7     (SUBGOAL OF 11)
         SET: FROM-PEG = PEG-1, OTHER-PEG = PEG-3
         OBJECT 8: (PEG-1(DISK-4 YES) PEG-2(DISK-3 YES) PEG-3(DISK-1 YES DISK-2 YES))

4 GOAL 15 APPLY MOVE-DISK WITH TO-PEG = PEG-3, DISK = DISK-4, TO 8     (SUBGOAL OF 3)
         SET: FROM-PEG = PEG-1, OTHER-PEG = PEG-2

5 GOAL 16 REDUCE D2.2 ON 8         (SUBGOAL OF 15)


6 GOAL 17 APPLY MOVE-DISK WITH TO-PEG = PEG-2, DISK = DISK-2, TO 8     (SUBGOAL OF 16)
         SET: FROM-PEG = PEG-3, OTHER-PEG = PEG-1

7 GOAL 18 REDUCE D1.1 ON 8         (SUBGOAL OF 17)


8 GOAL 19 APPLY MOVE-DISK WITH TO-PEG = PEG-1, DISK = DISK-1, TO 8     (SUBGOAL OF 18)
         SET: FROM-PEG = PEG-3, OTHER-PEG = PEG-2
         OBJECT 9: (PEG-1(DISK-1 YES DISK-4 YES) PEG-2(DISK-3 YES) PEG-3(DISK-2 YES))

7 GOAL 20 APPLY MOVE-DISK WITH TO-PEG = PEG-2, DISK = DISK-2, TO 9     (SUBGOAL OF 17)
         SET: FROM-PEG = PEG-3, OTHER-PEG = PEG-1
         OBJECT 10: (PEG-1(DISK-1 YES DISK-4 YES) PEG-2(DISK-2 YES DISK-3 YES) PEG-3(-----
              ) )

5 GOAL 21 APPLY MOVE-DISK WITH TO-PEG = PEG-3, DISK = DISK-4, TO 10    (SUBGOAL OF 15)
         SET: FROM-PEG = PEG-1, OTHER-PEG = PEG-2
```

Fig. 60 (cont.).

6 GOAL 22 REDUCE D1.2 ON 13   (SUBGOAL OF 21)

7 GOAL 23 APPLY MOVE-DISK WITH TO-PEG = PEG-2, DISK = DISK-1, TO 10   (SUBGOAL OF 22)
          SET: FROM-PEG = PEG-1, OTHER-PEG = PEG-3
          OBJECT 11: (PEG-1(DISK-4 YES) PEG-2(DISK-1 YES DISK-2 YES DISK-3 YES) PEG-3(-----
          ))

6 GOAL 24 APPLY MOVE-DISK WITH TO-PEG = PEG-3, DISK = DISK-4, TO 11   (SUBGOAL OF 21)
          SET: FROM-PEG = PEG-1, OTHER-PEG = PEG-2
          OBJECT 12: (PEG-1(-----) PEG-2(DISK-1 YES DISK-2 YES DISK-3 YES) PEG-3(DISK-4 YES

2 GOAL 25 TRANSFORM 12 INTO DESIRED-OBJ   (SUBGOAL OF TOP-GOAL)

3 GOAL 26 REDUCE D3.3 ON 12   (SUBGOAL OF 25)

4 GOAL 27 APPLY MOVE-DISK WITH TO-PEG = PEG-3, DISK = DISK-3, TO 12   (SUBGOAL OF 26)
          SET: FROM-PEG = PEG-2, OTHER-PEG = PEG-1

5 GOAL 28 REDUCE D2.1 ON 12   (SUBGOAL OF 27)

6 GOAL 29 APPLY MOVE-DISK WITH TO-PEG = PEG-1, DISK = DISK-2, TO 12   (SUBGOAL OF 28)

          SET: FROM-PEG = PEG-2, OTHER-PEG = PEG-3

7 GOAL 30 REDUCE D1.3 ON 12   (SUBGOAL OF 29)

8 GOAL 31 APPLY MOVE-DISK WITH TO-PEG = PEG-3, DISK = DISK-1, TO 12   (SUBGOAL OF 30)
          SET: FROM-PEG = PEG-2, OTHER-PEG = PEG-1
          OBJECT 13: (PEG-1(-----) PEG-2(DISK-2 YES DISK-3 YES) PEG-3(DISK-1 YES DISK-4 YES
          ))

Fig. 60 (cont.).

```
7 GOAL 32 APPLY MOVE-DISK WITH TO-PEG = PEG-1, DISK = DISK-2, TO 13    (SUBGOAL OF 29)
          SET: FROM-PEG = PEG-2, OTHER-PEG = PEG-3
          OBJECT 14: (PEG-1(DISK-2 YES) PEG-2(DISK-3 /ES) PEG-3(DISK-1 YES DISK-4 YES))

5 GOAL 33 APPLY MOVE-DISK WITH TO-PEG = PEG-3, DISK = DISK-3, TO 14    (SUBGOAL OF 27)
          SET: FROM-PEG = PEG-2, OTHER-PEG = PEG-1

6 GOAL 34 REDUCE D1.1 ON 14    (SUBGOAL OF 33)

7 GOAL 35 APPLY MOVE-DISK WITH TO-PEG = PEG-1, DISK = DISK-1, TO 14    (SUBGOAL OF 34)
          SET: FROM-PEG = PEG-3, OTHER-PEG = PEG-2
          OBJECT 15: (PEG-1(DISK-1 YES DISK-2 YES) PEG-2(DISK-3 YES) PEG-3(DISK-4 YES))

4 GOAL 36 APPLY MOVE-DISK WITH TO-PEG = PEG-3, DISK = DISK-3, TO 15    (SUBGOAL OF 33)
          SET: FROM-PEG = PEG-2, OTHER-PEG = PEG-1
          OBJECT 16: (PEG-1(DISK-1 YES DISK-2 YES) PEG-2(-----) PEG-3(DISK-3 YES DISK-4 YES)
          ))

3 GOAL 37 TRANSFORM 16 INTO DESIRED-OBJ    (SUBGOAL OF 25)

4 GOAL 38 REDUCE D2.3 ON 16    (SUBGOAL OF 37)

5 GOAL 39 APPLY MOVE-DISK WITH TO-PEG = PEG-3, DISK = DISK-2, TO 16    (SUBGOAL OF 38)
          SET: FROM-PEG = PEG-1, OTHER-PEG = PEG-2

6 GOAL 40 REDUCE D1.2 ON 16    (SUBGOAL OF 39)
```

Fig. 60 (cont.).

```
7 GOAL 41 APPLY MOVE-DISK WITH TO-PEG = PEG-2, DISK = DISK-1, TO 16      (SUBGOAL OF 40)
         SET: FROM-PEG = PEG-1, OTHER-PEG = PEG-3
         OBJECT 17: (PEG-1(DISK-2 YES) PEG-2(DISK-1 YES) PEG-3(DISK-3 YES DISK-4 YES))

6 GOAL 42 APPLY MOVE-DISK WITH TO-PEG = PEG-3, DISK = DISK-2, TO 17      (SUBGOAL OF 39)
         SET: FROM-PEG = PEG-1, OTHER-PEG = PEG-2
         OBJECT 18: (PEG-1(-----) PEG-2(DISK-1 YES) PEG-3(DISK-2 YES DISK-3 YES DISK-4 YES
         ))

4 GOAL 43 TRANSFORM 18 INTO DESIRED-OBJ       (SUBGOAL OF 37)

5 GOAL 44 REDUCE D1,3 ON 18       (SUBGOAL OF 43)

6 GOAL 45 APPLY MOVE-DISK WITH TO-PEG = PEG-3, DISK = DISK-1, TO 18      (SUBGOAL OF 44)
         SET: FROM-PEG = PEG-2, OTHER-PEG = PEG-1
         OBJECT 19: (PEG-1(-----) PEG-2(-----) PEG-3(DISK-1 YES DISK-2 YES DISK-3 YES DISK-4
         YES))

5 GOAL 46 TRANSFORM 19 INTO DESIRED-OBJ       (SUBGOAL OF 43)

SUCCESS
```

that MOVE-DISK performs a desirable function if the variables TO-PEG and DISK have the respective values PEG-3 and DISK-4. The application of MOVE-DISK with these two variables so specified is attempted by creating GOAL 3. After specifying the remaining variables, FROM-PEG and OTHER-PEG, to be PEG-1 and PEG-2, respectively, GPS detects that the operator is infeasible because DISK-1, DISK-2, and DISK-3 are not on PEG-2. GOAL 4 is created to reduce the difference that DISK-3 is not on PEG-2, because it is the most difficult difference detected in attempting to apply the operator. However, it is less difficult than the difference for which GOAL 2 was created; otherwise GOAL 4 would have been considered undesirable. The only other legitimate variable specification for FROM-PEG and TO-PEG is PEG-2 and PEG-1, respectively, which would give rise to the difference that DISK-4 is not on PEG-2. Since this difference is as difficult as the difference for which GOAL 2 was created, GPS considers this variable specification to be undesirable.

GPS attempts to achieve GOAL 4 by moving DISK-3 to PEG-2, for which GOAL 5 was created. Since DISK-2 is not on PEG-3 (GOAL 6), GOAL 7 is created in an attempt to move DISK-2 to PEG-3. In order to achieve GOAL 7, DISK-1 is moved to PEG-2 (GOAL 8 and GOAL 9), which results in the new object, OBJECT 5. DISK-2 is moved to PEG-3 (GOAL 10) resulting in OBJECT 6.

In reattempting GOAL 4, GOAL 11 is created to move DISK-3 to PEG-2. After moving DISK-1 from PEG-2 to PEG-3 (GOAL 12 and GOAL 13), DISK-3 is moved to PEG-2 (GOAL 14) and GOAL 4 is achieved. The first fourteen goals are typical of the behavior of GPS on this task, and success is achieved at GOAL 46.

DISCUSSION

In moving a disk two constraints, which are usually stated somewhat independently, must be satisfied. Only the top disk on a peg can be moved, and it must be smaller than the top disk on the peg to which it is being moved. In MOVE-DISK these two constraints are replaced by the single TEST of PRETESTS. Combining the two constraints changes the problem formulation significantly, even though both formulations define the "same" problem.

The more usual formulation of MOVE-DISK would have the following PRETESTS:

1. X ON THE TO-PEG IS UNDEFINED FOR-ALL X
   SMALLER THAN THE-PARTICULAR DISK.

2. X ON THE FROM-PEG IS UNDEFINED FOR-ALL X
SMALLER THAN THE-PARTICULAR DISK.

With this formulation, GPS would find the task considerably more difficult.* Suppose, for example, that GPS wanted to move DISK-2 to PEG-3 and that DISK-1 and DISK-2 were on PEG-1 (GOAL 7 in Fig. 60). PEG-1 would be used for FROM-PEG and GPS would find only one difference,

DISK-1 should not be on PEG-1.

This difference contains no information about where DISK-1 should be moved, and might be moved to PEG-3 in an attempt to reduce the difference. However, using the formulation in Fig. 58, GPS detects the difference

DISK-1 should be on PEG-2,

(GOAL 8) because OTHER-PEG must equal PEG-2 in order for the variable specification to be legal. In reducing this difference, GPS considers it desirable to move DISK-1 to PEG-2 (GOAL 9) but undesirable to move DISK-1 to PEG-3.

An outstanding feature of GPS's behavior on the Tower of Hanoi is that GPS never makes a mistake. That is, GPS always chooses to reduce a difference that leads to the selection of the best operator. As noted above, this is not the case when the PRETESTS in MOVE-DISK consist of two separate constraints. Thus, formulating the PRE-TESTS as a single constraint is necessary for GPS always to select the correct operator. Another factor that allows GPS to select the correct operators in this formulation is that the types of differences and their relative difficulty are in some sense optimal. For many tasks a good set of differences and a good DIFF-ORDERING are difficult to obtain.

There is another problem solver that solves the Tower of Hanoi, called GAKU (Hormann, 1965). It approaches the task quite differently than GPS. First, GAKU solves the three-disk Tower of Hanoi by trial and error. Then the solution to the four-disk task is obtained by generalizing the solution to the three-disk task; the five-disk solution is obtained by generalizing the four-disk solution; etc. Hence GAKU

* In attempting the four-disk version of the Tower of Hanoi, GPS would exhaust memory before finding a solution. GPS could probably find the solution to the three-disk version.

solves this task by searching for a solution in a space of solutions, whereas GPS searches for the solution in a space of situations.

PROVING THEOREMS EXPRESSED IN THE FIRST-ORDER PREDICATE CALCULUS

The first-order predicate calculus, sometimes called the first-order predicate logic or quantification theory, is a formal language system that has received much attention in attempts to construct theorem-proving programs. [For a representative sample, see Davis and Putman (1960), Friedman (1963), Gilmore (1960), Robinson (1963, 1965), Wang (1960, 1961) and Wos *et al.* (1964).]*

The primitive symbols of this logic are

parentheses	(,);
logical connectives	$\sim$, &, $\vee$, $\supset$, $\equiv$;
predicate letters	$P, Q, R, \ldots$;
individual names	$a, b, c, \ldots$;
variables	$u, v, w, \ldots$;
quantifiers	$\exists$, $\forall$.

Parentheses serve their normal purpose of delimiting groups of symbols. The logical connectives stand for negation, conjunction, disjunction, implication, and equivalence, respectively. An atomic formula is a predicate letter followed by a "(," followed by a string of several individual names or variables separated by commas, followed by a ")"—e.g., $P(a, u, a)$. The intent of the quantifiers can best be given by example: $(\exists u) P(u)$ is true if and only if there exists some individual name, α, such that $P(\alpha)$ is true. $(\forall u)P(u)$ is true if and only if for every possible individual name, α, $P(\alpha)$ is true.

Formulas $F_1, F_2, F_3, \ldots$ of the calculus can be defined recursively as one of the following (where F_i and F_j are arbitrarily formulas):

an atomic formula

$\sim F_i$

---

* Note added in proof: Recently, there has been much activity in the area of mechanical theorem proving (Robinson, 1969). However, none of it is especially relevant for the elementary treatment considered here.

$$(F_i \& F_j)$$

$$(F_i \lor F_j)$$

$$(F_i \supset F_j)$$

$$(F_i \equiv F_j)$$

$$(\forall u)F_j$$

$$(\exists u)F_i$$

A formula may be either true or false, depending on the interpretations given to the predicate letters and individual names that occur in it. For example, $(\exists u)\,(P(b, u) \& Q(u))$ is true when $P(b, u)$ is understood as "b is the brother of u," $Q(u)$ is understood as "u is tall," and b is the name of someone within the scope of u with a tall brother.

Let a *ground formula* be either an atomic formula that does not contain variables, or the negation of such a formula. Then an interpretation, I, can be defined as a set of ground formulae with the following properties:

No atomic formula and its negation are members of I (I is consistent);

For every possible ground formula, either it or its negation is a member of I (I is complete).

A formula is *satisfiable* if there exists an interpretation for which it is true; otherwise, it is *unsatisfiable*. A formula is *valid*, if it is true for all possible interpretations. A formula is a *theorem* if and only if the formula is valid. It follows that the negation of a theorem must necessarily be unsatisfiable.

PREDICATE CALCULUS THEOREM PROVERS

Although several different approaches have been taken in constructing theorem-proving programs, we shall consider only the one that has received the most attention. The theoretical justification of this approach can be found in Davis and Putman (1960) and Robinson (1965). These theorem provers do not process formulas in the calculus directly, but first reduce the statement of the theorem to a normal form in order to simplify the theorem-proving process. In this normal form, an atomic formula can have functions $f, g, h, \ldots$ of variables within the scope of a predicate—e.g., $P(f(a))$—as well as individual names and variables. (The intent of these functions will be discussed later.) A *literal* is defined as an atomic formula or the negation of an atomic formula. The disjunction of a finite set of literals is called a *clause*, and the *empty clause* is denoted by □. The normal form of a theorem is the conjunction of a finite set of clauses. Instead of proving that a theorem is valid, the theorem provers prove that the negation of the theorem is unsatisfiable; i.e., a contradiction can be obtained.

Neither the logical connectives ⊃ and ≡, nor the quantifiers ∀ and ∃, appear in the normal form. However, there is no loss of generality in the use of this normal form, because any formula in the calculus can be reduced to it. Implication and equivalence can be defined in terms of conjunction, negation, and disjunction, and can be removed by repeated application of these definitions. ∀ does not appear in the normal form, because by convention all variables are universally quantified. All occurrences of ∃ are removed by replacing all of the variables quantified by ∃ with functions of the universally quantified variables on which they depend. For example, the normal form of the formula $(\forall u)(\exists v)(\forall w)P(u,v,w)$, is $P(u,f(u),w)$. The variables u and w are universally quantified by convention. In order for the formula to be true, there must exist a value of v that will make the formula true for every possible value of w. But this value of v does not have to be the same for every possible value of u. It can be a function of u; hence, v can be replaced by a function of u, i.e., $f(u)$. On the other hand, in the formula $(\exists v)(\forall u)(\forall w)P(u,v,w)$, whose normal form is $P(u,f,w)$, the value of v must be independent of both u and w; i.e., f must be a constant.

Only a single inference principle, the *Resolution Principle*, is used (Robinson, 1965; Wos *et al.*, 1964). From any two clauses, C and D, a *resolvent* of C and D can be inferred, which has the following properties:

L is a literal in C, and M is a literal in D.

The resolvent is a new clause consisting of all of the literals in C and D with the exception of L and M.

Either L or M but not both contain a ~.

Except for the ~, L and M are identical or can be made identical by substituting for variables, functions, individual names, or other variables.

Any substitutions that must be made in L and M in order to make them identical are also made in the resolvent.

If there are no L and M that fulfill the above conditions, C and D will have no resolvents; and if L and M are not uniquely specified by the above conditions, C and D will have more than one resolvent.

If S is any set of clauses, the nth resolution of S, denoted by $\mathfrak{R}^n(S)$, is defined as

$\mathfrak{R}^1(S)$ is all members of S together with all resolvents of all pairs of members of S;

For $n \geq 1$, $\mathfrak{R}^{n+1}(S) = \mathfrak{R}^1(\mathfrak{R}^n(S))$.

Then the theoretical basis of the theorem prover is

Resolution Theorem: If S is any finite set of clauses, then S is unsatisfiable if and only if $\mathfrak{R}^n(S)$ contains $\square$, for some $n \geq 1$.

Theorem provers based on the Resolution Theorem attempt to prove the unsatisfiability of a set of clauses by inferring $\square$. The proof of the unsatisfiability of a set S of clauses (proof of a theorem) consists of a sequence of clauses, each of which is either a member of S or the resolvent of two earlier clauses in the sequence. The final member of the sequence is $\square$. No such theorem prover can guarantee that it can either prove or disprove an arbitrary theorem in a fixed amount of time (and computer memory) because the proof sequence can be, according to the Resolution Theorem, arbitrarily long.

A simple example of the normal form of a theorem is the conjunction of the three clauses

$$Q(b); \qquad\qquad\qquad (1)$$
$$\sim Q(u) \lor P(f(u)); \qquad\qquad\qquad (2)$$
$$\sim P(v). \qquad\qquad\qquad (3)$$

This theorem can be proved by first inferring the resolvent,

$$P(f(b)), \qquad\qquad\qquad (4)$$

of (1) and (2). In forming this resolvent, the two literals containing a Q cancel out by substituting b for u. Then $\Box$, which is a resolvent of (3) and (4), can be inferred.

GPS FORMULATION

GPS can prove theorems expressed in the normal form just described. Its proof techniques are very similar to the theorem provers we have just discussed in that it searches for $\Box$ by producing the resolvents of clauses.

Figure 61 is the formulation for GPS of the task of proving the first-order predicate calculus theorem[*]

$$(\exists u)(\exists y)(\forall z)((P(u,y) \supset (P(y,z)\&P(z,z)))\&$$
$$((P(u,y)\&Q(u,y)) \supset (Q(u,z)\&Q(z,z))))).$$

This theorem has a long history as a sample problem for theorem provers (Davis and Putnam, 1960; Gilmore, 1960; Robinson, 1963). The early theorem provers found it difficult, whereas it is trivial for more recent programs.

TOP-GOAL in Fig. 61 is a statement of the problem. The INITIAL-OBJ is the statement of the theorem in normal form. The negation of the theorem, after removing the quantifiers and implication, is

$$\sim((\sim P(u, y) \vee (P(y, f(u, y)) \& P(f(u, y), f(u, y)))) \&$$
$$(\sim(P(u, y) \& Q(u, y)) \vee (Q(u, f(u, y)) \& Q(f(u, y), f(u, y)))))).$$

The INITIAL-OBJ is the expression written as a conjunction of the clauses STATEMENT-1, STATEMENT-2, and STATEMENT-3. Due to the limitation of computer character sets, in the clauses in Fig. 61, all lowercase letters are replaced by capital letters; the tilde "$\sim$" is replaced by minus "—." There must be a space between all symbols in the clauses in Fig. 61 because "space" is the delimiter of words in the external representation of GPS.

Each clause is an OBJECT-SCHEMA, expressed as a linear string of symbols (translated in the LIST mode), and is converted into a tree structure internally. This conversion routine, designed to process the objects and the operators of mathematical tasks, assumes that each node of OBJECT-SCHEMAs has two ATTRIBUTES—SIGN and SYMBOL. Figures 62a and 62b show the tree-structure representation of STATE-

---

[*] The source of this formula is Church (1956, p. 265, No. 5). The notation used by Church is different from the notation used here.

```
RENAME     (

    AND  =  ,

    )

DECLARE        (

    F  ■ UNARY-CONNECTIVE

    MAIN  =  FEATURE

    P  ■ UNARY-CONNECTIVE

    Q  ■ UNARY-CONNECTIVE.

    V  ■ N-ARY-CONNECTIVE

    V...  =  N-ARY-CONNECTIVE

    ,  ■ N-ARY-CONNECTIVE

    -  ■ UNARY-CONNECTIVE

    )

LIST        (

    INITIAL-OBJ  ■ ( STATEMENT-1 AND STATEMENT-2 AND STATEMENT-3 )

    STATEMENT-1  =  ( P ( U , Y ) )

    STATEMENT-2  =  ( - P ( Y , F ( U , Y ) ) V - P ( F ( U , Y ) , F ( U , Y ) )

                    V Q ( U , Y ) )

    STATEMENT-3  =  ( - P ( Y , F ( U , Y ) ) V - P ( F ( U , Y ) , F ( U , Y ) )

                    V - Q ( U , F ( U , Y ) ) V - Q ( F ( U , Y ) , F ( U ,

                    Y ) ) )

    DESIRED-OBJ  =  ( FALSE )

    OPR-1  ■ ( ( B AND - B ) YIELDS FALSE )

    OPR-2  ■ ( ( ( B V... C ) AND - B ) YIELDS C )

    OPR-3  ■ ( ( ( B V... C ) AND ( - B V... D ) ) YIELDS ( C V D ) )

    )

TASK-STRUCTURES        (
```

Fig. 61. Specification for GPS of the task of proving a theorem expressed in the predicate calculus.

```
TOP-GOAL = ( TRANSFORM THE INITIAL-OBJ INTO THE DESIRED-OBJ . )

MAIN = ( SYMBOL )

BASIC-MATCH = ( COMP-FEAT-LIST ( MAIN ) )

COMP-OBJECTS = ( BASIC-MATCH )

DIFF-ORDERING = ( MAIN )

TABLE-OF-CONNECTIONS = ( ( MAIN OPR-1 OPR-2 OPR-3 ) )

LIST-OF-OPR = ( OPR-1 OPR-2 OPR-3 )

LIST-OF-VAR = ( B C D Y U )

   )

END
```

Fig. 61 (cont.).

MENT-3, respectively. (Figure 62c will be discussed later.) The ATTRIBUTEs of the nodes are implicit.

INITIAL-OBJ is a SET of OBJECT-SCHEMAS. (AND is the new name for comma [,] in this task; see RENAME.) GPS considers it to be the source of derivation of STATEMENT-1, STATEMENT-2, and STATEMENT-3, so that all objects derived from them will also have INITIAL-OBJ as their source of derivation. Thus, INITIAL-OBJ is a set that grows as new objects are generated during problem solving.

The DESIRED-OBJ, which represents □, consists of a single node that has the value NULL for the ATTRIBUTE "SYMBOL."

This task has three operators, OPR-1, OPR-2, and OPR-3. Each operator has as an input two OBJECT-SCHEMAs, which are separated by AND in Fig. 61. For example, the input to OPR-2 is two OBJECT-SCHEMAs having the forms

$$B \text{ v} \ldots C \qquad \text{and} \qquad -B,$$

where B and C are variables and v... is a connective.

The OBJECT-SCHEMA

$$B \text{ v} \ldots C$$

represents a clause that is the disjunction of the literal B and other literals. C represents the disjunction of all the literals in the OBJECT-SCHEMA except B. The reason for this representation will be discussed below.

COMP-OBJECTS and BASIC-MATCH indicate that the only type of

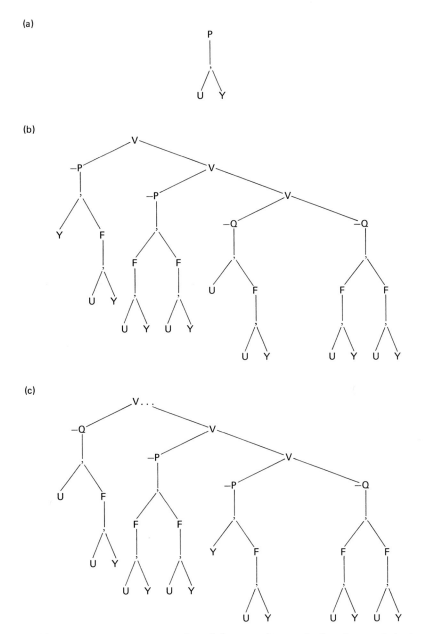

Fig. 62. Tree-structure representation of three predicate calculus objects. Only the values of the ATTRIBUTEs are shown.

difference to be detected in matching two OBJECT-SCHEMAS is MAIN and that it should be checked for only at the TOP-NODE of the OBJECT-SCHEMAS. This simple match is sufficient for this task because matching two OBJECT-SCHEMAS, which is done only in the TRANSFORM-METHOD, always has □ (DESIRED-OBJ) as one of the inputs. Thus, only the values of the ATTRIBUTE "SYMBOL" of TOP-NODE need be checked; the rest of the OBJECT-SCHEMAS is ignored.

DIFF-ORDERING is only a formality for this task because there is only one type of difference. TABLE-OF-CONNECTIONS is also a formality for this task. It provides no information about the desirability of the operators because, according to it, all of the operators have the capability of reducing the only type of difference—MAIN.

LIST-OF-OPR indicates that the three operators need to be converted into their internal representation after being translated. The variables used in this task are given in LIST-OF-VAR.

Included in the presentation of this task are three criteria for selecting members from a SET of OBJECT-SCHEMAS. Since there is no provision in the external representation for expressing these criteria, which are used in SELECT goals, they are given to GPS as IPL structures and do not appear in Fig. 61. They are

SMALLEST   Assigns highest priority to OBJECT-SCHEMAS (clauses) that contain the smallest number of literals (e.g., GOAL 2 in Fig. 63).

LIT-SIGN   Assigns priority to those OBJECT-SCHEMAS (clauses) that contain a literal whose SIGN and predicate letter are the same as the SIGN and predicate letter of the first literal in the criterion OBJECT-SCHEMA, and if the criterion object contains only a single literal, then the OBJECT-SCHEMA must contain only a single literal.

NO-LIT   Assigns priority to those OBJECT-SCHEMAS (clauses) that contain a single literal if the criterion OBJECT-SCHEMA is a single literal; otherwise, it must contain more than one literal.

The purpose of these criteria will become clear in the discussion of the behavior of GPS on this task.

Like the selection criteria, the immediate operators of this task are given to GPS as IPL structures and do not appear in Fig. 61. Besides ,substitution (which is standard) an immediate operator is needed to permute the literals in a clause when necessary.

Behavior of GPS

Figure 63 shows the behavior of GPS in solving the task in Fig. 61. To achieve TOP-GOAL, GPS recognizes that INITIAL-OBJ is a SET of OBJECT-SCHEMAS and generates GOAL 2 to find the member of the set that appears to be most easily transformed into DESIRED-OBJ. STATEMENT-1 is selected because it contains the fewest number of literals, and GOAL 3 is created in an attempt to achieve GOAL 1. GPS notices that the values of the ATTRIBUTE "SYMBOL" at the TOP-NODE of the two OBJECT-SCHEMAS in GOAL 3 are different and creates GOAL 4 to reduce this difference. According to TABLE-OF-CONNECTIONS, OPR-1 has the capability of reducing the difference and thus GOAL 5 is created.

In attempting GOAL 5 GPS notices that OPR-1 has two OBJECT-SCHEMAS as an input, and the TWO-INPUT-OPERATOR-METHOD (pp. 57–58) is selected for achieving GOAL 5. The first step in this method is to decide which of the input forms ($-B$ or B) corresponds to STATEMENT-1; GOAL 6 is created for this purpose. Since both input forms and STATEMENT-1 are clauses that contain only one literal, GPS decides that either input form can be used and selects the input form $-B$. The next step in the TWO-INPUT-OPERATOR-METHOD matches the input form selected to STATEMENT-1 (GOAL 7) to determine whether they can be made identical through the substitution of variables.[*] The result of GOAL 7 (OPERATOR 10) is OPR-1 after STATEMENT-1 has been matched to the input form—i.e., after $P(U, Y)$ is substituted for $-B$. At this point, GPS knows that the input form of OPERATOR 10, $P(U, Y)$, has already been supplied, even though Fig. 63 does not indicate this. The resultant object can be produced after supplying the other input, which can be any OBJECT-SCHEMA in the set INITIAL-OBJ. Thus, the next step in the TWO-INPUT-OPERATOR-METHOD (GOAL 8) is to select the OBJECT-SCHEMA to which OPERATOR 10 can most easily be applied. No OBJECT-SCHEMA in INITIAL-OBJ contains only a single literal whose SIGN is "$-$" and predicate letter is P; thus, GOAL 8 as well as GOAL 5 fails.

In retrying GOAL 4, GPS generates GOAL 9 because OPR-2 may reduce the difference. GPS, by the result of GOAL 10, decides that STATEMENT-1 should be matched to the input form $-B$ because it, like STATEMENT-1, contains only a single literal. GOAL 11 is successful, and its result is the partially applied OPERATOR 11.

[*] Note that there are two types of variables in this problem: those that occur as arguments of predicates and functions (Y and U), which stand ultimately for constants in the domain of quantification; and those that occur in the GPS operators (B, C, D), which stand for predicates and disjunctions of predicates. Since the values are always assigned during the course of matching, no difficulties arise over the differing domains.

Fig. 63. Performance of GPS on the task of Fig. 61.

```
1 TOP-GOAL TRANSFORM INITIAL-OBJ INTO DESIRED-OBJ    (SUBGOAL OF NONE)

2 GOAL 2 SELECT FROM INITIAL-OBJ A/C SMALLEST OF DESIRED-OBJ    (SUBGOAL OF TOP-GOAL)
        STATEMENT-1 SELECTED

2 GOAL 3 TRANSFORM STATEMENT-1 INTO DESIRED-OBJ    (SUBGOAL OF TOP-GOAL)

3 GOAL 4 REDUCE MAIN ON STATEMENT-1    (SUBGOAL OF 3)

4 GOAL 5 APPLY OPR-1 TO STATEMENT-1    (SUBGOAL OF 4)

5 GOAL 6 SELECT FROM CONDITION OPR-1 A/C NO.-LIT OF STATEMENT-1    (SUBGOAL OF LEFT CONDITION 5)
        CONDITION RIGHT SELECTED

5 GOAL 7 APPLY LEFT CONDITION OPR-1 TO STATEMENT-1    (SUBGOAL OF 5)
        OPERATOR 10: ((P(J, Y) AND -P(U, Y)) YIELDS NULL)

5 GOAL 8 SELECT FROM INITIAL-OBJ A/C LIT-SIGN OF RIGHT CONDITION 10    (SUBGOAL OF 5)
        NONE SELECTED

4 GOAL 9 APPLY OPR-2 TO STATEMENT-1    (SUBGOAL OF 4)

5 GOAL 10 SELECT FROM CONDITION OPR-2 A/C NO.-LIT OF STATEMENT-1    (SUBGOAL OF RIGHT CONDITION 9)
         CONDITION RIGHT SELECTED

5 GOAL 11 APPLY RIGHT CONDITION OPR-2 TO STATEMENT-1    (SUBGOAL OF 9)
         OPERATOR 11: (((-P(U, Y) V... C) AND P(U, Y)) YIELDS C)

5 GOAL 12 SELECT FROM INITIAL-OBJ A/C LIT-SIGN OF LEFT CONDITION 11    (SUBGOAL OF 9)
         STATEMENT-3 SELECTED

5 GOAL 13 APPLY LEFT CONDITION 11 TO STATEMENT-2    (SUBGOAL OF 9)
         OBJECT 12: (-P(F(U, Y), F(U, Y)) V... Q(U, Y))
```

Fig. 63 (cont.).

3 GOAL 14 TRANSFORM 12 INTO DESIRED-OBJ   (SUBGOAL OF 3)

4 GOAL 15 REDUCE MAIN ON 12   (SUBGOAL OF 14)

5 GOAL 16 APPLY OPR-1 TO 12   (SUBGOAL OF 15)

6 GOAL 17 SELECT FROM CONDITION OPR-1 A/C NO.-LIT OF 12   (SUBGOAL OF 16)
           NONE SELECTED

5 GOAL 18 APPLY OPR-2 TO 12   (SUBGOAL OF 15)

6 GOAL 19 SELECT FROM CONDITION OPR-2 A/C NO.-LIT OF 12   (SUBGOAL OF 18)
           CONDITION LEFT SELECTED

6 GOAL 20 APPLY LEFT CONDITION OPR-2 TO 12   (SUBGOAL OF 18)
           OPERATOR 13: (((-P(F(U, Y), F(U, Y)) V..: Q(U, Y)) AND P(F(U, Y), F(U, Y))) YIELDS
           Q(U, Y))

6 GOAL 21 SELECT FROM INITIAL-OBJ A/C LIT-SIGN OF RIGHT CONDITION 13   (SUBGOAL OF 18)
           STATEMENT=1 SELECTED

6 GOAL 22 APPLY RIGHT CONDITION 13 TO STATEMENT=1   (SUBGOAL OF 18)
           OBJECT 14: Q(U, Y)

4 GOAL 23 TRANSFORM 14 INTO DESIRED-OBJ   (SUBGOAL OF 14)

5 GOAL 24 REDUCE MAIN ON 14   (SUBGOAL OF 23)

6 GOAL 25 APPLY OPR-1 TO 14   (SUBGOAL OF 24)

Fig. 63 (cont.).

7 GOAL 26 SELECT FROM CONDITION OPR-1 A/C NO.-LIT OF 14   (SUBGOAL OF LEFT CONDITION 25)
    CONDITION RIGHT SELECTED

7 GOAL 27 APPLY LEFT CONDITION OPR-1 TO 14   (SUBGOAL OF 25)
    OPERATOR 15! ((Q(U, Y) AND -Q(U, Y)) YIELDS NULL)

7 GOAL 28 SELECT FROM INITIAL-OBJ A/C LIT-SIGN OF RIGHT CONDITION 15   (SUBGOAL OF 25)
    NONE SELECTED

6 GOAL 29 APPLY OPR-2 TO 14   (SUBGOAL OF 24)

7 GOAL 30 SELECT FROM CONDITION OPR-2 A/C NO.-LIT OF 14   (SUBGOAL OF RIGHT CONDITION 29)
    CONDITION RIGHT SELECTED

7 GOAL 31 APPLY RIGHT CONDITION OPR-2 TO 14   (SUBGOAL OF 29)
    OPERATOR 16! (((-Q(U, Y) V... C) AND Q(U, Y)) YIELDS C)

7 GOAL 32 SELECT FROM INITIAL-OBJ A/C LIT-SIGN OF LEFT CONDITION 16   (SUBGOAL OF 29)
    STATEMENT-3 SELECTED

7 GOAL 33 APPLY LEFT CONDITION 16 TO STATEMENT-3   (SUBGOAL OF 29)
    OBJECT 17! (-P(F(U, Y), F(U, Y)) V... -P(Y, F(U, Y)) V -Q(F(U, Y), F(U, Y)))

5 GOAL 34 TRANSFORM 17 INTO DESIRED-OBJ   (SUBGOAL OF 23)

6 GOAL 35 REDUCE MAIN ON 17   (SUBGOAL OF 34)

7 GOAL 36 APPLY OPR-1 TO 17   (SUBGOAL OF 35)

9 GOAL 37 SELECT FROM CONDITION OPR-1 A/C NO.-LIT OF 17   (SUBGOAL OF 36)
    NONE SELECTED

7 GOAL 38 APPLY OPR-2 TO 17   (SUBGOAL OF 35)

Fig. 63 (cont).

```
8 GOAL 39 SELECT FROM CONDITION OPR-2 A/C NO.--LIT OF 17      (SUBGOAL OF LEFT CONDITION 38)
       CONDITION LEFT SELECTED

8 GOAL 40 APPLY, LEFT CONDITION OPJ-2 TO 17      (SUBGOAL OF 38)
       OPERATOR 18:  (((-P(F(U, Y), F(U, Y)) V... -P(Y, F(U, Y)) V -Q(F(U, Y), F(U, Y
             ))) AND P(F(U, Y), F(U, Y))) YIELDS (-P(Y, F(U, Y)) V -Q(F(U, Y), Y)
             , F(J, Y))))

8 GOAL 41 SELECT FROM INITIAL-OBJ A/C LIT-SIGN OF RIGHT  CONDITION 18      (SUBGOAL OF 38)
       STATEMENT-1 SELECTED

8 GOAL 42 APPLY RIGHT  CONDITION 18 TO STATEMENT-1      (SUBGOAL OF 38)
       OBJECT 19: (-P(Y, F(U, Y)) V... -Q(F(U, Y), F(U, Y)))

GOAL  43 TRANSFORM 19 INTO DESIRED-OBJ      (SUBGOAL OF 34)

7 GOAL 44 REDUCE MAIN ON 19      (SUBGOAL OF 43)

8 GOAL 45 APPLY OPR-1 TO 19      (SUBGOAL OF 44)

9 GOAL 46 SELECT FROM  CONDITION OPR-1 A/C NO.--LIT OF 19      (SUBGOAL OF 45)
       NONE SELECTED

8 GOAL 47 APPLY OPR-2 TO 19      (SUBGOAL OF 44)

9 GOAL 48 SELECT FROM CONDITION OPR-2 A/C NO.--LIT OF 19      (SUBGOAL OF LEFT CONDITION 47)
       CONDITION LEFT SELECTED

9 GOAL 49 APPLY  LEFT  CONDITION OPR-2 TO 19      (SUBGOAL OF 47)
       OPERATOR 20:  (((-P(Y, F(U, Y)) V... -Q(F(U, Y), F(U, Y))) AND P(Y, F(U, Y))) YIELDS
             -Q(F(U, Y), F(U, Y)))
```

Fig. 63 (cont.).

```
9   GOAL 50 SELECT FROM INITIAL-OBJ A/C LIT-SIGN OF RIGHT CONDITION 20       (SUBGOAL OF 47)
        STATEMENT-1 SELECTED

9   GOAL 51 APPLY RIGHT CONDITION 20 TO STATEMENT-1       (SUBGOAL OF 47)
        OBJECT 211 -Q(F(U, Y), F(U, Y))

7 GOAL 52 TRANSFORM 21 INTO DESIRED-OBJ       (SUBGOAL OF 43)

8 GOAL 53 REDUCE MAIN ON 21       (SUBGOAL OF 52)

9 GOAL 54 APPLY OPR-1 TO 21       (SUBGOAL OF 53)

10  GOAL 55 SELECT FROM CONDITION OPR-1 A/C NO.-LIT OF 21       (SUBGOAL OF LEFT CONDITION 54)
        CONDITION RIGHT SELECTED

10  GOAL 56 APPLY LEFT CONDITION OPR-1 TO 21       (SUBGOAL OF 54)
        OPERATOR 221 ((-Q(F(U, Y), F(U, Y)) AND Q(F(U, Y), F(U, Y))) YIELDS NULL)

10  GOAL 57 SELECT FROM INITIAL-OBJ A/C LIT-SIGN OF RIGHT CONDITION 22       (SUBGOAL OF 54)
        14 SELECTED

10  GOAL 58 APPLY RIGHT CONDITION 22 TO 14       (SUBGOAL OF 54)
        OBJECT 231 NULL

8 GOAL 59 TRANSFORM 23 INTO DESIRED-OBJ       (SUBGOAL OF 52)


SUCCESS
```

To find the other input for OPERATOR 11, GPS creates GOAL 12. STATEMENT-3 is selected because it contains more than one literal and one of them has "−" for its SIGN and P for its predicate letter. OPERATOR 11 is applied (GOAL 13) and OBJECT 12 is produced.

GPS tries to transform OBJECT 12 into the DESIRED-OBJ (GOAL 14). Since they are different, GPS attempts to apply OPR-1 to OBJECT 12 (GOAL 16). GOAL 17 is created in order to decide which input form should be matched to OBJECT 12. Both input forms in OPR-1 contain only one literal and OBJECT 12 has two; hence GPS considers the application of OPR-1 infeasible. In attempting GOAL 15 again, GOAL 18 is created.

GPS continues in similar fashion until □ is finally produced as a result of GOAL 59 and the success of GOAL 60 indicates that the TOP-GOAL has been achieved.

DISCUSSION

The formulation of this task for GPS is somewhat clumsy. To express the Resolution Principle, which is used as a single rule of inference by the predicate calculus theorem provers, three distinct operators are required. This clumsiness results from an inadequate representation for sets and operations on sets. For example, there is no convenient way to represent the union of two sets or the set formed by deleting a member from a set.

OBJECT-SCHEMAS do not represent the disjunction of a set of literals by an unordered set (as is the case for sum and product in integration). Rather, disjunction is treated as a binary logical connective. Figure 62b illustrates that the arguments of v are either literals or a disjunction of literals. Figure 62a is the representation of a clause composed of a single literal. Such a clause is represented by the literal itself and thus contains no v.

The operators must distinguish between OBJECT-SCHEMAS that contain only a single literal and those that contain more than one literal. In the one case, the literal that is deleted is at the TOP-NODE; in the other, it is at the LEFT node. The three operators are required to take care of the three situations, respectively, i.e.,

when both input clauses contain a single literal,

when only one input clause contains a single literal,

when neither input clause contains a single literal.

OPR-2 (the second situation) can have the single literal as either its first input or second input.

It is noteworthy that representing the resolution principle as three operators instead of one has a considerable effect on the problem solving. Often GPS tries the wrong operator first—e.g., GOAL 5— and does not realize the mistake until several goals have been generated. If the three operators were combined into one, the wrong operator could not possibly be selected. In solving the task in Fig. 61, fourteen goals (a quarter of the goals) are generated in attempting to apply inappropriate operators.

On the other hand, the fact that there are three operators instead of one is used beneficially by GPS. GPS attempts to apply OPR-1 and OPR-2 before applying OPR-3 because of their order in the TABLE-OF-CONNECTIONS. Since one of the inputs to OPR-1 (or similarly, OPR-2) contains only a single literal, the result conatins one less literal than the larger input. Thus, viewing the operator as a process for producing a modification of its multiliteral input, the output is always reduced in size. Reducing the number of literals in a clause is desirable because the main objective of the task is to reduce the number of literals in a clause to zero, i.e., to produce □. Applying OPR-1 and OPR-2 before applying OPR-3 is equivalent to the *unit preference strategy* used in Wos *et al.* (1964).

The commutativity and associativity of v is implicitly taken into consideration in applying an operator. Whenever the match detects a v... versus v, an immediate operator juggles the order of the literals in an object until the SIGN and predicate letter of the first literal are the same in the object and input form of the operator. For example, in GOAL 33

$$\sim Q(U, Y) \text{v} ... C$$

is matched to Fig. 62b. After detecting the v... versus v, an immediate operator rewrites Fig. 62b as Fig. 62c, replacing the v... with a v. Since Fig. 62c can be made identical to the input form by substituting for variables, OBJECT 17 can be produced.

It is very important that the problem formulation takes advantage of the commutativity of the literals in a clause implicitly, instead of stating it explicitly, as an operator. Otherwise, the problem tree would be considerably larger and the problem solver would spend a large portion of its time commuting literals in a clause.

Perhaps the most instructive part of this example is the light it casts upon the evolution of problem-solving programs. In LT, a theorem-proving program for the propositional calculus that is the predecessor of GPS, it was noted that the match routine was the source of most of the power of the program over a brute-force search. GPS may be considered as an attempt to generalize the match routine, based on that experience. The first predicate calculus theorem prover did in fact use brute-force search (Gilmore, 1960). From an efficiency point of view the main effect of the Resolution Principle was to re-introduce the possibility of matching (gaining, thereby, a vast increase in power).* And it is this feature that allows GPS to use the Resolution Principle in a natural way.

FATHER AND SONS TASK†

A father and his sons want to cross a river. The only means of conveyance is a small boat whose capacity is 200 pounds. Each son weighs 100 pounds while the father weighs 200 pounds. Assuming that the father and either son can operate the boat, how can they all reach the other side of the river? Of course, there is no way to cross the river except by boat.

GPS FORMULATION

Figure 64 gives a formulation of this task for GPS. TOP-GOAL is a statement of the problem. INITIAL-OBJ, whose tree structure is shown in Fig. 65, represents the situation in which the father, both of his sons, and the boat are on the LEFT bank of the river. The presence of the BOAT is designated by the value BOAT of the ATTRIBUTE "BOAT;" its absence is indicated by the absence of a value of the ATTRIBUTE "BOAT." DESIRED-OBJ is the OBJECT-SCHEMA that represents the situation in which the father, his two sons, and the boat are on the RIGHT bank of the river.

In this task, the only operator is SAIL, whose application has the effect of moving X fathers, Y sons, and the boat from the FROM-SIDE to the TO-SIDE. The first two TESTS in VAR-DOMAIN of SAIL indicate that FROM-SIDE and TO-SIDE stand for different banks of the river. The third and fourth TESTS require that someone must be in the boat to operate it and that the capacity of the boat must not be exceeded.

---

* The match of LT (p. 21) is the inner component of Robinson's Unification Algorithm (1965). The Unification Algorithm iterates the match over all pairs of formulas in the two clauses being resolved.

† The source of this task is a private communication from Paul Newell.

```
DECLARE    (

   BOAT  = ATTRIBUTE

   D-L  = FEATURE

   D-R  = FEATURE

   FATHERS  = ATTRIBUTE

   FINAL-OBJ  = OBJECT-SCHEMA

   FROM-SIDE  = LOC-PROG

   F-L  = FEATURE

   F-R  = FEATURE

   INITIAL-OBJ  = OBJECT-SCHEMA

   SAIL  = MOVE-OPERATOR

   SONS  = ATTRIBUTE

   SIDES  = SET

   S-L  = FEATURE

   S-R  = FEATURE

   TO-SIDE  = LOC-PROG

   WEIGHT  = EXPRES

   0-1  = SET

   0-1-2  = SET

   1-2  = SET

          )

TASK-STRUCTURES     (

   TOP-GOAL  = ( TRANSFORM THE INITIAL-OBJ INTO THE FINAL-OBJ . )

   INITIAL-OBJ  = ( LEFT ( SONS 2 FATHERS 1 BOAT BOAT )

                    RIGHT ( SONS 0 FATHERS 0 ) )

   FINAL-OBJ  = ( LEFT ( SONS 0 FATHERS 0 )

                   RIGHT ( FATHERS 1 SONS 2 BOAT BOAT ) )
```

Fig. 64. Specification for GPS of the Father and Sons task.

```
WEIGHT = ( X + X + Y )

SAIL = $ SAIL THE BOAT FROM THE FROM-SIDE TO THE TO-SIDE WITH X FATHERS
         AND Y SONS IN IT. $
         ( CREATION-OPERATOR
           VAR-DOMAIN
           1. THE FROM-SIDE IS AN EXCLUSIVE-MEMBER OF THE SIDES .
           2. THE TO-SIDE IS AN EXCLUSIVE-MEMBER OF THE SIDES .
           3. Y IS A CONSTRAINED-MEMBER OF 0-1 , THE CONSTRAINT IS THAT
              THE WEIGHT IS IN-THE-SET 1-2 .
           4. X IS A CONSTRAINED-MEMBER OF 0-1-2 , THE CONSTRAINT IS THAT
              THE WEIGHT IS IN-THE-SET 1-2 .
           MOVES
           1. MOVE THE BOAT AT THE FROM-SIDE TO THE BOAT AT THE TO-SIDE .
           2. DECREASE BY THE AMOUNT X THE FATHERS AT THE FROM-SIDE AND
              ADD IT TO THE FATHERS AT THE TO-SIDE .
           3. DECREASE BY THE AMOUNT Y THE SONS AT THE FROM-SIDE AND ADD
              IT TO THE SONS AT THE TO-SIDE .   )

SIDES = ( LEFT RIGHT )
0-1 = ( 0 1 )
0-1-2 = ( 0 1 2 )
1-2 = ( 1 2 )
S-L = ( THE SONS AT THE LEFT )
S-R = ( THE SONS AT THE RIGHT )
F-L = ( THE FATHERS AT THE LEFT )
F-R = ( THE FATHERS AT THE RIGHT )
D-L = ( THE BOAT AT THE LEFT )
D-R = ( THE BOAT AT THE RIGHT )
```

Fig. 64 (cont.).

```
BASIC-MATCH = ( COMP-FEAT-LIST ( F-R S-R D-R ) )

COMP-OBJECTS = ( BASIC-MATCH )

DIFF-ORDERING = ( 1. ( F-L F-R )

                  2. ( S-L S-R )

                  3. ( D-L D-R ) )

TABLE-OF-CONNECTIONS = ( ( COMMON-DIFFERENCE SAIL ) )

LIST-OF-VAR = ( FROM-SIDE TO-SIDE X Y )

OBJ-ATTRIB = ( FATHERS SONS BOAT )


END
```

Fig. 64 (cont.).

WEIGHT is the EXPRESS whose value is the number of hundred pounds in the boat. Thus, if the value of WEIGHT is greater than 0, someone must be in the boat, and if the value of WEIGHT is not greater than two, the capacity of the boat is not exceeded. Negative values for X and Y do not make sense.

The three TRANSFORMATIONs in SAIL move the BOAT, the FATHER, and the SONS, respectively, across the river. The four SETs "SIDES," "0-1," "0-1-2," and "1-2" are used in the specification of SAIL.

The six types of difference F-L, F-R, S-L, S-R, D-L (dock at left), and D-R are all stated relative to the TOP-NODE of an OBJECT-SCHEMA. The types of difference that pertain to the FATHERs are most difficult according to DIFF-ORDERING, while the easiest types of difference are those that pertain to the BOAT.

BASIC-MATCH and COMPARE-OBJECTS indicate that the only types of difference detected by the match are those that pertain to the RIGHT

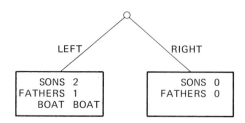

Fig. 65. Tree-structure representation of INITIAL-OBJ.

bank of the river. These types of difference are sufficient because what is not at the RIGHT must be at the LEFT.

TABLE-OF-CONNECTIONS designates SAIL to be relevant to reducing all types of difference and thus gives GPS no selectivity. OBJ-ATTRIB is a list of the ATTRIBUTEs of this task, and LIST-OF-VAR lists the variables that appear in Fig. 64.

NEW-OBJ is a selection criterion that is given to GPS as an IPL structure, hence does not appear in Fig. 64. It is used in several tasks and is described on page 130.

Behavior of GPS

Figure 66 shows the behavior of GPS in solving the task in Fig. 64. In attempting TOP-GOAL, GPS notices that neither the father, his sons, nor the boat is at the RIGHT bank of the river. GOAL 2 is generated because, according to DIFF-ORDEREING, F-R is more difficult than either D-R or S-R. To reduce this difference, SAIL, with X equal to 1 and TO-SIDE equal to RIGHT, is applied to the INITIAL-OBJ (GOAL 3, OBJECT 5).

Since there are not enough SONS at the RIGHT in OBJECT 5, (GOAL 4, GOAL 5), GPS attempts to move two of them to the RIGHT (GOAL 6). GPS notices that before it can apply this operator, the BOAT must be brought back to the LEFT (GOAL 7). Although bringing the BOAT back to the LEFT results in the INITIAL-OBJ (GOAL 8), it allows the two SONS to be moved to the RIGHT (GOAL 9, OBJECT 6).

After one of the SONS brings the BOAT to the LEFT, GPS moves the father to the RIGHT (GOAL 15). GPS attempts to move the remaining son at the LEFT across the river by bringing the BOAT back to the LEFT (GOAL 20). Since GPS does not realize that the other son was brought to the LEFT with the BOAT, only one son is moved to the RIGHT (GOAL 21), which causes GOAL 16 to be regenerated.

At this point, GPS realizes that it is in trouble and looks for something new to do. GOAL 23 is the expression of this, where OBJECT 4 is the SET of all objects derived from INITIAL-OBJ (it is generated internally by GPS). GOAL 25 is created because OBJECT 7 has never been transformed into the FINAL-OBJ and because it is derived from INITIAL-OBJ.

Since GOAL 25 does not lead to any new results, GOAL 30 is generated from GOAL 23, in an attempt to generate a new goal. After moving two sons across the river in OBJECT 9, GPS notices that it is successful (GOAL 33).

Fig. 66. Performance of GPS on the Father and Sons task.

```
1 TOP-GOAL TRANSFORM INITIAL-OBJ INTO FINAL-OBJ    (SUBGOAL OF NONE)

2 GOAL 2 REDUCE F-R ON INITIAL-OBJ    (SUBGOAL OF TOP-GOAL)

3 GOAL 3 APPLY SAIL WITH X = 1, TO-SIDE = RIGHT, TO INITIAL-OBJ    (SUBGOAL OF 2)
    SET: FROM-SIDE = LEFT, Y = 0
    OBJECT 5: (LEFT(FATHERS 0 SONS 2) RIGHT(FATHERS 1 SONS 0 BOAT BOAT))

2 GOAL 4 TRANSFORM 5 INTO FINAL-OBJ    (SUBGOAL OF TOP-GOAL)

3 GOAL 5 REDUCE S-R ON 5    (SUBGOAL OF 4)

4 GOAL 6 APPLY SAIL WITH Y = 2, TO-SIDE = RIGHT, TO 5    (SUBGOAL OF 5)
    SET: FROM-SIDE = LEFT, X = 0

5 GOAL 7 REDUCE D-L ON 5    (SUBGOAL OF 6)

6 GOAL 8 APPLY SAIL WITH TO-SIDE = LEFT, TO 5    (SUBGOAL OF 7)
    SET: FROM-SIDE = RIGHT, X = 1, Y = 0
    OBJECT INITIAL-OBJ: (LEFT(FATHERS 1 SONS 2 BOAT BOAT) RIGHT(FATHERS 0 SONS 0))

5 GOAL 9 APPLY SAIL WITH Y = 2, TO-SIDE = RIGHT, TO INITIAL-OBJ    (SUBGOAL OF 6)
    SET: FROM-SIDE = LEFT, X = 0
    OBJECT 6: (LEFT(FATHERS 1 SONS 0) RIGHT(FATHERS 0 SONS 2 BOAT BOAT))

3 GOAL 10 TRANSFORM 6 INTO FINAL-OBJ    (SUBGOAL OF 4)

4 GOAL 11 REDUCE F-R ON 6    (SUBGOAL OF 10)

5 GOAL 12 APPLY SAIL WITH X = 1, TO-SIDE = RIGHT, TO 6    (SUBGOAL OF 11)
    SET: FROM-SIDE = LEFT, Y = 0
```

Fig. 66 (cont.).

6 GOAL 13 REDUCE D-L ON 6   (SUBGOAL OF 12)

7 GOAL 14 APPLY SAIL WITH TO-SIDE = LEFT, TO 6   (SUBGOAL OF 13)
   SET: FROM-SIDE = RIGHT, X = 0, Y = 1
   OBJECT 7: (LEFT(FATHERS 1 SONS 1 BOAT BOAT) RIGHT(FATHERS 0 SONS 1))

6 GOAL 15 APPLY SAIL WITH X = 1, TO-SIDE = RIGHT, TO 7   (SUBGOAL OF 26)
   SET: FROM-SIDE = LEFT, Y = 0
   OBJECT 8: (LEFT(FATHERS 0 SONS 1) RIGHT(FATHERS 1 SONS 1 BOAT BOAT))

4 GOAL 16 TRANSFORM 8 INTO FINAL-OBJ   (SUBGOAL OF 10)

5 GOAL 17 REDUCE S-R ON 8   (SUBGOAL OF 16)

6 GOAL 18 APPLY SAIL WITH Y = 1, TO-SIDE = RIGHT, TO 8   (SUBGOAL OF 17)
   SET: FROM-SIDE = LEFT, X = 0

7 GOAL 19 REDUCE D-L ON 8   (SUBGOAL OF 18)

8 GOAL 20 APPLY SAIL WITH TO-SIDE = LEFT, TO 8   (SUBGOAL OF 19)
   SET: FROM-SIDE = RIGHT, Y = 1, X = 0
   OBJECT 9: (LEFT(FATHERS 0 SONS 2 BOAT BOAT) RIGHT(FATHERS 1 SONS 0))

7 GOAL 21 APPLY SAIL WITH Y = 1, TO-SIDE = RIGHT, TO 9   (SUBGOAL OF 18)
   SET: FROM-SIDE = LEFT, X = 0
   OBJECT 8: (LEFT(FATHERS 0 SONS 1) RIGHT(FATHERS 1 SONS 1 BOAT BOAT))

4 GOAL 16 TRANSFORM 8 INTO FINAL-OBJ   (SUBGOAL OF 10)

5 GOAL 23 TRANSFORM 4 INTO FINAL-OBJ   (SUBGOAL OF TOP-GOAL)

Fig. 66 (cont.).

```
6 GOAL 24 SELECT FROM 4 A/C NEW-OBJ OF FINAL-OBJ          (SUBGOAL OF 23)
         9 SELECTED

6 GOAL 25 TRANSFORM 7 INTO FINAL-OBJ          (SUBGOAL OF 23)

7 GOAL 26 REDUCE F-R ON 7          (SUBGOAL OF 25)

6 GOAL 15 APPLY SAIL WITH X = 1, TO-SIDE = RIGHT, TO 7          (SUBGOAL OF 26)
         SET: FROM-SIDE = LEFT, Y = 0
         OBJECT 8: (LEFT(FATHERS 0 SONS 1) RIGHT(FATHERS 1 SONS 1 BOAT BOAT))

4 GOAL 16 TRANSFORM 8 INTO FINAL-OBJ          (SUBGOAL OF 10)

4 GOAL 11 REDUCE F-R ON 6          (SUBGOAL OF 10)

5 GOAL 23 TRANSFORM 4 INTO FINAL-OBJ          (SUBGOAL OF TOP-GOAL)

6 GOAL 24 SELECT FROM 4 A/C NEW-OBJ OF FINAL-OBJ          (SUBGOAL OF 23)
         9 SELECTED

6 GOAL 30 TRANSFORM 9 INTO FINAL-OBJ          (SUBGOAL OF 23)

7 GOAL 31 REDUCE S-R ON 9          (SUBGOAL OF 30)

8 GOAL 32 APPLY SAIL WITH Y = 2, TO-SIDE = RIGHT, TO 9          (SUBGOAL OF 31)
         SET: FROM-SIDE = LEFT, X = 0
         OBJECT 12: (LEFT(FATHERS 0 SONS 0) RIGHT(FATHERS 1 SONS 2 BOAT BOAT))

7 GOAL 33 TRANSFORM 12 INTO FINAL-OBJ          (SUBGOAL OF 30)

SUCCESS
```

DISCUSSION

This task is very similar to the Missionaries and Cannibals task. Both tasks involve moving two different kinds of people across a river in a small boat, although the constraints are somewhat different. But their formulations for GPS are quite independent. This raises again the concept of a "task environment," which we dismissed earlier. For the original task of GPS, symbolic logic, the notion made sense: the task environment was the rules of logic; the tasks were individual theorems to be proved. For the Integration task we operated in essentially the same way, giving GPS two problems without changing anything else. But for the Missionaries and Cannibals and the Father and Sons task we found it easier to give separate task specifications. However, if the two specifications are laid side by side it becomes evident that much is the same, up to a change of names. The primary difference lies in the operator itself—exactly that part which seemed to be the main fixed feature of the task environment in logic and the Integration task.

The more interesting question is not why we did not exercise the care to assign identical names to the same concepts, so that the Father and Sons task could be given within the Missionaries and Cannibals task, but what additional apparatus it would take for GPS to note the similarities in the task and make some use of them.

MONKEY TASK

The Monkey task was invented by McCarthy (1963) as a typical problem for the Advice Taker program (McCarthy, 1959). A room contains a monkey, a box, and some bananas which are hanging from the ceiling. The monkey wants to eat the bananas, but he cannot reach them unless he is standing on the box when it is under the bananas. How can the monkey get the bananas? The answer is that the monkey must move the box under the bananas and climb on the box. The problem originates in the study of the problem-solving ability of primates. Its interest lies not in its difficulty, but in its being an example of a problem that is subject to common sense reasoning.

GPS FORMULATION

In the formulation of this task shown in Fig. 67, INITIAL-OBJ represents the monkey in the room. INITIAL-OBJ is an OBJECT-SCHEMA

```
DECLARE    (

   BOX'S-PLACE  = ATTRIBUTE

   CLIMB     = MOVE-OPERATOR

   CONTENTS=OF-MONKEY'S-HAND = ATTRIBUTE

   DESIRED-OBJ = DESCRIBED-OBJ

   D1 = FEATURE

   D2 = FEATURE

   D3 = FEATURE

   GET-BANANAS = MOVE-OPERATOR

   INITIAL-OBJ = OBJECT-SCHEMA

   MONKEY'S=PLACE = ATTRIBUTE

   MOVE-BOX = MOVE-OPERATOR

   PLACES = SET

   WALK      = MOVE-OPERATOR

   )

TASK-STRUCTURES    (

   TOP-GOAL = ( TRANSFORM THE INITIAL-OBJ INTO THE DESIRED-OBJ . )

   INITIAL-OBJ = ( MONKEY'S-PLACE PLACE-1 BOX'S-PLACE PLACE-2

                   CONTENTS-OF-MONKEY'S-HAND EMPTY )

   OBJ-ATTRIB = ( MONKEY'S-PLACE BOX'S-PLACE CONTENTS-OF-MONKEY'S-HAND )

   DESIRED-OBJ = ( TEX-DESCRIPTION

                   THE CONTENTS-OF-MONKEY'S-HAND EQUALS BANANAS . )

   PLACES = ( PLACE-1 PLACE-2 UNDER-BANANAS . )

   CLIMB = ( CREATION-OPERATOR

             PRETESTS

             1. THE MONKEY'S-PLACE EQUALS THE BOX'S-PLACE .

             MOVES
```

Fig. 67. Specification for GPS of the Monkey task.

```
            1. COPY ON-BOX AT THE MONKEY'S-PLACE . )
WALK = ( CREATION-OPERATOR

        VAR-DOMAIN

        X IS IN-THE-SET OF PLACES .

        MOVES

        COPY X AT THE MONKEY'S-PLACE . )
MOVE-BOX = ( CREATION-OPERATOR

            VAR-DOMAIN

            1. X IS IN-THE-SET OF PLACES .

            PRETESTS

            1. THE MONKEY'S-PLACE IS IN-THE-SET OF PLACES .

            2. THE MONKEY'S-PLACE EQUALS THE BOX'S-PLACE .

            MOVES

            1. COPY X AT THE MONKEY'S-PLACE .

            2. COPY X AT THE BOX'S-PLACE . )
GET-BANANAS = ( CREATION-OPERATOR

            PRETESTS

            1. THE BOX'S-PLACE EQUALS UNDER-BANANAS .

            2. THE MONKEY'S-PLACE EQUALS ON-BOX .

            MOVES

            1. COPY BANANAS AT THE CONTENTS-OF-MONKEY'S-HAND . )
D1 = ( MONKEY'S-PLACE )
D2 = ( BOX'S-PLACE )
D3 = ( CONTENTS-OF-MONKEY'S-HAND )
DIFF-ORDERING = ( D3 D2 D1 )
TABLE-OF-CONNECTIONS = ( ( COMMON-DIFFERENCE WALK CLIMB MOVE-BOX
                                        GET-BANANAS ) )
LIST-OF-VAR = ( X )
)
END
```

Fig. 67 (cont.).

consisting of only a single node with the three ATTRIBUTEs listed in OBJ-ATTRIB. There are four operators that represent the various acts that the monkey can perform. CLIMB is the operator whose application corresponds to the monkey climbing on the box. An application of WALK corresponds to the monkey walking to the place X, which must be on the floor of the room, i.e., in the set PLACES. MOVE-BOX represents the fact that the monkey can move the box to any place on the floor of the room, and GET-BANANAS is the statement that the monkey can get the bananas provided that the box is under the bananas and that he is standing on the box.

The three types of difference D1, D2, and D3, corresponding, respectively, to an incorrect value of one of the three ATTRIBUTEs "MONKEY'S-PLACE," "BOX'S-PLACE," and "CONTENTS-OF-MONKEY'S-HAND." DIFF-ORDERING indicates that it is most difficult to change the contents of the monkey's hand, whereas the monkey can easily change his position. TABLE-OF-CONNECTIONS contains no information about the desirability of operators, except that operators are desirable to reducing differences. LIST-OF-VAR indicates that X is the only variable in Fig. 67.

BEHAVIOR OF GPS

Figure 68 shows how GPS solved the problem in Fig. 67. The monkey cannot reach the bananas in the initial configuration of the room (GOAL 1, GOAL 2, GOAL 3) because the box is not under the bananas (and because the monkey is not on the box, which is less important). In order to move the box under the bananas (GOAL 4, GOAL 5), the monkey must be standing beside the box; consequently, the monkey walks to the box (GOAL 6, GOAL 7) which results in the new configuration of the room—OBJECT 4. After the monkey moves the box under the bananas (GOAL 8, OBJECT 5), he still cannot reach the bananas (GOAL 9) because he is not standing on the box. Therefore the monkey climbs on the box (GOAL 10, GOAL 11, OBJECT 6) and finally plucks the bananas from the ceiling (GOAL 11, GOAL 12, OBJECT 7).

DISCUSSION

INITIAL-OBJ and all OBJECT-SCHEMAs derived from INITIAL-OBJ are models of the various configurations of the room. They are not complete models of the room; e.g., none of them contains any information about things hanging from the ceiling. But they contain sufficient detail of the room for this simple problem.

```
1  TOP-GOAL  TRANSFORM  INITIAL-OBJ  INTO  DESIRED-OBJ          (SUBGOAL  OF  NONE)

2  GOAL  2  REDUCE  D3  ON  INITIAL-OBJ          (SUBGOAL  OF  TOP-GOAL)

3  GOAL  3  APPLY  GET-BANANAS  TO  INITIAL-OBJ          (SUBGOAL  OF  2)

4  GOAL  4  REDUCE  D2  ON  INITIAL-OBJ          (SUBGOAL  OF  3)

5  GOAL  5  APPLY  MOVE-BOX  WITH  X  =  UNDER-BANANAS,  TO  INITIAL-OBJ          (SUBGOAL  OF  4)

6  GOAL  6  REDUCE  D1  ON  INITIAL-OBJ          (SUBGOAL  OF  5)

7  GOAL  7  APPLY  WALK  WITH  X  =  PLACE-2,  TO  INITIAL-OBJ          (SUBGOAL  OF  6)
        OBJECT  4:  (MONKEY'S-PLACE  PLACE-2  BOX'S-PLACE  PLACE-2  CONTENTS-OF-MONKEY'S-HAND
        EMPTY)

6  GOAL  8  APPLY  MOVE-BOX  WITH  X  =  UNDER-BANANAS,  TO  4          (SUBGOAL  OF  5)
        OBJECT  5:  (MONKEY'S-PLACE  UNDER-BANANAS  BOX'S-PLACE  UNDER-BANANAS  CONTENTS-OF-MONKEY'S-HAND
        EMPTY)

4  GOAL  9  APPLY  GET-BANANAS  TO  5          (SUBGOAL  OF  3)

5  GOAL  10  REDUCE  D1  ON  5          (SUBGOAL  OF  9)

.6  GOAL  11  APPLY  CLIMB  TO  5          (SUBGOAL  OF  10)
        OBJECT  6:  (MONKEY'S-PLACE  ON-BOX  BOX'S-PLACE  UNDER-BANANAS  CONTENTS-OF-MONKEY'S-HAND
        EMPTY)

5  GOAL  12  APPLY  GET-BANANAS  TO  6          (SUBGOAL  OF  9)
        OBJECT  7:  (MONKEY'S-PLACE  ON-BOX  BOX'S-PLACE  UNDER-BANANAS  CONTENTS-OF-MONKEY'S-HAND
        BANANAS)

2  GOAL  13  TRANSFORM  /  INTO  DESIRED-OBJ          (SUBGOAL  OF  TOP-GOAL)

SUCCESS
```

Fig. 68. Performance of GPS on the Monkey task.

The representation of the problem in an Advice Taker problem solver—e.g., the program developed by Black (1964)—is quite different. There, the initial configuration of the room is not a single entity that models the situation, as in GPS's representation, but a group of independent linguistic expressions that describe the situation. In solving this task, the program deduces new linguistic expressions and not new room configurations. For example, in solving this task, Black's program deduces the linguistic expressions:

> The monkey can move the box under the
> bananas.

> The monkey can stand on the box when
> it is under the bananas.

These linguistic expressions describe only part of a possible room configuration in much the same way the DESIRED-OBJ describes only part of a room configuration.

Both representations have advantages. Linguistic expressions are good for representing imperfect information that is difficult to represent in a model; e.g., the monkey is in one of two places. On the other hand, models contain implicit information that need not be stated explicitly; e.g., the monkey can be in only one place at a time, or two squares are adjacent on a chess board. Which of these two representations is better probably depends upon the task, and for some tasks, such as the Monkey task, they are probably equally good. This issue is discussed in Newell and Ernst (1965).

THREE COINS PUZZLE

In the Three Coins puzzle (Filipiak, 1942), there are three coins sitting on a table. Both the first and third coins show tails, while the second coin shows heads. The problem is to make all three coins show the same—either heads or tails—in precisely three moves. Each move consists of turning over any two of the three coins. For example, if the first move consisted of turning over the first and third coins, all of the coins would show heads in the resulting situation. But the task is not solved, because only one move was taken instead of the required three.

```
RENAME    (

   COIN-1 = FIRST

   COIN-2 = SECOND

   COIN-3 = THIRD

        )

DECLARE    (

   BOTTOM = ATTRIBUTE

   COINS = SET

   DESIRED-OBJ = DESCRIBED-OBJ

   D1 = FEATURE

   D2 = FEATURE

   D3 = FEATURE

   D4 = FEATURE

   FLIP-COINS = MOVE-OPERATOR

   INITIAL-OBJ = OBJECT-SCHEMA

   MOVES-REMAINING = ATTRIBUTE

   MOVES-TAKEN = ATTRIBUTE

   TOP = ATTRIBUTE

   X = LOG-PROG

   Y = LOG-PROG

        )

TASK-STRUCTURES    (

   TOP-GOAL = ( TRANSFORM THE INITIAL-OBJ INTO THE DESIRED-OBJ . )

   INITIAL-OBJ = ( MOVES-REMAINING 3 MOVES-TAKEN 0

                      COIN-1 ( BOTTOM HEADS TOP TAILS )

                      COIN-2 ( BOTTOM TAILS TOP HEADS )

                      COIN-3 ( BOTTOM HEADS TOP TAILS ) )
```

Fig. 69. Specification for GPS of the Three Coins puzzle.

```
DESIRED-OBJ = ( TEX-DESCRIPTION
                    1. THE TOP OF COIN-2 EQUALS THE TOP OF COIN-3 .
                    2. THE TOP OF COIN-3 EQUALS THE TOP OF COIN-1 .
                    3. THE MOVES-REMAINING EQUALS 0 . )
COINS = ( COIN-1 COIN-2 COIN-3 )
FLIP-COINS = ( $ TURN COINS X AND Y OVER $ CREATION-OPERATOR
                    VAR-DOMAIN
                    1. X IS AN EXCLUSIVE-MEMBER OF THE COINS .
                    2. Y IS AN EXCLUSIVE-MEMBER OF THE COINS .
                    PRETESTS
                    1. THE MOVES-REMAINING IS GREATER-THAN 0 .
                    MOVES
                    1. DECREASE BY THE AMOUNT 1 THE MOVES-REMAINING AND
                        ADD IT TO THE MOVES-TAKEN .
                    2. MOVE THE BOTTOM OF X TO THE TOP OF X .
                    3. MOVE THE BOTTOM OF Y TO THE TOP OF Y .
                    4. MOVE THE TOP OF X TO THE BOTTOM OF X .
                    5. MOVE THE TOP OF Y TO THE BOTTOM OF Y .
    D1 = ( TOP OF COIN-1 )
    D2 = ( TOP OF COIN-2 )
    D3 = ( TOP OF COIN-3 )
    D4 = ( MOVES-REMAINING )
    DIFF-ORDERING = ( ( D1 D2 D3 D4 ) )
    TABLE-OF-CONNECTIONS = ( ( COMMON-DIFFERENCE FLIP-COINS ) )
    LIST-OF-VAR = ( X Y )
    OBJ-ATTRIB = ( TOP BOTTOM MOVES-REMAINING MOVES-TAKEN )
    )
END
```

Fig. 69 (cont.).

GPS FORMULATION

In Fig. 69, which gives the GPS formulation of the task, INITIAL-OBJ represents the situation in which the first and third coins show tails and the second coin shows heads. The tree-structure representation of INITIAL-OBJ is given in Fig. 70. Each node, except the TOP-NODE, represents a coin and has two ATTRIBUTES, TOP and BOTTOM, the values of which are the sides of the coin showing and not showing, respectively. The ATTRIBUTES of the TOP-NODE—MOVES-TAKEN and MOVES-REMAINING—keep track of the number of moves that are involved in producing the OBJECT-SCHEMA.

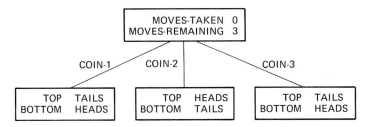

Fig. 70. Tree-structure representation of INITIAL-OBJ in the Three Coins puzzle.

The DESIRED-OBJ represents the OBJECT-SCHEMAs in which the TOPs of all three coins are the same and the MOVES-REMAINING is 0 (precisely three moves were involved in producing the OBJECT-SCHEMA). TOP-GOAL is the statement of the problem.

The only operator in this task is FLIP-COINS, which turns over any two of the three coins. FLIP-COINS also increments by 1 the value of the MOVES-TAKEN and decrements by 1 the value of the MOVES-REMAINING.

The types of difference of this task are D1, D2, D3, (the TOPs of the various coins) and D4 (MOVES-REMAINING). Others, such as BOTTOM of COIN-1, were not included because they could never be detected. DIFF-ORDERING signifies that all of the types of difference are equally difficult to reduce. TABLE-OF-CONNECTIONS indicates that FLIP-COINS is desirable to reduce any type of difference.

LIST-OF-VAR designates X and Y to be variables, and the ATTRIBUTES of this task are listed in OBJ-ATTRIB.

BEHAVIOR OF GPS

Figure 71 is the behavior of GPS in finding a solution to the task in Fig. 69. GPS notices that COIN-2 is not the same as COIN-3 (TOP-

```
1 TOP-GOAL TRANSFORM INITIAL-OBJ INTO DESIRED-OBJ        (SUBGOAL OF NONE)

2  GOAL 2 REDUCE D2 ON INITIAL-OBJ        (SUBGOAL OF TOP-GOAL)

3   GOAL 3 APPLY FLIP-COINS WITH X = COIN-2, TO INITIAL-OBJ        (SUBGOAL OF 2)
            SET: Y = COIN-1
            OBJECT 4: (MOVES-REMAINING 2 MOVES-TAKEN 1 COIN-1(TOP HEADS BOTTOM TAILS) COIN-2
                      (TOP TAILS BOTTOM HEADS) COIN-3(TOP TAILS BOTTOM HEADS))

2  GOAL 4 TRANSFORM 4 INTO DESIRED-OBJ        (SUBGOAL OF TOP-GOAL)

3   GOAL 5 REDUCE D3 ON 4        (SUBGOAL OF 4)

4    GOAL 6 APPLY FLIP-COINS WITH X = COIN-3, TO 4        (SUBGOAL OF 5)
            SET: Y = COIN-1
            OBJECT 5: (MOVES-REMAINING 1 MOVES-TAKEN 2 COIN-1(TOP TAILS BOTTOM HEADS) COIN-2
                      (TOP TAILS BOTTOM HEADS) COIN-3(TOP HEADS BOTTOM TAILS))

3   GOAL 7 TRANSFORM 5 INTO DESIRED-OBJ        (SUBGOAL OF 4)

4    GOAL 8 REDUCE D2 ON 5        (SUBGOAL OF 7)

5     GOAL 9 APPLY FLIP-COINS WITH X = COIN-2, TO 5        (SUBGOAL OF 8)
            SET: Y = COIN-1
            OBJECT 6: (MOVES-REMAINING 0 MOVES-TAKEN 3 COIN-1(TOP HEADS BOTTOM TAILS) COIN-2
                      (TOP HEADS BOTTOM TAILS) COIN-3(TOP HEADS BOTTOM TAILS))

4    GOAL 10 TRANSFORM 6 INTO DESIRED-OBJ        (SUBGOAL OF 7)

SUCCESS
```

Fig. 71. Performance of GPS on the Three Coins puzzle.

GOAL) and, in an attempt to reduce this difference (GOAL 2), GOAL 3 is created. OBJECT 4 is produced by turning over the first and second coins.

Since in OBJECT 4, COIN-3 is not the same as COIN-1 (GOAL 4, GOAL 5), GPS turns over the first and third coins (GOAL 6) to produce OBJECT 5. Again, COIN-2 is not the same as COIN-3, and the first and second coins are turned over (GOAL 7, GOAL 8, GOAL 9). In attempting GOAL 10, GPS notices that it has solved the problem.

DISCUSSION

In the DESIRED-OBJ, the order of the arguments (for expedience) is such that GPS does not make a mistake. GPS would make a mistake if the TESTs in the DESIRED-OBJ were

1. THE TOP OF COIN-1 EQUALS THE TOP OF COIN-2.
2. THE TOP OF COIN-2 EQUALS THE TOP OF COIN-3.

Using this DESIRED-OBJ, the TOPs of the coins would not all be the same in the result of GOAL 9. FLIP-COINS could not be applied to this object because the MOVES-REMAINING is 0. (DECREASE requires its first argument to be greater than 0.) Consequently, TRY-OLD-GOALS-METHOD would be evoked, which would cause a different feasible variable specification in applying an operator. This new result of an old APPLY goal would lead to a solution shortly.

The two ATTRIBUTEs "TOP" and "BOTTOM" could be replaced by a single ATTRIBUTE "ORIENTATION," whose value would be either HEADS or TAILS. With this formulation, the second and third TRANS-FORMATIONs of FLIP-COINS would be replaced by the single TRANS-FORMATION

MOVE-FUNCTION OF THE ORIENTATION OF X TO THE ORIENTATION OF X, THE FUNCTION IS F1.

F1 is the function whose value is TAILS when its argument is HEADS and vice-versa. The task is quite trivial, although it manages to get in puzzle books. It does have the interesting aspect that its solution is constrained to a fixed number of operator applications. Many other tasks have this same property.* This property can be represented by

* The matchstick problem used in Katona (1940) is another one.

associating with each object a counter that indicates the number of operator applications involved in producing the object.

PARSING SENTENCES

Generative grammars of certain languages can be defined by a set of phrase structure rules (Chomsky, 1957). Words in the language are divided into classes called parts of speech. If a word can be used as the part of speech α, it is a member of the class α. In general, a word is a member of several parts-of-speech classes. In Fig. 72, the part of

Rules

1. S ← NP VP NP .   6. NP ← ⟨noun⟩
2. S ← NP VBP AP .   7. VP ← ⟨adverb⟩ ⟨verb⟩
3. AP ← AP ⟨adjective⟩   8. VP ← ⟨verb⟩
4. AP ← ⟨adjective⟩   9. VBP ← ⟨adverb⟩ ⟨verb-be⟩
5. NP ← AP ⟨noun⟩   10. VBP ← ⟨verb-be⟩

Definition of Symbols

S	sentence	VP	verb phrase
NP	noun phrase	VBE	verb phrase for to be
AP	adjective phrase		

Fig. 72. Phrase-structure rules for a simple grammar.

speech class α is indicated by $\langle\alpha\rangle$. The meaning, for example, of Rule 3 is that an adjective phrase (*AP*) followed by a word that can be used as an adjective is an adjective phrase according to the grammar.

Parsing sentences can be accomplished by using these rules as replacement rules; i.e., any occurrence of the right side of a rule can be replaced by the left side of the rule. Consider the example of parsing, according to the grammar in Fig. 72, the sentence

Free variables cause confusion.

Assuming that *free* can be used as an adjective, an application of Rule 4 produces

NP cause confusion.

The use of Rules 6 and 8 (assuming that *cause* is a verb and *confusion* rt="headG SENTENCES1ment>

is a noun) yields

NP VP NP,

which is a sentence according to Rule 1.

GPS FORMULATION

Figure 73 is the GPS formulation of the task of parsing, according to the grammar in Fig. 72, the sentence

Free variables cause confusion.

INITIAL-OBJ represents the sentence to be parsed. After translation, it is converted by a special routine for this task to the tree-structure representation in Fig. 74.

The DESIRED-OBJ, which is also processed by the conversion routine, is an OBJECT-SCHEMA consisting of a single node that has SENTENCE as the value of the ATTRIBUTE "PS." PS stands for "part of speech" (which is a poor name for the ATTRIBUTE; "grammatical type" would be better). TOP-GOAL is the statement that the problem is to show that INITIAL-OBJ is a SENTENCE.

There are only two ATTRIBUTEs (OBJ-ATTRIB) in this formulation. The value of WORD is always an English word. The value of PS is always a grammatical type defined by one of the rules of the grammar, i.e., the correspondent to the left side of one of the ten rules in Fig. 72. Each node of an OBJECT-SCHEMA represents either a part of speech (PS) or a word. Thus, precisely one of the two ATTRIBUTEs, "WORD" or "PS," has a value at every node of every OBJECT-SCHEMA. This convention is implicit in the formulation of the operators of this task.

There are ten operators, one corresponding to each of the ten rules in Fig. 72. The function of each of these operators is to replace an occurrence of the left side of the rule with the right side of the rule. s1 in Fig. 73 corresponds to the first rule in Fig. 72. It is a FORM-OPERATOR, which is converted (by the same special routine that converts INITIAL-OBJ, DESIRED-OBJ, and s2) to the tree structure in Fig. 75. Similarly, s2 corresponds to the second rule in Fig. 72.

Each WORD in INITIAL-OBJ is the SET of the parts of speech for which the WORD can be used. (Since PERIOD cannot be used as any part of speech, it is not a SET but a CONSTANT.) For example, CAUSE is the SET of the two elements NOUN and VERB, because CAUSE can be used as either a noun or a verb. The first TEST in the PRETESTS of

```
RENAME     (

   NEXT = FIRST

   NEXT-OF-NEXT = FIRST-FIRST

       )

DECLARE    (

   FREE = SET

   VARIABLES = SET

   CAUSE = SET

   CONFUSION = SET

   PS = ATTRIBUTE

   WORD = ATTRIBUTE

   D1 = FEATURE

   A1 = MOVE-OPERATOR

   A2 = MOVE-OPERATOR

   N = MOVE-OPERATOR

   N1 = MOVE-OPERATOR

   V1 = MOVE-OPERATOR

   V2 = MOVE-OPERATOR

   V-B1 = MOVE-OPERATOR

   V-B2 = MOVE-OPERATOR

       )

LIST (

   DESIRED-OBJ = ( SENTENCE )

   INITIAL-OBJ = ( FREE VARIABLES CAUSE CONFUSION PERIOD )

   S1 = ( ( NOUN-PHRASE VERB-PHRASE NOUN-PHRASE PERIOD ) YIELDS SENTENCE )

   S2 = ( ( NOUN-PHRASE VERB-BE-PHRASE ADJECTIVE-PHRASE PERIOD ) YIELDS
          SENTENCE )
```

Fig. 73. Specification for GPS of the task of parsing a sentence.

```
         )

TASK-STRUCTURES  (

   TOP-GOAL = ( TRANSFORM THE INITIAL-OBJ INTO THE DESIRED-OBJ . )

   OBJ-ATTRIB = ( PS WORD )

   FREE = ( NOUN ADJECTIVE VERB ).

   VARIABLES = ( NOUN )

   CAUSE = ( NOUN VERB )

   CONFUSION = ( NOUN )

   N = (    $ ADJ-PHRASE NOUN $ CREATION-OPERATOR

            PRETESTS

            1. NOUN IS IN-THE-SET OF THE NEXT WORD .

            2. ADJECTIVE-PHRASE EQUALS THE PS .

            MOVES

            1. COPY NOUN-PHRASE AT THE PS .

            2. MOVE THE NEXT-OF-NEXT TO THE NEXT . )

   A1 = (  $ADJ-PHRASE ADJS   CREATION-OPERATOR

            PRETESTS

            1. ADJECTIVE IS IN-THE-SET OF THE NEXT WORD .

            2. THE PS EQUALS ADJECTIVE-PHRASE .

            MOVES

            1. MOVE THE NEXT-OF-NEXT TO THE NEXT .

            2. COPY ADJECTIVE-PHRASE AT THE PS .          )

   A2 = (  $ADJS   CREATION-OPERATOR

            PRETESTS

            1. ADJECTIVE IS IN-THE-SET OF THE WORD .

            MOVES

            1. REMOVE THE WORD .
```

Fig. 73 (cont.).

```
            2. COPY ADJECTIVE-PHRASE AT THE PS .          )
N1 = ( $ NOUN $ CREATION-OPERATOR
    PRETESTS
    1. NOUN IS IN-THE-SET OF THE WORD .
    MOVES
    2. REMOVE THE WORD .
    3. COPY NOUN-PHRASE AT THE PS .  )
V1 = ( $ADVERB VERB$  CREATION-OPERATOR
       PRETESTS
       1. VERB IS IN-THE-SET OF THE NEXT WORD .
       2. ADVERB IS IN-THE-SET OF THE WORD .
       MOVES
       1. REMOVE THE WORD .
       2. COPY VERB-PHRASE AT THE PS .
       3. MOVE THE NEXT-OF-NEXT TO THE NEXT . )
V2 = ( $VERB$ CREATION-OPERATOR
       PRETESTS
       1. VERB IS IN-THE-SET OF THE WORD .
       MOVES
       1. REMOVE THE WORD  .
       2. COPY VERB-PHRASE AT THE PS .          )
V-B1 = ( $ADVERB VERB-BE$  CREATION-OPERATOR
         PRETESTS
         1. VERB-BE IS IN-THE-SET OF THE NEXT WORD .
         2. ADVERB IS IN-THE-SET OF THE WORD .
         MOVES
         1. REMOVE THE WORD .
         2. COPY VERB-BE-PHRASE AT THE PS .
```

Fig. 73 (cont.).

```
         3. MOVE THE NEXT-OF-NEXT TO THE NEXT . )
V-B2 = ( $VERB-BE$  CREATION-OPERATOR

         PRETESTS

         1. VERB-BE IS IN-THE-SET OF THE WORD .

         MOVES

         1. REMOVE THE WORD .

         2. COPY VERB-BE-PHRASE AT THE PS .       )
D1 = ( PS )

COMPARE-OBJECTS = ( BASIC-MATCH )

BASIC-MATCH = ( COMP-FEAT-LIST ( D1 ) SUBEXPRESSIONS )

DIFF-ORDERING = ( D1 )

TABLE-OF-CONNECTIONS = ( ( D1 S1 S2 V1 V2 V-B1 V-B2 A1 A2 N N1 ) )

LIST-OF-OPR = ( S1 S2 )

         )

END
```

Fig. 73 (cont.).

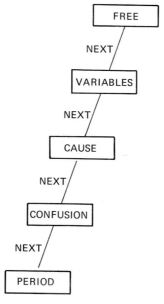

Fig. 74. Tree-structure representation of INITIAL-OBJ. The words at the nodes are values of the ATTRIBUTE "WORD."

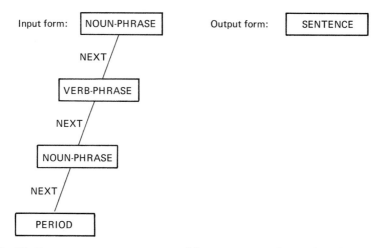

Input form: NOUN-PHRASE   Output form: SENTENCE

Fig. 75. Tree-structure representation of the operator s1. The words at the nodes are values of the ATTRIBUTE "PS," except for PERIOD, which is a value of WORD.

N, which is the MOVE-OPERATOR representation of Rule 6 in Fig. 72, is satisfied if the NEXT WORD can be used as a NOUN; thus, the TEST is satisfied if the NEXT WORD is CAUSE.

The first TRANSFORMATION in N changes the PS to NOUN-PHRASE. (According to the second TEST in PRETESTS, PS has the value ADJEC-TIVE-PHRASE.) The second TRANSFORMATION of N has the effect of deleting the NEXT WORD from the string of WORDs and PSs repre-sented by the OBJECT-SCHEMA.

The only type of difference used in this task is D1, which pertains to the value of the ATTRIBUTE "PS." The type of difference that refers to the value of WORD is not used, since the value of this ATTRIBUTE cannot be changed. (Some of the operators REMOVE the value of WORD from a node but none replaces it with a different value.)

COMPARE-OBJECTS and BASIC-MATCH indicate that the match tests whether the value of PS at all corresponding nodes of two OBJECT-SCHEMAs are identical. DIFF-ORDERING is a formality for this task because D1 is the only type of difference; and TABLE-OF-CONNEC-TIONS signifies that all of the operators are relevant to reducing D1. LIST-OF-OPR indicates that s1 and s2 must be processed by the con-version routine after thay have been translated.

Because of the lack of selectivity provided by the TABLE-OF-CONNECTIONS, a desirability filter for FORM-OPERATORs was added to the REDUCE-METHOD before giving this task to GPS. To test the desirability of a FORM-OPERATOR, the FEATURE, which is the type of difference, is evaluated in the output form of the FORM-OPERATOR. If this value is the same as the value of the difference, the operator is considered desirable. The significance of this filter is discussed later.

BEHAVIOR OF GPS

Figure 76 illustrates how GPS solved the task in Fig. 73. In order to achieve TOP-GOAL, GPS attempts to reduce D1 on the TOP-NODE of INITIAL-OBJ (GOAL 2). GOAL 3 is created because S1 is considered desirable; i.e., the OBJECT-SCHEMA produced by an application of S1 has SENTENCE as the value of the FEATURE "D1." Since the value of PS at the TOP-NODE of INITIAL-OBJ is not NOUN-PHRASE (GOAL 4), GOAL 5 is created because N has the capability of alleviating this difference.

GPS attempts to apply A1 to INITIAL-OBJ (GOAL 6, GOAL 7), because the value of PS must be ADJECTIVE-PHRASE in order for N to be applicable. GPS notices that GOAL 7 is impossible because VARIABLES cannot be used as an ADJECTIVE. GOAL 8 is created in reattempting GOAL 6, and OBJECT 7 to which N can be applied is produced (GOAL 9, OBJECT 8). (This task uses a special routine for printing OBJECT-SCHEMAS in order to make them more legible; only the values of attributes are printed; LOC-PROGS and ATTRIBUTES are not printed.)

S1 cannot be applied to OBJECT 8 (GOAL 10), because the values of PS of the NEXT is not VERB-PHRASE. An attempt to apply V1 to the NEXT of OBJECT 8 (GOAL 11, GOAL 12) fails because CAUSE cannot be used as an ADVERB. But the application of V2 to the NEXT of OBJECT 8 produces OBJECT 9 (GOAL 13). Finally, noticing that CONFUSION can be used as a NOUN-PHRASE (OBJECT 10), S1 is applied and, since its result (OBJECT 11) is identical to the DESIRED-OBJ, the task is solved.

DISCUSSION

All of the operators of this task modify the value of PS at some node and thus are desirable for reducing the type of difference D1. However, for a particular difference, at most two operators are desirable in fact. For example, only S1 and S2 can alleviate the difference

the PS should be SENTENCE.

Only information about the types of difference and not about the values of differences can be put into the TABLE-OF-CONNECTIONS.

```
1 TOP-GOAL TRANSFORM INITIAL-OBJ INTO DESIRED-OBJ        (SUBGOAL OF NONE)

  2 GOAL 2 REDUCE D1 ON INITIAL-OBJ        (SUBGOAL OF TOP-GOAL)

    3 GOAL 3 APPLY S1 TO INITIAL-OBJ        (SUBGOAL OF 2)

      4 GOAL 4 REDUCE D1 ON INITIAL-OBJ        (SUBGOAL OF 3)

        5 GOAL 5 APPLY N TO INITIAL-OBJ        (SUBGOAL OF 4)

          6 GOAL 6 REDUCE D1 ON INITIAL-OBJ        (SUBGOAL OF 5)

            7 GOAL 7 APPLY A1 TO INITIAL-OBJ        (SUBGOAL OF 6)

            7 GOAL 8 APPLY A2 TO INITIAL-OBJ        (SUBGOAL OF 6)
                    OBJECT 7: (ADJECTIVE-PHRASE VARIABLES CAUSE CONFUSION PERIOD)
          6 GOAL 9 APPLY N TO 7        (SUBGOAL OF 5)
                  OBJECT 8: (NOUN-PHRASE CAUSE CONFUSION PERIOD)
      4 GOAL 10 APPLY S1 TO 8        (SUBGOAL OF 3)

        5 GOAL 11 REDUCE D1 ON  NEXT 8        (SUBGOAL OF 10)

          6 GOAL 12 APPLY V1 TO  NEXT 8        (SUBGOAL OF 11)

          6 GOAL 13 APPLY V2 TO  NEXT 8        (SUBGOAL OF 11)
                  OBJECT 9: (NOUN-PHRASE VERB-PHRASE CONFUSION PERIOD)
        5 GOAL 14 APPLY S1 TO 9        (SUBGOAL OF 10)

          6 GOAL 15 REDUCE D1 ON  NEXT  NEXT 9        (SUBGOAL OF 14)

            7 GOAL 16 APPLY N TO  NEXT  NEXT 9        (SUBGOAL OF 15)

            7 GOAL 17 APPLY N1 TO  NEXT  NEXT 9        (SUBGOAL OF 15)
                    OBJECT 10: (NOUN-PHRASE VERB-PHRASE NOUN-PHRASE PERIOD)
          6 GOAL 18 APPLY S1 TO 10        (SUBGOAL OF 14)
                  OBJECT 11: (SENTENCE)
  2 GOAL 19 TRANSFORM 11 INTO DESIRED-OBJ        (SUBGOAL OF TOP-GOAL)

SUCCESS
```

Fig. 76. Performance of GPS on the Parsing task.

Consequently, the TABLE-OF-CONNECTIONS in Fig. 73 does not contain sufficient selectivity, and an additional desirability filter for FORM-OPERATORS had to be given to GPS. On the other hand, the *desirability-selection* process for MOVE-OPERATORS gives GPS sufficient selectivity. If s1 and s2 (the only FORM-OPERATORS in Fig. 73) were expressed as MOVE-OPERATORS, the desirability filter would not need to be added. However, s1 and s2 were expressed as FORM-OPERATORS to demonstrate that the two different TYPES of operator can be used in the specification of a single task.

A great deal of effort has been devoted to the construction of efficient parsing algorithms for simple phrase structure grammars (Oettinger, 1965). The point of this example is not GPS's proficiency as a parser, but an illustration of the kinship between heuristic search and syntactic analysis. This kinship has also been noted by Amarel (1965) and Floyd (1964).

BRIDGES OF KÖNIGSBERG

Through the German town of Königsberg ran the river Pregel. In the river were two islands connected with the mainland and with each other by seven bridges as shown in Fig. 77. Could a person walk from some point in town and return to the same point after crossing each of the seven bridges once and only once?

In 1736 Euler proved that this task is impossible, and his proof stands as one of the early efforts in topology (Northrop, 1944). Nevertheless, we can give GPS the task of finding a path that starts at point E in Fig. 77, crosses all of the bridges precisely once and ends

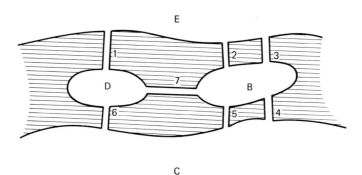

Fig. 77. A schematic of the seven bridges of Königsberg. The numbers 1, 2, . . . , 7 are labels for the bridges; the letters *B, C, D, E*, are labels for the different sections of the town.

at point E, even though we know *a priori* that a solution does not exist.

GPS FORMULATION

An OBJECT-SCHEMA in the formulation in Fig. 78 is a single node with up to eight ATTRIBUTEs (OBJ-ATTRIB). The value of CURRENT-POINT is either B, C, D, or E, corresponding to where GPS would be standing in Fig. 77. The values of the other ATTRIBUTEs indicate which bridges have been crossed. (BRIDGE-1 corresponds to the bridge labeled 1 in Fig. 77, BRIDGE-2 to the bridge labeled 2; and so on.) For example, BRIDGE-1 has been crossed if the value of the AT-TRIBUTE "BRIDGE-1" is CROSSED; otherwise, BRIDGE-1 has not been crossed.

TOP-GOAL is the statment of the task. INITIAL-OBJ represents the situation when GPS is standing at point E and has not crossed any bridges.

The DESIRED-OBJ is a DESCRIBED-OBJ that represents the situation when all of the bridges have been CROSSED and GPS is standing at point E. The first TEST in the DESIRED-OBJ requires that all of the ATTRIBUTEs in the SET "BRIDGES" have the value CROSSED. And the second TEST is satisfied if CURRENT-POINT has the value E.

The only operator in this task is CROSS, whose application corresponds to walking from the point OTHER-END cross the bridge X to the point NEXT-POINT. The third TEST in VAR-DOMAIN requires that X be in the SET "BRIDGES." Each member of BRIDGES is not an atomic symbol, but a data structure that is an encoding of the two points connected by the bridge; e.g., BRIDGE-1 connects E and D. The first two TESTs in VAR-DOMAIN signify that OTHER-END and NEXT-POINT stand for the two points connected by the bridge X.

The PRETESTS indicate that in order to cross the bridge X, GPS must be standing at one end of X and that GPS must not have previously crossed X. The MOVES designate that in the resultant object X is CROSSED and the value of CURRENT-POINT is NEXT-POINT. (According to the PRETESTS, the CURRENT-POINT must be OTHER-END in the object to which CROSS is applied.)

In the formulation of this task, there are eight differences, D1 ⋯ D8, each referring to the value of one of the eight ATTRIBUTEs. DIFF-ORDERING designates that the differences that refer to the status of a bridge, D1 ⋯ D7, are more difficult than D8 which refers to the CURRENT-POINT. CROSS is relevant to reducing any type of difference (TABLE-OF-CONNECTIONS), and LIST-OF-VAR lists the variables that appear in Fig. 78.

```
DECLARE

    BRIDGES = SET

    BRIDGE-1 = ATTRIBUTE

    BRIDGE-2 = ATTRIBUTE

    BRIDGE-3 = ATTRIBUTE

    BRIDGE-4 = ATTRIBUTE

    BRIDGE-5 = ATTRIBUTE

    BRIDGE-6 = ATTRIBUTE

    BRIDGE-7 = ATTRIBUTE

    CROSS = MOVE-OPERATOR

    CURRENT-POINT = ATTRIBUTE

    DESIRED-OBJ = DESCRIBED-OBJ

    D1 = FEATURE

    D2 = FEATURE

    D3 = FEATURE

    D4 = FEATURE

    D5 = FEATURE

    D6 = FEATURE

    D7 = FEATURE

    D8 = FEATURE

    ED = SET

    EB = SET

    CB = SET

    CD = SET

    DB = SET

    ENDS = ATTRIBUTE

    INITIAL-OBJ = OBJECT-SCHEMA
```

Fig. 78. Specification for GPS of the Bridges of Königsberg task.

```
      X = ATTRIBUTE
      )
TASK-STRUCTURES   (
    OBJ-ATTRIB = ( BRIDGE-1 BRIDGE-2 BRIDGE-3 BRIDGE-4 BRIDGE-5
                   BRIDGE-6 BRIDGE-7 CURRENT-POINT )
    TOP-GOAL = ( TRANSFORM THE INITIAL-OBJ INTO THE DESIRED-OBJ . )
    INITIAL-OBJ = ( CURRENT-POINT E )
    DESIRED-OBJ = ( TEX-DESCRIPTION
                          1. X EQUALS CROSSED , FOR-ALL X IN THE BRIDGES .
                          2. THE CURRENT-POINT EQUALS E .      )
    BRIDGES = ( BRIDGE-1 BRIDGE-2 BRIDGE-3 BRIDGE-4 BRIDGE-5 BRIDGE-6 BRIDGE-7 )
    CROSS = ( CREATION-OPERATOR
                  VAR-DOMAIN
                  1. OTHER-END IS AN EXCLUSIVE-MEMBER OF THE ENDS OF THE
                     PARTICULAR X .
                  2. NEXT-POINT IS AN EXCLUSIVE-MEMBER OF THE ENDS OF THE
                     PARTICULAR X .
                  3. X IS IN-THE-SET OF BRIDGES .
                  PRETESTS
                  1. CURRENT-POINT EQUALS THE OTHER-END .
                  2. X IS UNDEFINED .
                  MOVES
                  1. COPY CROSSED AT X .
                  2. COPY NEXT-POINT AT THE CURRENT-POINT . )
    BRIDGE-1 = ( ENDS ED )
    BRIDGE-2 = ( ENDS EB )
    BRIDGE-3 = ( ENDS EB )
```

Fig. 78 (cont.).

```
BRIDGE-4 = ( ENDS CB )

BRIDGE-5 = ( ENDS CB )

BRIDGE-6 = ( ENDS CD )

BRIDGE-7 = ( ENDS DB )

ED = ( E D )

EB = ( E B )

CB = ( C B )

CD = ( C D )

DB = ( D B )

D1 = ( BRIDGE-1 )

D2 = ( BRIDGE-2 )

D3 = ( BRIDGE-3 )

D4 = ( BRIDGE-4 )

D5 = ( BRIDGE-5 )

D6 = ( BRIDGE-6 )

D7 = ( BRIDGE-7 )

D8 = ( CURRENT-POINT )

DIFF-ORDERING = ( 1. ( D1 D2 D3 D4 D5 D6 D7 )

                  2. D8  )

TABLE-OF-CONNECTIONS = ( ( COMMON-DIFFERENCE CROSS ) )

LIST-OF-VAR = ( X NEXT-POINT OTHER-END )

)

END
```

Fig. 78 (cont.).

GPS often detects several of the types of difference D1, D2, ..., D7, between two objects. Since they are all equally difficult, GPS must arbitrarily select one and attempt to reduce it. For this reason, the TRANSFORM-METHOD was slightly generalized for this task. If an attempt to reduce a difference detected by the TRANSFORM-METHOD fails, the method does not necessarily fail. Instead, another equally difficult difference will be selected and the goal of reducing this difference will be generated. This modified TRANSFORM-METHOD was also used in the Missionaries and Cannibals task and is discussed in more detail on p. 130.

Behavior of GPS

Figure 79 illustrates how GPS attempted to solve the task in Fig. 78. In attempting TOP-GOAL, GPS detects the differences D1, ... D7, and since they are all equally difficult, GPS selects one, D7, to REDUCE (GOAL 2). GPS attempts to apply CROSS with X equal to BRIDGE-7 because it is relevant to reducing D7 on INITIAL-OBJ. GPS could CROSS BRIDGE-7 by walking from B to D if CURRENT-POINT had the value of B instead of E (GOAL 4). After crossing BRIDGE-2 (GOAL 5, OBJECT 4), BRIDGE-7 is CROSSED (GOAL 6, OBJECT 5).

Since BRIDGE-6 is not CROSSED in OBJECT 5 (GOAL 7, GOAL 8), GPS crosses it (GOAL 9, OBJECT 6). GPS attempts to CROSS BRIDGE-5 from B to C (GOAL 10, GOAL 11, GOAL 12) but cannot because the CURRENT-POINT in OBJECT 6 is C instead of B. Each bridge can be CROSSED in two directions, but GPS does not realize that BRIDGE-5 can be CROSSED in the other direction. To make the CURRENT-POINT B (GOAL 13), BRIDGE-4 is CROSSED (GOAL 14, OBJECT-7). BRIDGE-5 can be CROSSED in OBJECT-7 (GOAL 15), which produces OBJECT-8.

Since none of the bridges can be CROSSED in OBJECT-8, the attempts to CROSS BRIDGE-3 (GOAL 18) and BRIDGE-1 (GOAL 22) both fail. GPS reattempts GOAL 11 to no avail because all of the desirable operators have been tried. Another attempt to achieve GOAL 10 generates GOAL 25 because D4 is as difficult as D5. But attempting GOAL 25 eventually leads to the generation of a goal identical to GOAL 14, which is not retried. (This is the reason GOAL 27 is abandoned.) All other attempts to achieve GOAL 10 fail, because GPS fails to reduce D3 on OBJECT 6 (GOAL 29) and fails to reduce D1 on OBJECT 6 (GOAL 33).

In reattempting GOAL 7, GPS eventually produces OBJECT 9 (GOAL 50). GPS manages to cross six of the seven bridges in two different ways (OBJECT 12, OBJECT 13), but shortly thereafter exhausts its memory.

Discussion

Although GPS was given the problem of starting from and returning to point E, by slightly reformulating INITIAL-OBJ and DESIRED-OBJ the task could specify the problem of starting from and returning to an arbitrary point. The revised INITIAL-OBJ would be

(CURRENT-POINT X STARTING-POINT X)

and the DESIRED-OBJ would check whether the CURRENT-POINT

Fig. 79. Performance of GPS on the Bridges of Königsberg task.

```
1 TOP-GOAL TRANSFORM INITIAL-OBJ INTO DESIRED-OBJ    (SUBGOAL OF NONE)

2 GOAL 2 REDUCE D7 ON INITIAL-OBJ    (SUBGOAL OF TOP-GOAL)

3 GOAL 3 APPLY CROSS WITH X = BRIDGE-7, TO INITIAL-OBJ    (SUBGOAL OF 2)
    SET: OTHER-END = B, NEXT-POINT = D

4 GOAL 4 REDUCE D8 ON INITIAL-OBJ    (SUBGOAL OF 3)

5 GOAL 5 APPLY CROSS WITH NEXT-POINT = B, TO INITIAL-OBJ    (SUBGOAL OF 4)
    SET: OTHER-END = E, X = BRIDGE-2
    OBJECT 4: (BRIDGE-2 CROSSED CURRENT-POINT B)

4 GOAL 6 APPLY CROSS WITH X = BRIDGE-7, TO 4    (SUBGOAL OF 3)
    SET: OTHER-END = B, NEXT-POINT = D
    OBJECT 5: (BRIDGE-2 CROSSED BRIDGE-7 CROSSED CURRENT-POINT D)

2 GOAL 7 TRANSFORM 5 INTO DESIRED-OBJ    (SUBGOAL OF TOP-GOAL)

3 GOAL 8 REDUCE D6 ON 5    (SUBGOAL OF 7)

4 GOAL 9 APPLY CROSS WITH X = BRIDGE-6, TO 5    (SUBGOAL OF 8)
    SET: OTHER-END = D, NEXT-POINT = C
    OBJECT 6: (BRIDGE-2 CROSSED BRIDGE-6 CROSSED BRIDGE-7 CROSSED CURRENT-POINT C)

3 GOAL 10 TRANSFORM 6 INTO DESIRED-OBJ    (SUBGOAL OF 7)

4 GOAL 11 REDUCE D5 ON 6    (SUBGOAL OF 10)

5 GOAL 12 APPLY CROSS WITH X = BRIDGE-5, TO 6    (SUBGOAL OF 11)
    SET: OTHER-END = B, NEXT-POINT = C
```

Fig. 79 (cont.).

```
6 GOAL 13 REDUCE D8 ON 6        (SUBGOAL OF 12)

7 GOAL 14 APPLY CROSS WITH NEXT-POINT = B, TO 6        (SUBGOAL OF 13)
         SET: OTHER-END = C, X = BRIDGE-4
         OBJECT 7: (BRIDGE-2 CROSSED BRIDGE-4 CROSSED BRIDGE-6 CROSSED BRIDGE-7 CROSSED
                    CURRENT-POINT B)

6 GOAL 15 APPLY CROSS WITH X = BRIDGE-5, TO 7        (SUBGOAL OF 12)
         SET: OTHER-END = B, NEXT-POINT = C
         OBJECT 8: (BRIDGE-2 CROSSED BRIDGE-4 CROSSED BRIDGE-5 CROSSED BRIDGE-6 CROSSED
                    BRIDGE-7 CROSSED CURRENT-POINT C)

4 GOAL 16 TRANSFORM 8 INTO DESIRED-OBJ        (SUBGOAL OF 10)

5 GOAL 17 REDUCE D3 ON 8        (SUBGOAL OF 16)

6 GOAL 18 APPLY CROSS WITH X = BRIDGE-3, TO 8        (SUBGOAL OF 17)
         SET: OTHER-END = B, NEXT-POINT = E

7 GOAL 19 REDUCE D8 ON 8        (SUBGOAL OF 18)

8 GOAL 20 APPLY CROSS WITH NEXT-POINT = B, TO 8        (SUBGOAL OF 19)
         SET: OTHER-END = B, X = BRIDGE-7

5 GOAL 21 REDUCE D1 ON 8        (SUBGOAL OF 16)

6 GOAL 22 APPLY CROSS WITH X = BRIDGE-1, TO 8        (SJBGOAL OF 21)
         SET: OTHER-END = D, NEXT-POINT = E

7 GOAL 23 REDUCE D8 ON 8        (SUBGOAL OF 22)
```

Fig. 79 (cont.).

```
8 GOAL 24 APPLY CROSS WITH NEXT-POINT = D, TO 8    (SUBGOAL OF 23)
    SET: OTHER-END = B, X = BRIDGE-7

4 GOAL 11 REDUCE D5 ON 6    (SUBGOAL OF 10)

4 GOAL 25 REDUCE D4 ON 6    (SUBGOAL OF 10)

5 GOAL 26 APPLY CROSS WITH X = BRIDGE-4, TO 6    (SUBGOAL OF 25)
    SET: OTHER-END = B, NEXT-POINT = C

6 GOAL 27 REDUCE D8 ON 6    (SUBGOAL OF 26)

4 GOAL 29 REDUCE D3 ON 6    (SUBGOAL OF 10)

5 GOAL 30 APPLY CROSS WITH X = BRIDGE-3, TO 6 ,    (SUBGOAL OF 29)
    SET: OTHER-END = B, NEXT-POINT = E

6 GOAL 31 REDUCE D8 ON 6    (SUBGOAL OF 30)

4 GOAL 33 REDUCE D1 ON 6    (SUBGOAL OF 10)

5 GOAL 34 APPLY CROSS WITH X = BRIDGE-1, TO 6    (SUBGOAL OF 33)
    SET: OTHER-END = D, NEXT-POINT = E

6 GOAL 35 REDUCE D8 ON 6    (SUBGOAL OF 34)

7 GOAL 36 APPLY CROSS WITH NEXT-POINT = D, TO 6    (SUBGOAL OF 35)
    SET: OTHER-END = B, X = BRIDGE-7
```

Fig. 79 (cont.).

3 GOAL 8 REDUCE D6 ON 5   (SUBGOAL OF 7)

3 GOAL 37 REDUCE D5 ON 5   (SUBGOAL OF 7)

4 GOAL 38 APPLY CROSS WITH X = BRIDGE-5, TO 5   (SUBGOAL OF 37)
        SET: OTHER-END = B, NEXT-POINT = C

5 GOAL 39 REDUCE D8 ON 5   (SUBGOAL OF 38)

6 GOAL 40 APPLY CROSS WITH NEXT-POINT = B, TO 5   (SUBGOAL OF 39)
        SET: OTHER-END = B, X = BRIDGE-7

3 GOAL 41 REDUCE D4 ON 5   (SUBGOAL OF 7)

4 GOAL 42 APPLY CROSS WITH X = BRIDGE-4, TO 5   (SUBGOAL OF 41)
        SET: OTHER-END = B, NEXT-POINT = C

5 GOAL 43 REDUCE D8 ON 5   (SUBGOAL OF 42)

3 GOAL 45 REDUCE D3 ON 5   (SUBGOAL OF 7)

4 GOAL 45 APPLY CROSS WITH X = BRIDGE-3, TO 5   (SUBGOAL OF 45)
        SET: OTHER-END = B, NEXT-POINT = E

5 GOAL 47 REDUCE D8 ON 5   (SUBGOAL OF 46)

3 GOAL 49 REDUCE D1 ON 5   (SUBGOAL OF 7)

Fig. 79 (cont.).

```
4 GOAL 50 APPLY CROSS WITH X = BRIDGE-1, TO 5      (SUBGOAL OF 49)
        SET: OTHER-END = D, NEXT-POINT = E
        OBJECT 9: (BRIDGE-1 CROSSED BRIDGE-2 CROSSED BRIDGE-7 CROSSED CURRENT-POINT E)

3 GOAL 51 TRANSFORM 9 INTO DESIRED-OBJ      (SUBGOAL OF 7)

4 GOAL 52 REDUCE D6 ON 9      (SUBGOAL OF 51)

5 GOAL 53 APPLY CROSS WITH X = BRIDGE-6, TO 9      (SUBGOAL OF 52)
        SET: OTHER-END = D, NEXT-POINT = C

6 GOAL 54 REDUCE D8 ON 9      (SUBGOAL OF 53)

7 GOAL 55 APPLY CROSS WITH NEXT-POINT = D, TO 9      (SUBGOAL OF 54)
        SET: OTHER-END = B, X = BRIDGE-7

4 GOAL 56 REDUCE D5 ON 9      (SUBGOAL OF 51)

5 GOAL 57 APPLY CROSS WITH X = BRIDGE-5, TO 9      (SUBGOAL OF 56)
        SET: OTHER-END = B, NEXT-POINT = C

6 GOAL 58 REDUCE D8 ON 9      (SUBGOAL OF 57)

7 GOAL 59 APPLY CROSS WITH NEXT-POINT = B, TO 9      (SUBGOAL OF 58)
        SET: OTHER-END = E, X = BRIDGE-3
        OBJECT 10: (BRIDGE-1 CROSSED BRIDGE-2 CROSSED BRIDGE-3 CROSSED BRIDGE-7 CROSSED
                    CURRENT-POINT B)

6 GOAL 60 APPLY CROSS WITH X = BRIDGE-5, TO 10      (SUBGOAL OF 57)
        SET: OTHER-END = B, NEXT-POINT = C
        OBJECT 11: (BRIDGE-1 CROSSED BRIDGE-2 CROSSED BRIDGE-3 CROSSED BRIDGE-5 CROSSED
                    BRIDGE-7 CROSSED CURRENT-POINT C)
```

Fig. 79 (cont.).

```
4  GOAL 61 TRANSFORM 11 INTO DESIRED-OBJ          (SUBGOAL OF 51)

5  GOAL 62 REDUCE D6 ON 11          (SUBGOAL OF 61)

6  GOAL 63 APPLY CROSS WITH X = BRIDGE-6, TO 11          (SUBGOAL OF 62)
        SET: OTHER-END = D, NEXT-POINT = C

7  GOAL 64 REDUCE D8 ON 11          (SUBGOAL OF 63)

8  GOAL 65 APPLY CROSS WITH NEXT-POINT = D, TO 11          (SUBGOAL OF 64)
        SET: OTHER-END = C, X = BRIDGE-6
   OBJECT 12: (BRIDGE-1 CROSSED BRIDGE-2 CROSSED BRIDGE-3 CROSSED BRIDGE-5 CROSSED
              BRIDGE-6 CROSSED BRIDGE-7 CROSSED CURRENT-POINT D)

7  GOAL 66 APPLY CROSS WITH X = BRIDGE-6, TO 12          (SUBGOAL OF 63)
        SET: OTHER-END = D, NEXT-POINT = D

7  GOAL 64 REDUCE D8 ON 11          (SUBGOAL OF 63)

5  GOAL 67 REDUCE D4 ON 11          (SUBGOAL OF 61)

6  GOAL 68 APPLY CROSS WITH X = BRIDGE-4, TO 11          (SUBGOAL OF 67)
        SET: OTHER-END = B, NEXT-POINT = C

7  GOAL 69 REDUCE D8 ON 11          (SUBGOAL OF 68)

8  GOAL 70 APPLY CROSS WITH NEXT-POINT = B, TO 11          (SUBGOAL OF 69)
        SET: OTHER-END = C, X = BRIDGE-4
   OBJECT 13: (BRIDGE-1 CROSSED BRIDGE-2 CROSSED BRIDGE-3 CROSSED BRIDGE-4 CROSSED
              BRIDGE-5 CROSSED BRIDGE-7 CROSSED CURRENT-POINT B)

7  GOAL 71 APPLY CROSS WITH X = BRIDGE-4, TO 13          (SUBGOAL OF 68)
```

EQUALS the STARTING-POINT instead of point E. X would be bound by applying an operator to the INITIAL-OBJ.

Eventually, GPS would give up on this task, because it would run out of things to do. But GPS would have tried all possibilities before this happened. In attempting a TRANSFORM goal, a difference is generated for each bridge that is not CROSSED. The modified TRANS-FORM-METHOD will generate a REDUCE goal for each of these differences, and GPS will attempt to CROSS the bridge to which the difference pertains. However, GPS would not realize it had disproved the problem by exhaustion.

In attempting most impossible tasks, GPS would not attempt to search the entire problem space because some parts of the space would appear undesirable (according to DIFF-ORDERING and TABLE-OF-CONNECTIONS). However, in this task most GOALS appear equally desirable because the difference types D1 ⋯ D7 are all equally difficult according to DIFF-ORDERING. A better DIFF-ORDERING and a better set of difference types would increase GPS's selectivity. But even if GPS could use more sophisticated types of differences (than the FEATUREs used currently), it is not clear what types of difference should be used to increase GPS's selectivity.

The impossibility of this problem lies in the topological properties of the city. By studying the properties, Euler discovered the problem to be impossible. GPS cannot see the impossibility, because it sets out to CROSS bridges instead of discovering topological properties of the city. Such limitations in problem-solving programs are discussed in more detail in Newell (1965).

WATER JUG TASK

Given a five-gallon jug and an eight-gallon jug, how can precisely two gallons be put into the five-gallon jug? Since there is a sink nearby, a jug can be filled from the tap and can be emptied by pouring its contents down the drain. Water can be poured from one jug into another, but no measuring devices are available other than the jugs themselves.*

This is only a particular water-jug task. In others, the number of jugs, the sizes of the jugs, and the amount of water desired may be different, but the general problem is the same. Sometimes, as an addi-

* The source of this problem is No. 19 in Mott-Smith (1954).

```
SKIP-WORDS        (

   GALLONS

        )

RENAME   (

   JUG-1  =  FIRST

   JUG-2  =  SECOND

        )

DECLARE    (

   FINAL-OBJ  =  DESCRIBED-OBJ

   INITIAL-OBJ  =  OBJECT-SCHEMA

   EMPTY-JUG  =  MOVE-OPERATOR

   FILL-JUG  =  MOVE-OPERATOR

   CREATE-WATER  =  MOVE-OPERATOR

   DESTROY-WATER  =  MOVE-OPERATOR

   D1-1  =  FEATURE

   D1-2  =  FEATURE

   D2-1  =  FEATURE

   D2-2  =  FEATURE

   CONTENTS  =  ATTRIBUTE

   MAXIMUM  =  ATTRIBUTE

   SPACE  =  ATTRIBUTE

   JUGS  =  SET

   NUMBERS  =  SET

   X  =  LOC-PROG

   Y  =  LOC-PROG

        )

TASK-STRUCTURES    (
```

Fig. 80. Specification for GPS of the Water Jug task.

INITIAL-OBJ = (JUG-1 (CONTENTS IS 0   SPACE IS 5 GALLONS

                        MAXIMUM IS 5 GALLONS)

                JUG-2 (CONTENTS IS 0 SPACE IS 8 GALLONS

                        MAXIMUM IS 8 GALLONS))

OBJ-ATTRIB = (CONTENTS SPACE MAXIMUM)

FINAL-OBJ = (THE TEX-DESCRIPTION IS THE CONTENTS OF JUG-1 EQUALS 2

                GALLONS .)

TOP-GOAL = (TRANSFORM THE INITIAL-OBJ INTO THE FINAL-OBJ .)

CREATE-WATER = ($ FILL JUG X WITH WATER FROM THE TAP $

                    CREATION-OPERATOR

                    VAR-DOMAIN

                    X IS A CONSTRAINED-MEMBER OF THE JUGS , THE CONSTRAINT

                    IS THAT THE CONTENTS OF X DOES NOT-EQUAL THE MAXIMUM OF

                    X .

                    MOVES

                    1. COPY THE MAXIMUM OF X AT THE CONTENTS OF X .

                    2. COPY 0 AT THE SPACE IN X .   )

DESTROY-WATER = ($ POUR AWAY ALL OF THE WATER IN JUG X $

                    CREATION-OPERATOR

                    VAR-DOMAIN

                    X IS A CONSTRAINED-MEMBER OF THE JUGS , THE CONSTRAINT

                    IS THAT THE CONTENTS OF X DOES NOT-EQUAL 0

                    MOVES

                    1. COPY THE MAXIMUM OF X AT THE SPACE IN X .

                    2. COPY 0 AT THE CONTENTS OF X .   )

EMPTY-JUG = $ EMPTY ALL OF JUG X INTO JUG Y $

                (CREATION-OPERATOR

Fig. 80 (cont.).

VAR-DOMAIN

1. X IS AN EXCLUSIVE-MEMBER OF THE JUGS .

2. Y IS AN EXCLUSIVE-MEMBER OF THE JUGS .

3. Z IS IN-THE-SET OF NUMBERS .

PRETESTS

1. THE CONTENTS OF X EQUALS Z .

MOVES

1. DELETE THE AMOUNT Z FROM THE SPACE IN Y AND
   ADD IT TO THE CONTENTS OF Y .

2. COPY 0 AT THE CONTENTS OF X .

3. COPY THE MAXIMUM OF X AT THE SPACE IN X .   )

FILL-JUG = $ EMPTY PART OF JUG X INTO JUG Y $

(CREATION-OPERATOR

VAR-DOMAIN

·1. X IS AN EXCLUSIVE-MEMBER OF THE JUGS .

2. Y IS AN EXCLUSIVE-MEMBER OF THE JUGS .

3. Z IS IN-THE-SET OF NUMBERS .

PRETESTS

1. THE SPACE IN Y EQUALS Z .

MOVES

1. DELETE THE AMOUNT Z FROM THE CONTENTS OF X
   AND ADD IT TO THE SPACE IN X .

2. COPY THE MAXIMUM OF Y AT THE CONTENTS OF Y .

3. COPY 0 AT THE SPACE IN Y .   )

NUMBERS = (1 2 3 4 5)

JUGS = (JUG-1 JUG-2)

D1-1 = (THE CONTENTS OF JUG-1 .)

D1-2 = (THE SPACE IN JUG-1 .)

Fig. 80 (cont.).

```
D2-1 = ( THE CONTENTS OF JUG-2 . )

D2-2 = ( THE SPACE IN JUG-2 . )

DIFF-ORDERING = ( ( D1-1 D1-2 D2-1 D2-2 ) )

TABLE-OF-CONNECTIONS = ( ( COMMON-DIFFERENCE FILL-JUG EMPTY-JUG

                                      DESTROY-WATER CREATE-WATER ) )

LIST-OF-VAR = ( X Y Z )

   )

  END .
```

Fig. 80 (cont.).

tional constraint, no water can be poured down the drain.* This type of task has been used extensively in psychological experiments designed to investigate certain aspects of human behavior (Luchins and Luchins, 1959).

GPS FORMULATION

Figure 80 is the formulation of the task for GPS. INITIAL-OBJ, the OBJECT-SCHEMA whose tree structure representation is shown in Fig. 81, is the situation when both the five-gallon jug and the eight-gallon jug are empty. A jug is represented by a node that has three ATTRIBUTEs, listed in OBJ-ATTRIB:

> MAXIMUM, whose value is the size of the jug;
>
> CONTENTS, whose value is the amount of water in the jug;
>
> SPACE, whose value is the size of the jug minus the amount of water in the jug.

SPACE is clearly superfluous, but it simplifies the statement of the operators.

FINAL-OBJ consists of a single TEST to be applied at the TOP-NODE of an OBJECT-SCHEMA. FINAL-OBJ represents the situation when there are two gallons in the five-gallon jug, and TOP-GOAL is the statement of the problem.

---

* For example, given a three-liter jug and a five-liter jug, both of which are empty, and given an eight-liter jug full of ale, how can two men split the ale? In this task, a jug cannot be filled from the tap and, of course, none of the ale can be poured down the drain.

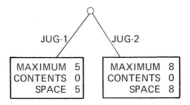

Fig. 81. Tree-structure representation of INITIAL-OBJ in Fig. 80.

There are four operators in this task. CREATE-WATER corresponds to filling jug X from the tap. VAR-DOMAIN of CREATE-WATER requires that X be a jug that is not full. DESTROY-WATER corresponds to pouring the contents of jug X down the drain. According to its VAR-DOMAIN, X must be a jug that is not empty.

EMPTY-JUG and FILL-JUG are the operators for pouring Z gallons[*] of water from jug X into jug Y. Z must be in the SET "NUMBERS"—i.e., an integer between 1 and 5 inclusively. Since the five-gallon jug is always one of the jugs, Z cannot be more than 5, and it is never a fractional part of a gallon. An application of EMPTY-JUG corresponds to pouring all of the contents of jug X into jug Y. In order to do this the contents Z of jug X must fit into jug Y. If this is not the case, the first TRANSFORMATION, which adds the water to jug Y, will fail. The other two TRANSFORMATIONs have the effect of removing the water from jug X.

FILL-JUG is used to fill jug Y with water from the contents of jug X. The first TRANSFORMATION removes the water from jug X and will not be applicable unless there is more water in X than there is SPACE in Y. The other two TRANSFORMATIONs add the water to jug Y.

The types of difference for this task, D1-1, D1-2, D2-1, and D2-2, refer to the CONTENTS and SPACE of the two jugs. DIFF-ORDERING and TABLE-OF-CONNECTIONS are a mere formality for this task because, for lack of something better, all differences are considered equally difficult. Likewise, all of the operators are considered relevant to reducing all types of difference. Thus, these data structures contain no information about the nature of the problem.

LIST-OF-VAR indicates that X, Y, and Z are variables.

NEW-OBJ is a selection criterion given to GPS as an IPL-V structure; hence, it does not appear in Fig. 80. It is used to select from a SET of OBJECT-SCHEMAS those members that do not appear in the statement

---

[*] Z, which stands for an amount of water, should not be confused with X and Y, which stand for jugs.

of any TRANSFORM goal generated thus far. This task and several others use this criterion in the TRANSFORM-SET-METHOD (see pp. 130–131 for a detailed discussion). The rationale is that a new goal can be created by transforming an object that fulfills this criterion into the desired situation.

BEHAVIOR OF GPS

Figure 82 shows how GPS solved the task in Fig. 80. The only difference between INITIAL-OBJ and FINAL-OBJ (TOP-GOAL) that GPS found is that the amount of water in the five-gallon jug should be increased by two gallons. To reduce this difference (GOAL 2), GPS tries to apply FILL-JUG with Y being the five-gallon jug (GOAL 3). This operator is considered desirable because it has the effect of increasing the amount of water in the five-gallon jug even though, if successful, it would increase the amount of water by five gallons instead of two gallons. GOAL 3 is abandoned by GPS because, before the operator could be applied, the amount of water in the eight gallon jug must be increased by at least five gallons, which is as difficult as increasing the amount of water in the five gallon jug.

In reattempting GOAL 2, GPS tries to pour precisely two gallons of water into the five-gallon jug from the eight-gallon jug (GOAL 4). In order to do this, the eight gallon jug must contain precisely two gallons, and GOAL 4 is abandoned. GOAL 5 is created in another attempt to achieve GOAL 2 because CREATE-WATER with X equal to the five-gallon jug has the desirable effect of increasing the amount of water in the five-gallon jug.

In OBJECT-4, the five gallon jug contains too much water (GOAL 6, GOAL 7) and GOAL 8 is generated in an attempt to pour three gallons out of the five-gallon jug. In OBJECT 5 (the result of GOAL 9) the five-gallon jug does not contain enough water (GOAL 10, GOAL 11) and the water in the eight-gallon jug is poured into the five gallon jug (GOAL 12), which results in the previously generated OBJECT 4. Since the goal of transforming OBJECT 4 into FINAL-OBJ is not a new goal, GPS does not try to attempt it, but looks for something else to do.

GOAL 14 is created in an attempt to generate a new goal. OBJECT 3, which is generated internally, is the SET of all OBJECT-SCHEMAs derived from the INITIAL-OBJ. However, GOAL 15 and thus GOAL 14 fail, since all of the OBJECT-SCHEMAs in OBJECT 3 have been used in a TRANSFORM GOAL.

As a last resort, GPS tries previously generated goals in an attempt to produce new results. In reattempting GOAL 2, GPS finds that it has

Fig. 82. Performance of GPS on the Water Jug task.

```
1  TOP-GOAL TRANSFORM INITIAL-OBJ INTO FINAL-OBJ          (SUBGOAL OF NONE)

2  GOAL 2 REDUCE D1-1 ON INITIAL-OBJ          (SUBGOAL OF TOP-GOAL)

3  GOAL 3 APPLY FILL-JUG WITH Y = JUG-1, TO INITIAL-OBJ          (SUBGOAL OF 2)
          SET: X = JUG-2, Z = 5

3  GOAL 4 APPLY EMPTY-JUG WITH Z = 2, Y = JUG-1, TO INITIAL-OBJ          (SUBGOAL OF 2)
          SET: X = JUG-2

3  GOAL 5 APPLY CREATE-WATER WITH X = JUG-1, TO INITIAL-OBJ          (SUBGOAL OF 2)
          OBJECT 4: (JUG-1(SPACE 0 CONTENTS 5 MAXIMUM 5) JUG-2(SPACE 8 CONTENTS 0 MAXIMUM
                     8))

2  GOAL 6 TRANSFORM 4 INTO FINAL-OBJ          (SUBGOAL OF TOP-GOAL)

3  GOAL 7 REDUCE D1-1 ON 4          (SUBGOAL OF 6)

4  GOAL 8 APPLY FILL-JUG WITH Z = 3, X = JUG-1, TO 4          (SUBGOAL OF 7)
          SET: Y = JUG-2

4  GOAL 9 APPLY EMPTY-JUG WITH X = JUG-1, TO 4          (SUBGOAL OF 7)
          SET: Y = JUG-2, Z = 5
          OBJECT 5: (JUG-1(SPACE 5 CONTENTS 0 MAXIMUM 5) JUG-2(SPACE 3 CONTENTS 5 MAXIMUM
                     8))

3  GOAL 10 TRANSFORM 5 INTO FINAL-OBJ          (SUBGOAL OF 6)

4  GOAL 11 REDUCE D1-1 ON 5          (SUBGOAL OF 10)
```

Fig. 82 (cont.).

```
5 GOAL 12 APPLY FILL-JUG WITH Y = JUG-1, TO 5      (SUBGOAL OF 11)
          SET: X = JUG-2, Z = 5
          OBJECT 4: (JUG-1(SPACE 0 CONTENTS 5 MAXIMUM 5) JUG-2(SPACE 8 CONTENTS 0 MAXIMUM
          8))

2 GOAL 6 TRANSFORM 4 INTO FINAL-OBJ          (SUBGOAL OF TOP-GOAL)

3 GOAL 14 TRANSFORM 3 INTO FINAL-OBJ         (SUBGOAL OF TOP-GOAL)

4 GOAL 15 SELECT FROM 3 A/C NEW-OBJ OF FINAL-OBJ      (SUBGOAL OF 14)
          NONE SELECTED

2 GOAL 2 REDUCE D1-1 ON INITIAL-OBJ          (SUBGOAL OF TOP-GOAL)

3 GOAL 14 TRANSFORM 3 INTO FINAL-OBJ         (SUBGOAL OF TOP-GOAL)

2 GOAL 2 REDUCE D1-1 ON INITIAL-OBJ          (SUBGOAL OF TOP-GOAL)

3 GOAL 7 REDUCE D1-1 ON 4      (SUBGOAL OF 6)

4 GOAL 17 APPLY DESTROY-WATER WITH X = JUG-1, TO 4      (SUBGOAL OF 7)
          OBJECT INITIAL-OBJ: (JUG-1(SPACE 5 CONTENTS 0 MAXIMUM 5) JUG-2(SPACE 8 CONTENTS
          0 MAXIMUM 8))

1 TOP-GOAL TRANSFORM INITIAL-OBJ INTO FINAL-OBJ      (SUBGOAL OF NONE)

3 GOAL 7 REDUCE D1-1 ON 4      (SUBGOAL OF 6)

2 GOAL 2 REDUCE D1-1 ON INITIAL-OBJ          (SUBGOAL OF TOP-GOAL)
```

Fig. 82 (cont.).

```
3 GOAL 7 REDUCE D1-1 ON 4        (SUBGOAL OF 5)

2 GOAL 2 REDUCE D1-1 ON INITIAL-OBJ        (SUBGOAL OF TOP-GOAL)

4 GOAL 11 REDUCE D1-1 ON 5        (SUBGOAL OF 10)

5 GOAL 19 APPLY EMPTY-JUG WITH X = 2, Y = JUG-1, TO 5        (SUBGOAL OF 11)
         SET: X = JUG-2

5 GOAL 20 APPLY CREATE-WATER WITH X = JUG-1, TO 5        (SUBGOAL OF 11)
          OBJECT 6: (JUG-1(SPACE-0 CONTENTS 5 MAXIMUM 5) JUG-2(SPACE 3 CONTENTS 5 MAXIMUM
                    8))

4 GOAL 21 TRANSFORM 6 INTO FINAL-OBJ        (SUBGOAL OF 10)

5 GOAL 22 REDUCE D1-1 ON 6        (SUBGOAL OF 21)

6 GOAL 23 APPLY FILL-JUG WITH Z = 3, X = JUG-1, TO 6        (SUBGOAL OF 22)
          SET: Y = JUG-2
          OBJECT 7: (JUG-1(SPACE 3 CONTENTS 2 MAXIMUM 5) JUG-2(SPACE 0 CONTENTS 8 MAXIMUM
                    8))

5 GOAL 24 TRANSFORM 7 INTO FINAL-OBJ        (SUBGOAL OF 21)

SUCCESS
```

already tried all of the desirable operators. GOAL 14 and GOAL 2 are abandoned because all of the methods for achieving these goals have been exhausted.*

In reattempting GOAL 7, GPS creates GOAL 17 because DESTROY-WATER with X equal to the five-gallon jug decreases the contents of the five-gallon jug. Unfortunately, GOAL 17 leads to an old object, INITIAL-OBJ, and an old GOAL, TOP-GOAL, and again GPS retries unfinished goals.

After fumbling a bit, GPS decides to retry GOAL 11. GOAL 19 is considered infeasible, and GOAL 20 results in OBJECT 6, which has five gallons in both jugs. After filling the eight-gallon jug with the five-gallon jug (GOAL 23), GPS notices that it has solved the problem (GOAL 24).

DISCUSSION

Often in specifying a water-jug task the jug that is to contain the desired quantity of water is not given. The task of producing two gallons in either jug can be specified by reformulating the FINAL-OBJ in Fig. 81 as

ONE OF THE TWO-GALLON-TESTS IS TRUE,

where TWO-GALLON-TESTS is

1. THE CONTENTS OF JUG-1 EQUALS 2.

2. THE CONTENTS OF JUG-2 EQUALS 2.

However, the current *object-difference* process is not sophisticated enough to produce a difference when a disjunctive set of TESTs (indicated by TRUE) is not satisfied. There is no conceptual difficulty in generalizing the *object-difference* process. But the difference produced should be the easiest difference, because satisfying any TEST will do.

An alternative for the FINAL-OBJ is not to use a DESCRIBED-OBJ, but to use a set of OBJ-SCHEMAs, each of which represents a particular final configuration. To do this we would have to have a method (which we do not have) that would transform an INITIAL-OBJ into a set. GPS does have the converse method, TRANSFORM-SET-METHOD, which

---

* All goals that were selected to be tried will be printed. Some of these goals are never really attempted because all of the methods have been tried to exhaustion.

goes from a set to a single FINAL-OBJ; and it does have the analogous method for operators, FORM-OPR-TO-SET-METHOD. There would be no difficulty in adding the desired method, except that we have agreed to hold the methods constant.

The use of differences in this task seems to be a rather ineffective means of guiding the problem solving. None of the APPLY goals generate subgoals. If a difference is detected in applying an operator, it is always as difficult as the difference which the application of the operator is supposed to reduce, because all of the types of difference are considered equally difficult (see DIFF-ORDERING). In such cases, GPS rejects the variable specification produced by the feasibility-selection process for MOVE-OPERATORs. A better set of types of difference and a better ordering on them might improve GPS's performance on this task. However, even if GPS could use more sophisticated types of difference (than FEATURE), it is unclear what types of difference would improve the problem solving. GPS might need some additional problem-solving mechanisms, e.g., planning, in order to be more proficient at the task.

LETTER SERIES COMPLETION

The task of Letter Series Completion, which is found in aptitude tests, is that of adding the next few letters to a series of letters. Several computer programs for solving this task (and similar tasks) have been constructed (Pivar and Finkelstein, 1964; Simon and Kotovsky, 1963; Williams, 1966). A simple example of this task is as follows:

$$B \; C \; B \; D \; B \; E \; \_ \; \_$$

The two blanks indicate that the next two letters of the series must be supplied. The answer to this task is that the next two letters are B and F, respectively. This answer is based on the hypothesis that all odd letters of the series are B's and the even letters of the series are in the order of their occurrence in the English alphabet.

In general, the next few letters of a series are derived from some general description of the series. However, there are many different series whose first several letters are those given in the task. For example another continuation of the above sequence is:

$$B \; C \; B \; D \; B \; E \; B \; C \; B \; D \; B \; E \; B \; C \ldots$$

But the correct answer is to be based on the "simplest" description of the series. No satisfactory general formulation of simplicity exists, of course. This matters little to the use of such problems in an aptitude test, where simplicity is understood to rest on ferreting out the underlying structure of the series that makes it redundant.[*]

WILLIAMS' FORMULATION OF THE TASK

Donald Williams has designed a program (Williams, 1966) that does aptitude test problems, among which is the Letter Series Completion task. The formulation of this task for GPS was adapted from his formulation. Williams' program is aimed at doing many different types of aptitude-test problem; however, we are concerned only with how it handles the Letter Series Completion task.

The program knows certain *relations* among the letters of an alphabet. Listed in the order of their simplicity, the relations used by the program are as follows (the examples are taken from the English alphabet):

same	e.g., *B* is the same as *B*;
next	e.g., *C* is the next letter after *B*;
next after next	e.g., *D* is the next after next letter after *B*;
predecessor	e.g., *A* is the predecessor of *B*.

In attempting to find a description of a letter series, the program assigns relations between pairs of letters in the series. Thus, it might decide that the *first letter is the same as the fifth*. We need a term to refer to a relation with its pair of operands, and will use the term *relationship*. Thus, the relation *same* can enter into a number of relationships.

The simplicity of a relationship is determined mainly by the simplicity of its relation. If two relationships have identical relations, the simpler one is the one whose operands are separated by fewer letters in the series. For example, in the series above, the relationship *the first letter is the same as the third letter* is simpler than the

---

[*] Note that our second extension above was generated by a rule—simply iterate the sequence as given—that is clearly inappropriate, even though it is universally applicable and extremely simple to state and use.

relationship *the first letter is the same as the fifth letter;* but the latter is simpler than the relationship *the next letter of the alphabet follows the first letter of the series.*

The program discovers a relationship by scanning the series from left to right. It always attempts to find a relationship between the *current letter* and a letter to the right of the *current letter.* The *current letter* is initially the first letter in the series, and upon assigning a relationship between the *current letter* and another letter, the other letter becomes the new *current letter.* Thus, the scan does not necessarily move uniformly through the series, but jumps ahead as it successfully establishes relationships among letters that are not necessarily adjacent in the series.

The remainder of the techniques used by Williams' program on this task will be illustrated by an example rather than described generally. In attempting to solve the above example (using the English alphabet), the program begins by looking for the simplest relationship between the *current letter* (first letter) and some other letter. According to the program's definition of simplicity, it assigns the relationship *the first letter is the same as the third letter* and looks for the simplest relationship between the new *current letter* (third letter) and some letter to the right of it. It then assigns the relationship *the third letter is the same as the fifth letter.*

At this point, it notices that both relationships assigned are equivalent; i.e., the relation is *same* in both and there is one letter between both first and third and fifth. Consequently, it checks to see whether the fifth letter, which is the *current letter,* is the *same* as the seventh letter. Since the seventh letter is a blank, it assigns *B* to be the seventh letter and assigns the relationship *the seventh is the same as the fifth.*

In checking whether the ninth letter is the *same* as the seventh, it notices that there is no ninth letter and assigns the second letter to be the new *current letter* because it is the first letter not previously used in a relationship. The simplest relationship—*the fourth letter in the series is the next of the alphabet after the second letter in the series*— is assigned, and the *current letter* becomes the fourth letter. Again the simplest relationship—*the sixth letter is next after the fourth letter*—is assigned. Since the last two relationships are the same, the program checks to see whether the eighth is the *next* after the sixth. Since the eighth letter is a blank, *F* is assigned to be the eighth letter of the series and the problem is solved.

The way Williams' program approaches this problem might seem strange because it assigns relationships until it stumbles across the answer.* Never does it hypothesize a complete description of the entire series (e.g., the odd letters are *B*'s; the even letters are in sequence in the alphabet), and check to see whether the description correctly describes the letters given.† Nevertheless, the program is quite proficient at the Letter Series Completion task.

GPS FORMULATION

The transcription of the task

$$B \; C \; B \; D \; B \; E \; \underline{\quad} \; \underline{\quad}$$

into the external representation of GPS, given in Fig. 83, is considerably less direct than the other tasks we have discussed. The main reason is that the objects are not different letter series, but are partial descriptions of letter series. That is, an object is a series together with relationships on the various letters in the series.

Each node of an OBJECT-SCHEMA represents a position in a series. The TOP-NODE represents the first position of the series; the node ONE (the new name of FIRST) from the TOP-NODE represents the second position in the series; the node TWO from the TOP-NODE represents the third position in series, etc. Each node except the last has precisely one branch leading from it to the node representing the following position in the series. The value of the ATTRIBUTE "LETTER" of a node is the letter in the position of the series represented by the node. Figure 84 illustrates the tree-structure representation of the INITIAL-OBJ—the series to be completed. In Fig. 84, α and β are variables, created by a special routine that converts INITIAL-OBJ in Fig. 83 into the tree structure in Fig. 84. Each blank must be replaced by a distinct variable, else GPS would consider that they all stand for the same letter.

A relationship on a pair of letters in a series is represented by the ATTRIBUTE "RELATION"‡ at the node representing the leftmost letter of the pair. The relation (e.g., *same*) is the value of RELATION. The other letter of the relationship is designated by the value of the ATTRIBUTE "INTERVAL." For example, the respective values SAME

---

* It does not always assign the correct relationships, and in such cases finds it necessary to go back and try different relationships.

† Such a technique is used in Simon and Kotovsky (1963).

‡ "RELATION" is used as an ATTRIBUTE in this task and should not be confused with the RELATIONs of GPS, e.g., EQUALS and CONSTRAINED-MEMBER.

```
RENAME    (

    ONE  =  FIRST

    TWO  =  FIRST-FIRST

    THREE  =  FIRST-FIRST-FIRST

       )

DECLARE   (

    DESIRED-OBJ  =  DESCRIBED-OBJ

    APPLY-CURRENT-RELATION  =  MOVE-OPERATOR

    APPLY-LAST  =  MOVE-OPERATOR

    APPLY-RELATION  =  MOVE-OPERATOR

    CURRENT-RELATION  =  ATTRIBUTE

    INTERVAL  =  ATTRIBUTE

    LETTER  =  ATTRIBUTE

    RELATION  =  ATTRIBUTE

    D1  =  FEATURE

    D2  =  FEATURE

    QUOTE-Y  =  FEATURE

    INTERVALS  =  SET

    RELATIONS  =  SET

          )

  LIST   (

     INITIAL-OBJ  =  (  B  C  B  D  B  E  -  -  )

          )

TASK-STRUCTURES    (

    TOP-GOAL  =  (  TRANSFORM  THE  INITIAL-OBJ  INTO  THE  DESIRED-OBJ  ;  )

    DESIRED-OBJ  =  (  SUBEXPRESSION-TESTS

                   1.  A  RELATION  IS  DEFINED  ;
```

Fig. 83. Specification for GPS of the Letter Series Completion task.

```
              2. THE CURRENT-RELATION IS UNDEFINED .   )
APPLY-RELATION = ( CREATION-OPERATOR

                  VAR-DOMAIN

                  1. Y IS IN-THE-SET OF INTERVALS .

                  2. X IS IN-THE-SET OF RELATIONS .

                  PRETESTS

                  1. THE LETTER OF Y EQUALS THE FUNCTION X OF THE LETTER .

                  MOVES

                  1. COPY X AT THE RELATION .

                  2. COPY X AT THE CURRENT-RELATION OF Y .

                  3.  COPY QUOTE-Y IN THE INTERVAL OF Y .

                  4.  COPY QUOTE-Y IN THE INTERVAL .

                      )

APPLY-CURRENT-RELATION = ( CREATION-OPERATOR

                          VAR-DOMAIN

                          1. X EQUALS THE CURRENT-RELATION  .

                          2. Y EQUALS THE INTERVAL .

                          PRETESTS

                          1. THE LETTER OF Y EQUALS THE FUNCTION X OF THE

                             LETTER .

                          MOVES

                          1. COPY THE CURRENT-RELATION AT THE RELATION .

                          2. MOVE THE CURRENT-RELATION TO THE

                             CURRENT-RELATION OF Y .

                          3. COPY QUOTE-Y IN THE INTERVAL OF Y .

                      )

APPLY-LAST = ( CREATION-OPERATOR
```

Fig. 83 (cont.).

```
                    VAR-DOMAIN
                    1. Y EQUALS THE INTERVAL .
                    PRETESTS
                    1. THE LETTER OF Y IS JNDEFINED .
                    MOVES
                    1. REMOVE THE CURRENT-RELATION .
                    2. COPY LAST AT THE RELATION .        )
        INTERVALS = ( ONE TWO THREE )
        RELATIONS = ( SAME NEXT  )
        DIFF-ORDERING = ( D1 D2 )
        D1 = ( CURRENT-RELATION )
        D2 = ( RELATION )
        TABLE-OF-CONNECTIONS = ( 1. ( D1 APPLY-CURRENT-RELATION APPLY-LAST )
                                 2. ( D2 APPLY-RELATION ) )
        NEXT = ( B C C D D E E F  )
        SAME = ( B B C C D D E E F ⊦  )
        QUOTE-Y = ( QUOTE Y )
        OBJ-ATTRIB = ( LETTER CURRENT-RELATION RELATION INTERVAL )
        LIST-OF-VAR = ( X Y )
            )
END
```

Fig. 83 (cont.).

and TWO of the ATTRIBUTEs "RELATION" and "INTERVAL" at a node represent the relationship that the LETTER at the node is the SAME as the LETTER at the second position to the right.

TOP-GOAL is the statement of the problem. As in Williams' formulation, GPS does not set out to fill in the blanks. Rather, it attempts to assign relationships to the series, filling in the blanks (substituting for the variables) whenever necessary. DESIRED-OBJ requires that all nodes have a value of the ATTRIBUTE "RELATION." Since none of the relationships can involve a blank, this ensures that all of the blanks have been filled.

The ATTRIBUTE "CURRENT-RELATION" of a node indicates that the node represents the *current letter* of the series. The second TEST in

DESIRED-OBJ gives rise to a difference detected at a node that has a value of CURRENT-RELATION. In order to reduce this difference, a RELATION must be added to this node. The use of CURRENT-RELATION in this formulation corresponds to the fact that the *current letter* is always one of the letters in a relationship assigned by Williams' program.

There are three operators, each of which assigns a relationship. APPLY-RELATION is used to assign the simplest relationship. It as-

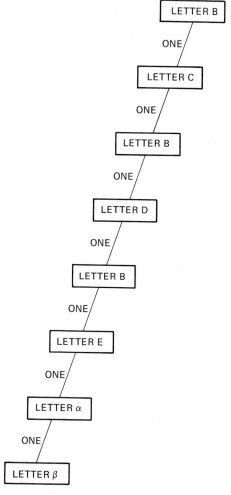

Fig. 84. Tree-structure representation of INITIAL-OBJ in Fig. 83 (α and β are variables).

sumes that the *current letter* is the point of application. X is the relation of the relationship being assigned. Y is the distance between the letters of the relationship. For example, if Y is ONE, the two letters are adjacent; if Y is TWO, one letter separates them, etc.

PRETESTS of APPLY-RELATION requires that the pair of letters satisfy the relation X. For example, if X is SAME and Y is TWO, PRETESTS will be satisfied in applying APPLY-RELATION to the TOP-NODE of INITIAL-OBJ because the first and third letters of the series are both B's.

The first and fourth TRANSFORMATIONs of APPLY-RELATION assign a relationship to an OBJECT-SCHEMA. They add the attribute–value pairs RELATION X and INTERVAL Y to the node at which APPLY-RELATION is applied. The other two TRANSFORMATIONs serve the purpose of marking the new *current letter* and noting the relationship assigned by the operator at the new *current letter*.

APPLY-CURRENT-RELATION applies the previously assigned relationship at the *current letter* marked by the ATTRIBUTE "CURRENT-RELATION." This operator is the same as APPLY-RELATION, except that the legitimate values of the variable are more restricted, and that the node to which it is applied must have a value of the ATTRIBUTE "CURRENT-RELATION." X and Y must have the values of the AT-TRIBUTEs "CURRENT-RELATION" and "INTERVAL," respectively.

APPLY-LAST is used to handle the case when the letter that should be a distance Y from the *current letter* does not exist, e.g., the ninth letter in INITIAL-OBJ. LAST is copied at the RELATION of the *current letter* to indicate that it has been considered. CURRENT-RELATION is removed so that the node at which the operator is being applied will no longer be considered the *current letter*.

DIFF-ORDERING ranks D1, which refers to the value of CURRENT-RELATION, as the more important type of difference. It is detected only at a node that has a value of CURRENT-RELATION, and since such a node corresponds to Williams' *current letter*, the next operator must be applied at that node.

TABLE-OF-CONNECTIONS lists APPLY-CURRENT-RELATION and APPLY-LAST as desirable for reducing D1, because they affect CUR-RENT-RELATION. Even though they also affect RELATION, they are not considered desirable for reducing D2, which pertains to RELATION, because a goal of reducing D2 is generated only when the OBJECT-SCHEMA does not contain a CURRENT-RELATION.

NEXT is a list of pairs of letters. The first letter of each pair is a letter of the alphabet, the second is the following letter of the alphabet. It is used in the PRETESTS of APPLY-RELATION and APPLY-CURRENT-

RELATION (a possible value of X) as a FUNCTION of one argument. For a particular value, α, of the argument, the value of the function is the second letter of the pair whose first letter is α. For example, NEXT of C is D. SAME has the same role as NEXT. It is a list of pairs of letters in which both letters in each pair are the same.

In some of the TRANSFORMATIONs of the operators, QUOTE-Y is an argument of an OPERATION. The value of the QUOTE-Y is always Y, e.g., ONE or TWO. Since Y is used as a LOC-PROG, normally the value of the argument Y is the node of an OBJECT-SCHEMA to which Y refers instead of the LOC-PROG itself. Thus, QUOTE-Y had to be used instead of Y.

OBJ-ATTRIB is a list of all the ATTRIBUTEs for this task, and LIST-OF-VAR is a list of the variables that appear in Fig. 83.

BEHAVIOR OF GPS

Figure 85 shows the behavior of GPS on the task in Fig. 83. In attempting TOP-GOAL, GPS notices that none of the nodes of INITIAL-OBJ has a RELATION and creates GOAL 2 to reduce this difference at the TOP-NODE (which corresponds to the leftmost letter). To achieve GOAL 2, GPS attempts to apply APPLY-RELATION with none of its variables specified (GOAL 3) because, regardless of their values, the operator is considered to be desirable.

GOAL 3 results in OBJECT 4, which has been assigned the relationship *the first letter is the same as the third letter*. There is a special print routine for the OBJECT-SCHEMAs of this task. The positions in the series (nodes in the OBJECT-SCHEMAs) are separated by commas and no LOC-PROGs appear in the printout of an OBJECT-SCHEMA. The TOP-NODE (leftmost position of the series) of OBJECT 4 has three attribute–value pairs:

LETTER   B;

RELATION   SAME;

INTERVAL   TWO.

This asserts the relationship that the second letter to the right is also a *B*. Henceforth, nodes of OBJECT SCHEMAs will be referred to by their corresponding position in the series.

In OBJECT 4 the third position of the series, the only position other than the first that has an ATTRIBUTE other than LETTER, has the attribute–value pairs

Fig. 85. Performance of GPS on the Letter Series Completion task.

```
1  TOP-GOAL TRANSFORM INITIAL-OBJ INTO DESIRED-OBJ        (SUBGOAL OF NONE)

2  GOAL 2 REDUCE D2 ON INITIAL-OBJ          (SUBGOAL OF TOP-GOAL)

3  GOAL 3 APPLY APPLY-RELATION TO INITIAL-OBJ          (SUBGOAL OF 2)
          SET: Y = TWO, X = SAME
          OBJECT 4: (LETTER B RELATION SAME INTERVAL TWO, LETTER C, LETTER B CURRENT-RELATION
                     SAME INTERVAL TWO, LETTER D, LETTER B, LETTER E, LETTER -, LETTER -)

2  GOAL 4 TRANSFORM 4 INTO DESIRED-OBJ          (SUBGOAL OF TOP-GOAL)

3  GOAL 5 REDUCE D1 ON ONE ONE 4          (SUBGOAL OF 4)

4  GOAL 6 APPLY APPLY-CURRENT-RELATION TO ONE ONE 4          (SUBGOAL OF 5)
          SET: X = SAME, Y = TWO
          OBJECT 5: (LETTER B RELATION SAME INTERVAL TWO, LETTER C, LETTER B RELATION SAME
                     INTERVAL TWO, LETTER D, LETTER B CURRENT-RELATION SAME INTERVAL TWO,
                     LETTER E, LETTER -, LETTER -)

3  GOAL 7 TRANSFORM 5 INTO DESIRED-OBJ          (SUBGOAL OF 4)

4  GOAL 8 REDUCE D1 ON ONE ONE ONE 5          (SUBGOAL OF 7)

5  GOAL 9 APPLY APPLY-CURRENT-RELATION TO ONE ONE ONE ONE 5          (SUBGOAL OF 8)
          SET: X = SAME, Y = TWO
          OBJECT 6: (LETTER B RELATION SAME INTERVAL TWO, LETTER C, LETTER B RELATION SAME
                     INTERVAL TWO, LETTER D, LETTER B RELATION SAME INTERVAL TWO, LETTER E
                     , LETTER B CURRENT-RELATION SAME INTERVAL TWO, LETTER -)

4  GOAL 10 TRANSFORM 6 INTO DESIRED-OBJ          (SUBGOAL OF 7)

5  GOAL 11 REDUCE D1 ON ONE ONE ONE ONE ONE 6          (SUBGOAL OF 10)
```

Fig. 85 (cont.).

```
6 GOAL 12 APPLY APPLY-CURRENT-RELATION TO ONE ONE ONE ONE ONE ONE 6       (SUBGOAL OF 11)
     SET: X = SAME, Y = TWO

6 GOAL 13 APPLY APPLY-LAST TO ONE ONE ONE ONE ONE ONE 6      (SUBGOAL OF 11)
     SET: Y = TWO
     OBJECT 7: (LETTER B RELATION SAME INTERVAL TWO, LETTER C, LETTER E RELATION SAME
               INTERVAL TWO, LETTER D, LETTER B RELATION SAME INTERVAL TWO, LETTER E
               , LETTER B RELATION LAST INTERVAL TWO, LETTER -)

5 GOAL 14 TRANSFORM 7 INTO DESIRED-OBJ      (SUBGOAL OF 10)

6 GOAL 15 REDUCE D2 ON ONE 7      (SUBGOAL OF 14)

7 GOAL 16 APPLY APPLY-RELATION IO ONE 7       (SUBGOAL OF 15)
     SLT: Y = TWO, X = NEXT
     OBJECT 8: (LETTER B RELATION SAME INTERVAL TWO, LETTER C RELATION NEXT INTERVAL
               TWO, LETTER D CURRENT-RELATION NEXT
               INTERVAL TWO, LETTER B RELATION SAME INTERVAL TWO, LETTER E, LETTER B
               RELATION LAST INTERVAL TWO, LETTER -)

6 GOAL 17 TRANSFORM 8 INTO DESIRED-OBJ      (SUBGOAL OF 14)

7 GOAL 18 REDUCE D1 ON ONE ONE ONE X      (SUBGOAL OF 17)

9 GOAL 19 APPLY APPLY-CURRENT-RELATION TO ONE ONE ONE ONE 8       (SUBGOAL OF 18)
     SET: X = NEXT, Y = TWO
     OBJECT 9: (LETTER B RELATION SAME INTERVAL TWO, LETTER C RELATION NEXT INTERVAL
               TWO, LETTER B RELATION SAME INTERVAL TWO, LETTER D RELATION NEXT INTERVAL
               TWO, LETTER B RELATION SAME INTERVAL TWO, LETTER E CURRENT-RELATION NEXT
               INTERVAL TWO, LETTER B RELATION LAST INTERVAL TWO, LETTER -)

7 GOAL 20 TRANSFORM 9 INTO DESIRED-OBJ      (SUBGOAL OF 17)
```

Fig. 85 (cont.).

8 GOAL 21 REDUCE D1 ON ONE ONE ONE ONE ONE 9   (SUBGOAL OF 20)

9 GOAL 22 APPLY APPLY-CURRENT-RELATION TO ONE ONE ONE ONE ONE 9   (SUBGOAL OF 21)
    SET: X = NEXT, Y = TWO
    OBJECT 10: (LETTER B RELATION SAME INTERVAL TWO, LETTER C RELATION NEXT INTERVAL
        TWO, LETTER B RELATION SAME INTERVAL TWO, LETTER D RELATION NEXT INTERVAL
        TWO, LETTER B RELATION SAME INTERVAL TWO, LETTER E RELATION NEXT INTERVAL
        TWO, LETTER B RELATION LAST INTERVAL TWO, LETTER F CURRENT-RELATION
        NEXT INTERVAL TWO)

8 GOAL 23 TRANSFORM 10 INTO DESIRED-OBJ   (SUBGOAL OF 20)

9 GOAL 24 REDUCE D1 ON ONE ONE ONE ONE ONE 10   (SUBGOAL OF 23)

10 GOAL 25 APPLY APPLY-CURRENT-RELATION TO ONE ONE ONE ONE ONE 10   (SUBGOAL OF 24)
    SET: X = NEXT, Y = TWO

10 GOAL 26 APPLY APPLY-LAST TO ONE ONE ONE ONE ONE ONE 10   (SUBGOAL OF 24)
    SET: Y = TWO
    OBJECT 11: (LETTER B RELATION SAME INTERVAL TWO, LETTER C RELATION NEXT INTERVAL
        TWO, LETTER B RELATION SAME INTERVAL TWO, LETTER D RELATION NEXT INTERVAL
        TWO, LETTER B RELATION SAME INTERVAL TWO, LETTER E RELATION NEXT INTERVAL
        TWO, LETTER B RELATION LAST INTERVAL TWO, LETTER F RELATION LAST INTERVAL
        TWO)

9 GOAL 27 TRANSFORM 11 INTO DESIRED-OBJ   (SUBGOAL OF 23)

SUCCESS

LETTER   B;

CURRENT-RELATION   SAME;

INTERVAL   TWO.

This indicates that the third position in OBJECT 4 corresponds to the *current letter* and that the previously assigned relationship is *the current letter is the same as the second letter to the right of it.*

In attempting GOAL 4, GPS notices that SAME is the CURRENT-RELATION of the third position. To remove this attribute–value pair (GOAL 5), APPLY-CURRENT-RELATION is applied to the third position in OBJECT 4 (GOAL 6). Note that ONE indicates one place to the right; e.g., ONE ONE 4 in GOAL 5, and GOAL 6 refers to two places to the right of the first position, which is the third position. OBJECT 5 is produced by assigning the relationship *the third letter is the same as the fifth letter.*

B is substituted for the first blank in order to achieve GOAL 9, and *F* is substituted for the second blank in achieving GOAL 22. The result of GOAL 26 is a complete description of the series, and the success of GOAL 27 indicates that TOP-GOAL is successful.

DISCUSSION

The formulation of the task in Fig. 83 has several peculiarities. The definition of simplicity of a relationship is buried in the VAR-DOMAIN of APPLY-RELATION. Since the MOVE-OPERATOR-METHOD tries legitimate variable specifications in the order in which they turn up, they must turn up in the correct order if the simplest relationship is to be assigned first. Thus, if the order of the two TESTS in VAR-DOMAIN were changed, the simplest relationship would not necessarily be assigned by an application of APPLY-RELATION. For example, GOAL 3 would assign the relationship *the second letter is the NEXT after the first letter.*

The communication between operators seems rather strange. An application of APPLY-RELATION in some sense designates to which position GPS will attempt to apply the next operator and that it will be either APPLY-CURRENT-RELATION or APPLY-LAST. These peculiarities are both derived from making GPS find the simplest description of the series. DESIRED-OBJ indicates that any complete description of the series is sufficient, and the simplicity of the description results from the order in which operators are applied.

Another peculiarity is replacing the goal of filling in the blank with the goal of finding a complete description of the series. Since there must be some restrictions on how the series is completed (else any answer would be correct), the latter goal seems to be a reasonable way of stating the problem.

The purpose of posing this task to GPS is not basically to illustrate how the Letter Series Completion task can be formalized. This has been done more elegantly and efficiently in the work already cited. However, the performance of GPS in Fig. 85 does illustrate how this task can be approached by searching for a suitable description of the series in a space of descriptions. In this respect, the formulation of this task is similar to the GPS-like formulation of the Binary Choice task in Feldman *et al.* (1963) (discussed on p. 28), where the space searched was a space of hypotheses.

CHAPTER VII

SUMMARY AND DISCUSSION

The presentation of the material is now complete. We have formulated a problem of generality for problem-solving programs, which we investigated by getting GPS to perform a number of different tasks. By the nature of the study, the major lessons have emerged during the attempts to extend GPS to these additional tasks. It remains only to discuss the case from a more general view and to tie together some loose ends. However, we have presented much detail—undoubtedly, we have told many readers more than they wish to know. In consequence, some of the shape of the study may well have been lost. It might be useful to begin with a brief recapitulation of the whole story.

RECAPITULATION

THE APPROACH

HEURISTIC SEARCH. This research approaches the construction of a general problem solver by way of a general paradigm of problem solving: heuristic search (Newell and Ernst, 1965). In simplified form the heuristic-search paradigm posits objects and operators, where an operator can be applied to an object to produce either a new object or a signal that indicates inapplicability. A heuristic-search problem has the following formulation:

Given: an initial situation represented as an object;

a desired situation represented as an object;

a set of operators;

Find: a sequence of operators that will transform the initial situation into the desired situation.

The first operator of the solution sequence is applied to the initial situation, the other operators are applied to the result of the application of the preceding operators, and the result of the application of the last operator in the sequence is the desired situation.

The operators are rules for generating objects, and thus define a tree of objects. Each node of the tree represents an object, and each branch of a node represents the application of an operator to the object at the node. The branch leads to the node that represents the object produced by the application of the operator. A method for solving a heuristic-search problem is searching the tree, defined by the initial situation and the operators, for a path to the desired situation.

Even though we know of no obvious heuristic-search formulation for many problems, heuristic search derives its appeal from its generality, which has been empirically demonstrated by its wide use in other research efforts in problem solving (discussed in Chapter II).

PROBLEMS OF GENERALITY.   The power of a problem solver is indicated by the effectiveness of its problem-solving techniques, while its generality is indicated by the domain of problems it can deal with. Generality and power are not independent, for both depend strongly upon the internal representation. The internal representation is pulled in two directions. On the one hand, it must be general enough so that problems can be translated into it. On the other hand, it must be specific enough so that the problem-solving techniques can be applied. Thus, there are many different problems of generality, one for each set of problem-solving techniques, and the difficulty of achieving generality depends upon the variety and complexity of the techniques.

This research investigates a particular problem of generality: that of extending the generality of GPS while maintaining its power—i.e., its techniques—at a fixed level. This involves extending the internal representation of GPS in such a way that its problem-solving methods remain applicable, while the domain of problems translatable into its internal representation is broadened. Thus, this research is concerned mainly with representational issues. Different issues would arise in generalizing the internal representation of a problem solver that employed markedly different techniques than those of GPS. In this respect, the research has the nature of a case study.

GPS

GPS attempts to solve problems by tree search, as does any heuristic-search program. But to guide the search, GPS employs a general technique called *means–ends analysis*—selecting the means to be used with a view towards the end to be reached. Means–ends analysis is accomplished by taking differences between what is given and what is wanted, e.g., between two objects, or between an object and the class of objects to which an operator can be applied. A difference designates some undesirable feature of an object. GPS uses the difference to select a desirable operator—one that is relevant to reducing the difference. For example, in attempting the original problem, GPS detects a difference, if one exists, between the initial situation and the desired situation. Assuming that a relevant operator exists and that it can be applied to the initial situation, GPS applies it and produces a new object. GPS rephrases the original problem by replacing the initial situation with the new object and then repeats the process. The problem is solved when an object is generated that is identical to the desired situation.

The problem-solving techniques of GPS are embodied in a set of *methods*, which are applied by a *problem-solving executive*. To solve a problem, the problem-solving executive selects a relevant method and applies it. Subproblems (goals) may be generated by the method in an attempt to simplify the problem. In such cases the main problem may be abandoned temporarily by the problem-solving executive for the purpose of solving the subproblem. Subproblems are attempted in the same way as the main problem: by selecting a relevant method.

Chapter III describes the problem-solving executive and the methods. For this summary we are interested only in the demands that the problem-solving methods of GPS place on the internal representation. Each of these demands, listed below, requires that GPS abstract certain information from the internal representation. The process by which this is done may be different for different represen tations, but the information abstracted does not depend on the representation. Thus, these demands provide the boundary conditions of our *particular problem of generality.*

OBJECT COMPARISON. GPS must be able to compare two objects to determine whether they represent the same situation.

OBJECT DIFFERENCE. If two objects do not represent the same situation, GPS must be able to detect differences between them that summarize their dissimilarity.

OPERATOR APPLICATION. GPS must be able to apply an operator to an object. The result of this process is either an object or a signal that the application is not feasible.

OPERATOR DIFFERENCE. If it is infeasible to apply an operator to an object, GPS must be able to produce differences that summarize why the application is infeasible.

DESIRABILITY SELECTION. For any difference GPS must be able to select from all operators of a task those operators that are relevant to reducing the difference. (Of course, this selection need not be perfect.)

FEASIBILITY SELECTION. For any object GPS must be able to select from all the operators those that will be applicable to the object. This is meant to cover the case where the internal representation permits several operators of limited range to be combined in a single operator of wider range, such that the application of the unified operator does not decompose simply to the sequential application of the two suboperators. (Again, *feasibility selection* need not be perfect.)

CANONIZATION. GPS must be able to find the canonical names of certain types of data structure. Canonization arises from GPS's strategy for comparing two data structures. If they have canonical names, they are equivalent only if they have the same name. On the other hand, if two data structures do not have canonical names, they are equivalent only if they are equivalent in their structure and content.

INTERNAL REPRESENTATION OF GPS-2-5

The current version of GPS (i.e., GPS-2-6) was developed by modifying an earlier version, GPS-2-5. GPS-2-5, together with its predecessors, solved only three kinds of problem, being limited mainly by inadequate facilities for representing tasks. The internal representation of a task for GPS (any version) consists of several different kinds of data structure:

objects	TABLE-OF-CONNECTIONS
operators	DIFF-ORDERING
differences	COMPARE-OBJECTS
goals	declarations

Chapter IV described the above types of data structure, setting forth how they are given in specifying a problem. Here, we shall only review the representation of objects and operators, since these provide the main representational issues. Differences are the only other data structure whose representation in GPS is not the same as in GPS-2-5. Their representation depends to a large extent on the representation of objects and operators. We give below the representation used in GPS-2-5. The modifications constituting the current GPS are given in the next section in connection with the representational issues that gave rise to them.

OBJECTS. In GPS-2-5, objects were represented by tree structures encoded in IPL description lists. Each node of a tree structure can have an arbitrary number of branches leading from it to other nodes. In addition to branches, each node can have a local description consisting of an arbitrary number of attribute–value pairs. The tree structure in Fig. 86 for example, represents the initial situation in the Missionaries and Cannibals task. The node to which the LEFT branch leads represents the left bank of the river, and the node to which the RIGHT branch leads represents the right bank. The local description at the node to which the LEFT branch leads indicates that three missionaries, three cannibals, and the boat are at the LEFT.

The use of variables in a tree structure allows a class of objects to be represented as a single data structure, called a *schema*. For example, Fig. 87 is the *schema* representing $\int e^u \, du$, where u is a variable. This *schema* represents a large class of objects, all having the same form but different values for u. GPS assumes that all three struc-

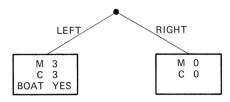

Fig. 86. Tree-structure representation of the initial situation in the Missionaries and Cannibals task.

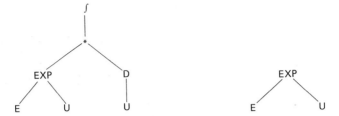

Fig. 87. Tree structure representation of $\int e^u\, du$.

Fig. 88. Tree structure representation of e^u.

tures may contain variables and it is prepared to process them as classes of objects.

OPERATORS. In GPS-2-5, an operator was represented by giving schemas for its input and output objects. (They were called form operators.) Assuming that u is a variable, Fig. 87 is the *schema* of the input of the operator $\int e^u\, du = e^u$, and Fig. 88 is the *schema* of the output. Such an operator can be applied only to a member of the class of objects represented by the input *schema*.

REPRESENTATIONAL ISSUES

The representational issues that were investigated arose from various properties of tasks that could not be dealt with adequately by GPS-2-5. For some tasks the difficulty was removed by generalizing the representation. The issues arising from other tasks could not be handled within the framework of the existing program.

DESIRED SITUATION. In many tasks the desired situation is a class of objects that could not be represented in GPS-2-5. In integration, for example, the desired situation is any expression that does not contain $\int$. A *schema* cannot represent this class of objects because all of the members do not have the same form. For this reason the representation of the desired situation had to be generalized.

In introducing a new representation for the desired situation, some new processes are required to abstract information from the representation; a new *object-comparison* process, so that GPS can compare an object to the desired situation; and a new *object-difference* process, so that GPS can detect differences between an object and the desired situation. *Object comparison* and *object difference* are the only demands (see pp. 91–92) of GPS's problem-solving method that are affected by the introduction of a new representation for the desired situation.

The generalization of the desired situation consists of a set of constraints, called a DESCRIBED-OBJ. A set of constraints represents a class of objects; namely, those objects that satisfy all of the constraints. The desired object in the Integration task can be represented by the single constraint:

No symbol in the expression is an $\int$.

Each constraint in a DESCRIBED-OBJ is a data structure, called a TEST, that consists of a RELATION and several arguments (in most cases, two). In the previous example,

> the RELATION is NOT-EQUAL;
>
> the first argument is a symbol;
>
> the second argument is $\int$.

This constraint is quantified "for all" symbols. GPS can recognize NOT-EQUAL as a RELATION it understands (currently GPS understands fifteen RELATIONs). On the other hand, GPS understands only the generic form of the arguments, which are task dependent.

OPERATORS. The operators of many tasks, particularly mathematical calculi, could be represented conveniently in GPS-2-5. However, the operators of other tasks, e.g., the Missionaries and Cannibals, could not. To alleviate this difficulty a new representation of operators was added, called MOVE-OPERATORs. A MOVE-OPERATOR consists of a group of TESTs and a group of TRANSFORMATIONs. The TESTs, which are the same as the TESTs in a DESCRIBED-OBJ, must be satisfied in order for the operator to be applicable, and the TRANSFORMATIONs indicate how the resultant object differs from the input object.

A TRANSFORMATION is a data structure that consists of an OPERATION and several arguments. GPS knows the semantics of the OPERATIONs, but as in TESTs, only knows the generic form of the arguments, which are task dependent. Currently, GPS understands six OPERATIONs. A typical TRANSFORMATION (from the Missionaries and Cannibals operator that moves X missionaries, Y cannibals, and the BOAT from LEFT to RIGHT) is

> DECREASE the number of missionaries at the
> LEFT by X and increase the number of missionaries
> at the RIGHT by X.

In this TRANSFORMATION the OPERATION is DECREASE and the arguments are X, the number of missionaries at the LEFT, and the missionaries at the RIGHT.

The introduction of MOVE-OPERATORs in GPS required the addition of new processes so that the problem-solving methods could be applied to this new representation. New processes were needed for *operator application, operator difference, desirability selection*, and *feasibility selection*. The MOVE-OPERATOR representation was designed to make these processes possible.

A key feature of the MOVE-OPERATOR representation is its transparent structure. Each of the new processes analyzes this structure in order to extract the necessary information. Another desirable property of a MOVE-OPERATOR is its structural similarity to DESCRIBED-OBJ. This similarity causes the MOVE-OPERATOR processes to be similar to the DESCRIBED-OBJ processes, and thus all of these processes use the same basic subroutines. For example, the *operator-difference* process for MOVE-OPERATORs and the *object-difference* process for DESCRIBED-OBJ are nearly identical.

UNORDERED SETS. Some tasks require the representation of unordered sets. Multiplication, for example, can be represented as an *n*-ary function of a set of arguments whose order is irrelevant. An unordered set can be represented in GPS-2-5 as an object representing an ordered set, together with an operator for permuting the elements of the set. This representation has the drawback that discovering the identity of two sets requires several applications of the permutation operators. The permutation operator would be unnecessary if the identity test could take into consideration implicitly the fact that the two sets are unordered.

The objects of GPS were generalized to represent unordered sets by permitting the nodes to be tagged either ordered or unordered. Although it seems simple, this generalization complicates considerably the *object-comparison, object-difference, operator-application, operator-difference,* and *canonization* processes. These processes were generalized for the Integration task so that the nodes of objects and operators could be unordered. Although the generalized processes were more complex and less efficient, there was a saving in total effort because of an overall reduction in the problem space.

The main complication of unordered sets is the necessity for discovering which pairs of elements should be placed in correspondence. Few difficulties arise if the elements are structures consisting wholly of constants. But if variables occur, multiple possibilities for correspondence can exist. To see the identity of two unordered sets may require finding a particular pattern of correspondences. Chapter V discusses this matter in more detail and describes how the generalized processes (*object comparison*, etc.) deal with the problem.

LARGE OBJECTS. Memory limits permit GPS to solve only simple problems. However, for some tasks the objects are so large that not even simple problems can be solved before its memory is exhausted. For example, straightforward representation of a chess board in GPS requires a thousand memory locations, so that very few objects can be stored in memory.

There are two distinct difficulties with GPS's use of memory: first, GPS saves in memory all objects generated during problem solving; second, each object is an independent representation of a total situation, i.e., there is no provision for dealing with fragments of situations. These difficulties, especially the second, appeared to require changes too extensive to be dealt with in this research.

DIFFERENCES. In generalizing GPS, the representation of differences was degraded. Each difference in GPS can pertain only to the value of one attribute of one node of an object. More global differences, such as the total number of occurrences of a symbol in an object, which could be represented in GPS-2-5, cannot be represented in the present GPS. They would introduce considerable complexity in the *operator-difference, object-difference,* and *desirability selection* processes. Thus, the generalization of these processes for MOVE-OPERATORs and DESCRIBED-OBJs was accomplished by simplifying the representation of differences.

Differences, although not part of the heuristic-search paradigm, are central to means–ends analysis, which is the main technique of GPS. Many tasks were not given to GPS because their simple differences would not guide adequately GPS's search for a solution. For example, many of the logic tasks solved by GPS-2-5 cannot be solved by GPS because of the lack of direction provided by the simplified differences. However, the representation of differences was adequate for the eleven tasks that were given to GPS.

TASKS

The various modifications described in Chapter V and summarized above permit GPS to perform a considerable range of tasks. Chapter VI contains the demonstration of this, where each task is described and discussed in detail. Here we will make only a remark or two about each.

MISSIONARIES AND CANNIBALS. GPS and one of its predecessors, GPS-2-2, both solved the Missionaries and Cannibals task.
The representation of the task in GPS was quite different from that
in GPS-2-2. The latter contained information about the operators
that the current GPS discovers for itself. GPS-2-2 was given ten operators, one for each of the different travel situations, along with information about the desirability of each for reducing the various types of
difference. GPS is given only a single operator, which moves X missionaries and Y cannibals across the river. In applying this operator
GPS specifies the variables (X, Y, and the direction of the boat) so
that the operator will perform a desirable function.

GPS-2-2 was given a desirability filter for operators that prevented
it from attempting to move more missionaries and cannibals across
the river than there were on the side from which they were being
moved. Such a separate filter is unnecessary in GPS, because GPS
never considers applying such an infeasible operator.

INTEGRATION. In the Integration task, multiplication and
addition are represented as n-ary functions of an unordered set of
arguments. Thus the commutativity and associativity of multiplication
and addition are expressed implicitly instead of by explicit operators.
If they are given to GPS as explicit operators, the problem space
would increase, which would prevent GPS from solving some trivial
integrals.

SAINT (Slagle, 1963), a program that is quite proficient at symbolic integration, also represents the commutativity and associativity of multiplication and addition implicitly. Other similarities and
some dissimilarities between SAINT and GPS are discussed in
Chapter VI.

TOWER OF HANOI. The Tower of Hanoi is a task for which
means–ends analysis is very effective. GPS never makes a mistake on
this task, mainly because the differences and the DIFF-ORDERING are
in some sense optimal.

PROVING THEOREMS IN THE PREDICATE CALCULUS. GPS
proved a simple theorem in the first-order predicate calculus. The formulation of this problem is basically the same as that in Robinson
(1965). In fact, the natural correspondence between the Resolution
Principle and the match routine in GPS (and in LT before it) is sufficiently close to reveal that predicate calculus theorem provers have
followed an evolution from brute-force search (Gilmore, 1960) back
toward the mechanisms that were incorporated in the earliest heuristic problem solvers. [Match routines similar in function to those in

LT and GPS exist in SAINT (Slagle, 1963) and in the geometry program (Gelernter, 1959).]

FATHER AND SONS.   The Father and Sons task is very similar to the Missionaries and Cannibals task. Both involve moving two different kinds of people across a river in a small boat. The constraints are somewhat different, leading to different operators. In consequence, the Father and Sons task was specified independently of the Missionaries and Cannibals task.

MONKEY TASK.   The Monkey task was formulated by McCarthy (1963) as a typical (though very simple) problem for the Advice Taker (McCarthy, 1959). GPS's formulation of this task may be contrasted with the formulation for a typical Advice Taker program (Black, 1964). In GPS the objects are models of room configurations whereas the objects in Black's program are linguistic expressions that describe certain aspects of the room configurations.

THREE COINS.   The peculiarity of the Three Coins task lies in the fact that the solution is constrained to a fixed number of operator applications. This constraint was handled in GPS by expanding the object representation to include a counter that indicates how many operator applications were used in producing the object. In the desired situation the counter must have a particular value.

PARSING SENTENCES.   Much research effort has been devoted to constructing efficient parsing algorithms for simple phase-structure grammars. The point of this example in the present work is not GPS's proficiency as a parser, but illustration of the kinship between heuristic search and syntactic analysis.

BRIDGES OF KÖNIGSBERG.   The Bridges of Königsberg is the only impossible task that was given to GPS. Although GPS's behavior is not aimless (it crosses six bridges in two different ways), GPS cannot see the impossibility, because that lies in the topological properties of the bridges. GPS only attempts to cross bridges, having no way of viewing the problem as a whole.

WATER JUG TASK.   For the Water Jug task, means–ends analysis seems to be a rather ineffective heuristic as demonstrated by the fact that GPS stumbled onto the solution. Better (though more complex) differences than the ones provided to GPS do exist.

LETTER SERIES COMPLETION TASK.   The Letter Series Completion task is the only one whose solution requires inductive reasoning. The formulation seems clumsy. However, the example demonstrates how the problem can be approached by searching for a suitable description in a space of descriptions. The Binary Choice task, which also requires inductive reasoning, was formulated in a similar way by Feldman *et al.* (1963),

THE LOGIC OF THE CASE

With the whole case study before us, let us reexamine the framework. We identified three global aspects of the situation: problem-solving power, amount of specification, and generality. These terms, although lacking precise definition, have served to structure the investigation. Thus, one cannot identify a meaningful problem of generality without in some sense holding constant both the problem-solving power and the amount of specification. Otherwise, it would not be possible to tell whether one program were more general than another. We need to examine in retrospect how we handled both of these boundaries to the investigation. The first two parts of this section will be devoted to this examination.

Generality can be measured by performance on a range of tasks. The wider this range, the more general GPS can be considered to be. But this inference needs closer scrutiny. What are the characteristics of the tasks that were actually given to GPS? In particular, should GPS's problem solving be coherent in some sense, to accept it as a general problem solver. We shall examine these two questions as the next two parts of this section. Finally, we need to inquire about the relationship of this study to learning, a concept that is often associated with generality.

HOLDING THE POWER CONSTANT

Lacking a good measure of the power of a problem solver, especially a measure that applies across tasks, we have identified power with the set of methods available for problem solving. This identification is very convenient for GPS, since the program has been organized deliberately as a collection of methods plus a method interpreter. Thus, holding power constant meant holding the methods constant. This was done easily enough in principle, simply by not modifying any part of GPS having to do with the methods. The ban was extended to the problem executive (i.e., the method interpreter) as well, since the executive performs several substantive functions, such as object and goal evaluation.

Actually, we did not keep our promise completely. We made the following two modifications:

TRANSFORM-METHOD   multiple differences lead to multiple
REDUCE GOALs (used in Missionaries and
Cannibals; Bridges of Königsburg);

REDUCE-METHOD   a filter to eliminate undesirable operators
(used in the Parsing task).

The first of these is a rather universal requirement of GPS's problem
solving, which we have used from time to time [e.g., in GPS-2-2
(Newell, 1963)], but did not have in the GPS-2-5 formulation. By the
nature of the match routines and the way differences are defined for
them, more than one difference between expressions is possible
and even likely. The modification provides the simplest scheme for
dealing with this multiplicity: setting up REDUCE GOALs in the order
of difficulty of their differences.

The second modification is a standard way of introducing additional
selectivity into a heuristic-search program. The selectivity of GPS's
search arises mainly from two sources: representing operators and
objects so that match routines can make appropriate "direct" selec-
tions without generating all of the possible operators (or objects);
and using differences to select desirable operators. In addition it may
be possible to test operators for either desirability or feasibility before
they are applied. In LT, for example, a test of similarity between the
theorems and objects was used as a filter before the match (Newell
et al. 1957a). Again, in GPS-2-2 (Newell, 1963) the REDUCE-METHOD
contained preliminary tests for both desirability and feasibility,
although the tests were often left null for particular runs. However,
no such structure was put in GPS-2-5. Our modification was to add a
desirability filter.

The desirability filter was needed for the Parsing task because the
TABLE-OF-CONNECTIONS was too specialized, permitting selection of
operators only on the type of difference, and not on the value. The
Parsing task had only a single difference type, all the information
being carried in the value. MOVE-OPERATORs do provide selection
on difference values, but the Parsing task also contained FORM-OPER-
ATORS, for which the TABLE-OF-CONNECTIONS provided the only
selectivity. It seemed easier to add the filter than to generalize the
TABLE-OF-CONNECTIONS, although the latter certainly would have
been possible.

Thus, although we did modify the methods slightly for particular
tasks, in fact, both modifications were of a general, non-task-specific
nature that should have been part of the original repertoire of GPS-2-5.

A more serious change in the power of GPS was the degradation of the differences. The original versions of GPS used rather elaborate differences (e.g., the number of differing terms). But in order to extend GPS to MOVE-OPERATORs we limited the differences almost completely to FEATUREs; that is, to local differences. One may view this restriction in two ways. First, for tasks where only FEATURE differences are appropriate, the inability of GPS to handle more general differences is of no account: it does not diminish the program's power. At the same time, GPS is simply unable to handle tasks requiring more elaborate differences. Thus, the limitation on differences becomes a limitation of generality, not of power. On the other hand, if some tasks can be done using either FEATURE differences or more elaborate ones, the FEATUREs simply degrading the performance, then one is tempted to view the limitation as one of power, not of generality. Which view is appropriate depends on the nature of the task. For the form of propositional logic used as the first task of the earlier versions of GPS, the limitation turned out to be one of generality. GPS failed to solve even the simple problem of transforming $(Q \vee P) \cdot P$ into $P \cdot (\sim P \supset Q)$. Hence, we eliminated propositional logic from the list of tasks done by GPS. In general we do not understand the behavior of heuristic-search programs well enough to characterize in any general way the effect of degrading the differences.

One side effect of the agreement not to modify the methods was to preclude the extension of GPS to tasks in which some single higher concept was necessary to understand the structuring of the task. Perhaps the best example is games. To play a game, GPS must come to understand that there are two (or more) different players whose interests are opposed, so that sometimes it must analyze from one viewpoint, sometimes from another. This is not difficult to implement with new methods. But we have found no way to implement it within the existing structure. The same modification would enable GPS to behave in an active environment, since the real issue is not the game-like nature of the situation, but rather the existance of many active agents, each of which has to be considered in terms of its own laws of action.*

An analogous situation arises in getting GPS to do concept-formation tasks. The central idea is to work in the space of hypotheses. Thus, the differences that arise in the TRANSFORM-METHOD are not differences between objects—i.e., between the data structures representing hypotheses—but differences in derived behavior—i.e.,

---

* Such a method, of course, does not provide all of the apparatus needed to operate in real time; e.g., it does not have an interrupt capability.

between the predictions from the hypotheses and the facts. A simple modification of the MATCH-METHOD or of the TRANSFORM-METHOD would let GPS handle some of these tasks easily and naturally by giving it direct knowledge of when it is to use indirect differences. Actually, we did manage to get GPS to do one such task—the Series task—by melding the hypothesis and the exemplar into a single object, so that there was no issue of whether to match directly or indirectly.

It is quite clear that these modifications provide real increments to GPS's general knowledge about the world and how to solve problems in it. Thus, they should not be introduced without an awareness of the change they produce in the problem-solving power of GPS. Yet each of them is a relatively trivial change, and one does not feel that any serious modification of GPS has been made by introducing them.

HOLDING THE SPECIFICATION CONSTANT

If one does not control the information given in specifying a problem to a problem solver, then it is easy to construct very general problem solvers. These are simply executive shells that require of the specification that it tell how to solve the problem as well as what the problem is. To avoid such pitfalls it might seem sufficient simply to distinguish the "what" from the "how"—the statement of the problem from the methods used to solve it. But this is not so easily done. For, viewed broadly, the problem specification *is* a set of instructions to the problem solver on how to behave for a given problem, and the problem solver *is* a complex interpreter of these instructions. How else does different behavior arise when the same problem solver is put to work on different problems? Thus, the only distinction between "legitimate" and "illegitimate" specification of behavior for a problem solver is its degree of indirectness.

Our discussion of programming languages as problem solvers was meant to point up this issue. It suggested that no simple criteria could be found that would distinguish programming language from problem solver. The game-playing language of T. Williams (1965), which specifies the rules of a game in a command language, but with no more symbols than those of the "regular" description in a book like Hoyle, provided some supporting evidence.

Since we have no adequate characterization of the amount of specification of a problem, our course has been to provide a standard way of giving the problem. This is the external representation. At least we can discuss after the fact whether the amount and kinds of specification were appropriate. The main question in such a discussion is whether information has been given that seems unnecessary for the communication of the task, thus providing GPS with additional clues about how to solve the problem.

We recall from Chapter IV the list of structures in the internal representation necessary to specify a task, expanding it somewhat to indicate which items were given through the external representation:

Objects
 INITIAL-OBJ,DESIRED-OBJ

Operators
 MOVE-OPERATORs, FORM-OPERATORs

Goals
 TOP-GOAL

Differences

TABLE-OF-CONNECTIONS

DIFF-ORDERING

Match details
 COMP-OBJECTS, BASIC-MATCH, COMP-FEAT-LIST

Declarations
 RENAME, SKIP-WORDS, DECLARE, LIST-OF-VAR, LIST-OF-OPR, OBJ-ATTRIB, FEATUREs, SETs

Immediate operators (given in IPL)

Selection tests (given in IPL)

PROBLEM-SOLVING-EXECUTIVE tests and operators (given in IPL)

For some of the items in this list there is little doubt that they are necessary to the definition of the task. The objects and operators are clearly necessary, as is the TOP-GOAL. In giving these tasks to a human some of these items might be left out—e.g., TOP-GOAL, or some of the operators—but only because they were already understood. In this respect it should be noted that TOP-GOAL was the same for all eleven tasks; namely TRANSFORM THE INITIAL-OBJ INTO THE DESIRED-OBJ, and might have been left out.*

---

* But see Newell *et al.* (1960b) for an example where a REDUCE goal is TOP-GOAL.

Fig. 89. The Nine Dot Puzzle: Draw a connected path consisting of three straight-line segments that passes through all nine dots.

Similarly, the various declarations do not provide problem-solving information, but merely provide the semantics of the terms used in the other task structures. If we had been concerned with giving to GPS the same external representation of the task as is given a human, then we could have suppressed much of the declared information. Besides providing an extensive initial dictionary available in common for all tasks, a certain amount of specialization to the particular task would be necessary. For example, JUGS is a set of JUGs, but in context it must be specialized to be the set consisting of JUG-1 and JUG-2. The types (what is given under DECLARE) of many of the symbols are given implicitly by their use; e.g., differences are FEATUREs, and anything that appears on DIFF-ORDERING is a difference; therefore, anything on DIFF-ORDERING is a FEATURE. To mechanize this would require giving GPS additional general information, and also some modest inference techniques. The style of operation would be very much in the flavor of Raphael's SIR (1964) or Bobrow's STUDENT (1964).

The important point is that such a sophisticated translation process does not aid significantly in the solution of the problem, but serves only to define it. Actually, of course, there is a class of problems that depend for their problematic character on the misdefinition of the situation at the initial stages. A familiar one is the nine-dot puzzle, shown in Fig. 89, where the task is to draw a single line, made up of three straight-line segments, such that it passes through all nine points. The solution is rather straightforward with the right operators; the difficulty for humans apparently arises because they infer that the operators are confined to the space bounded by the dots. Having to give GPS an explicit list of operators or an explicit specialization for the problem in hand removes the possibility of this kind of problem.*

The list of specifications includes several items devoted to the

---

* We do not assert that GPS cannot be given such problems; only that to do so requires that the initial translation stages be handled as a problem domain for GPS, rather than that they be finessed by a special translation routine.

differences and how they are used: the differences themselves, the
TABLE-OF-CONNECTIONS, the DIFF-ORDERING, and a number of
details about the match. All this information is surely not usually
defined explicitly as part of a task. In fact, two main reservations have
been expressed about GPS through the years. One has been that the
DESIRED-OBJ has to be given as a definite object. This restriction has
been relieved to some extent in the present effort by generalizing
DESIRED OBJs to include DESCRIBED OBJs. The second concern has
been the need to provide differences. That so much information about
differences appears in all of the specifications shows that we have
not met this objection. The issue has several parts that are associated
conveniently with the different components of the specification.

Originally GPS had to be given routines for detecting differences,
and this seemed the most serious respect in which GPS was being
told how to solve the problem. Two schemes had been proposed
earlier for having GPS construct its own differences (Newell, 1962b;
Newell *et al.*, 1960b). In the present effort, the introduction of *characteristic lists* as a representation for objects also solves this part of the
problem, although it does so by restricting the differences to be
FEATUREs. Thus differences do not have to be specified for either
MOVE-OPERATORs or DESCRIBED-OBJs.

It does remain necessary to specify the differences to be detected
by the MATCH-METHOD; that is between objects represented as
schemas (which occur in FORM-OPERATORs and OBJECT-SCHEMAs).
This is done by the specification "COMP-OBJECTS = $(\cdots)$," where
the FEATUREs to be detected are listed inside the parentheses. However, it turns out that in all the cases we have actually treated the
specification reads "COMP-OBJECTS = (BASIC-MATCH)." That is to say,
the same FEATUREs are to be detected as in BASIC-MATCH, which is
the match used in the identity test. Thus, in fact, this additional
specification could have been deleted for the eleven tasks actually
tried.

The BASIC-MATCH specification (the list of FEATUREs to be detected
for identity) is somewhat anomalous also. Partly, it reflects the internal
representation which intermixes all attributes at a node, and thus
needs to distinguish those that define the object. However, the list
of FEATUREs could be inferred from an examination of the objects
given in the specification plus the features used by the operators.
Such an analysis would provide a maximal, hence sufficient, set. But
GPS may then be forced to check a number of redundant FEATUREs—
e.g., the state of both sides of the river in the Missionaries and Cannibals task. As it now stands, it would not detect the redundancy.

The TABLE-OF-CONNECTIONS is used to evoke the operators relevant to a difference between two objects or SCHEMAS. For a FORM-OPERATOR, it can be replaced by an analysis of the operator, as was shown earlier (Newell, 1962b), simply by matching the input form to the output form and detecting the differences. A similar analysis can be made for MOVE-OPERATORs; it is nowise different from the analyses already made in the program. However, it did not seem worthwhile to make this modification in GPS, since our attention was directed at the problems of representation.

The final aspect of the difference is the DIFF-ORDERING. No complete schemes have been proposed for having GPS discover the appropriate order of importance for the difference types. It is easy, of course, to imagine an adaptive scheme of the usual kind, in which the order is rearranged with experience. However, such a scheme provides no real insight into the nature of the differences or their order.

In this discussion we have taken for granted that, normally, difference information is not provided explicitly in presenting these tasks to humans. Thus, to provide such information to GPS is to give it additional information about how to solve the problem. Since there is some evidence that humans make use of the same methods as GPS (Newell and Simon, 1961b, 1961c),* one can inquire where they get their information about the differences. Part of the answer is surely that all tasks are imbedded in a web of prior knowledge that is well integrated with the language used to specify tasks. Thus, terms such as *delete, add, exchange,* and *replace* are all parts of the normal vocabulary, available to describe what has to be done to change one situation into another and to describe the effects of operators. General experience with these terms will provide orderings on the differences as well. These orderings may not be completely appropriate, of course, but neither are the orderings that we give GPS through the external representation.

The last three items on the list of specifications were given to GPS as IPL routines, hence were outside the external representation as defined in Chapter IV. The basic reason for not rationalizing these aspects of GPS, thus permitting a meaningful external representation of them, was the expectation that they would not vary over tasks (within the scope of this study). For example, substitution is performed via immediate operators, but is used with all *schemas,* and

---

* The evidence pertains to means–ends analysis generally, not to the individual methods as they are detailed in Chapter III.

so is viewed as part of GPS's basic equipment. Again, variation in the goal and object evaluation routines, which reside in the PROBLEM-SOLVING-EXECUTIVE, was not of interest for this study. However, just as with the methods, we did in fact make some changes in these processes, and they should be reviewed to determine what kind of information was thereby communicated to GPS, i.e., information that would define the problem or help solve it.

GPS can manipulate objects in only two ways: by operators, evoked by goals; and by immediate operators, evoked by the match routine. The peculiarity of the latter is that they are known to be necessary if a match is to succeed. Thus, they can be applied without setting up a goal, since the function of a goal is to provide a remembered choice point for reinitiating search in another direction. The immediate operators are therefore applied in the match routine, in the context in which the difference that evoked them was found. The match is able to continue after the immediate operator has been applied (if successful). Thus, the effect of making an operator an immediate operator is that the search tree is truncated, and a good deal of excess housekeeping (setting up goals, linking them together, etc.) is avoided.

That a given operation is possible in a task is certainly part of the definition of that task, and must be specified to GPS in some fashion. But whether a given operator should be handled in the special style of an immediate operator is not part of the task definition and conveys problem-solving information. This is quite clear in the case of the Integration task and the Predicate Calculus task, where immediate operators were used (although in different ways) to attain commutativity and associativity directly. In fact, much of the point of the Integration task is to observe the necessity of having an unordered match. On the other hand, although the ability to deal with unordered objects was introduced for particular tasks, it is certainly part of the general equipment of a problem solver, just as substitution is.

The only other place where immediate operators are specified for a particular task is in simplifying expressions in the Integration task. It is an important heuristic in dealing with algebraic expressions that they should be kept in a canonical form as defined by certain simplification operations (e.g., $X+0 \to X$, $X \cdot 1 \to X$, etc.). The use of this heuristic is communicated to GPS by making all these operations immediate operators (tied to appropriate differences that detect them). Actually, part of the reduction to canonical form (the "flattening" of expressions, such as $X+(Y+Z) \to X+Y+Z$) is achieved by processing the total expression after it has been produced, rather than by applying immediate operators. This is equivalent to rewriting each main operator as a sequence of two operators, e.g., INTEGRATE, SIMPLIFY. In fact, we implemented it by augmenting the NEW-OBJECT path of the PROBLEM-SOLVING-EXECUTIVE (see Fig. 13). This was the one modification of the PROBLEM-SOLVING-EXECUTIVE that occurred in the eleven tasks.

The criterion used by a SELECT goal was given to GPS (as an IPL structure) for each task in which it was appropriate. One criterion, NEW-OBJECT, was used in three tasks: Missionaries and Cannibals, Fathers and Sons, and the Water Jug task. The others were unique to a single task: SIMILARITY, for Integration; and SMALLEST, LIT-SIGN, and NO-LIT for the Predicate Calculus task. NEW-OBJECT could well be part of GPS's general store of knowledge; but the other criteria convey information about how to solve a specific task. The issues here are similar to those with the differences, where one feels that GPS should either develop such heuristic information on its own in analyzing a particular task or have it as part of a general experience with prior tasks. Unlike the situation with differences, very little exploration of selection criteria has been done in working with GPS. Consequently, there exist no proposals for how GPS might obtain its own selection criteria.

We have now reviewed the variety of information given GPS in specifying a task. Besides the information necessary for the definition of a task, there are several items that indicate how to solve the problem: information about differences, about which operators should be immediate, and about selection criteria. Although some of this information represents general abilities that should be part of GPS, independent of task, a substantial amount is still specific to a task. Throughout this discussion on specification we have allowed ourselves to substitute the question of minimum specification for the question of holding the specification constant. The latter is what we need in order to be assured that an apparent generalization of a problem solver is not simply a series of unique problem solvers, each separately programmed via the problem specifications. On this score the study seems in reasonable shape, since the same information is given in all tasks (and also in the tasks for GPS-2-5). The important exception, the handling of unordered sets, is not only one of our deliberate modifications, but also one that should become parts of GPS's basic abilities. In the long run the question of minimization is the more fascinating, and it would be worthwhile to assess the current state of GPS in this respect. However, further analysis of this depends on trying to assess the contributions to problem-solving power of the various pieces of information that GPS uses. This is beyond the bounds of the present effort.

THE CLASS OF TASKS

The eleven tasks were meant to sample the variety of tasks that GPS is capable of doing. They were chosen with a view both to feasibility and diversity—but certainly nonsystematically. Good taxonomies of tasks do not yet exist. Still, it is clear that our tasks have much in common and that certain obvious kinds of task are not represented among them.

More important, the tasks all seem quite formal—mathematical problems and puzzles. They share this characteristic with most of the other tasks handled by heuristic-search programs. Though this would seem to be a major restriction, there are at least two cautions about treating it as such. First, when completely understood, all symbolic systems look formal, since they can consist only of arrangements of symbols and their manipulation. Thus, when one comes to understand a task from the point of view of symbol manipulation (as in GPS), then it will seem quite formal—more so than if it were simply overheard being given by one human to another.

The second caution relates to the additional mechanism required to input completely naturalistic, hence informal, versions of these tasks. Here, the STUDENT program of Bobrow (1964) provides an appropriate benchmark, for we do not usually view algebra word problems as examples of formal problems—indeed, their whole educational point is to provide instances of informal problems to be formalized. On the one hand the mechanisms of STUDENT are quite modest, consisting basically of a pattern-match capability and a number of rules written within this for interpreting the input sentences. On the other hand, STUDENT does not handle problems just as they come from textbooks on ninth-grade algebra. Substantial restrictions were placed on the freedom of the prose, and it remains unclear how much additional mechanism is required to handle the raw prose (which is still quite simple compared with the full range of English).

Many kinds of task simply are missing from the set of eleven. Among the more obvious are tasks that involve the extended use of arithmetic, tasks that involve a large data base, tasks that require taking into account other active agents, and tasks that require expertise. (Even where some expertise is normally assumed, as in integration, GPS approaches the task like a novice with a table of integrals.) Thus, GPS still extends only over a very restricted domain.

On the other hand, the inclusion of several tasks not of the classic game-playing or theorem-proving type must be taken as positive evidence of diversity. The Parsing task, the Series Completion task, and (however trivial its substance) the Monkey task all show breadth.

Unified Problem Solving

One possible model of a problem solver is a large collection of disjoint methods, connected by a single diagnostic routine that examines the problem, determines its type, and ships it off to the appropriate method. This can be called the "Big Switch" model of generality. It lies behind the idea discussed earlier of considering ALGOL plus a subroutine library to be a problem solver. To some extent general problem solvers must partake of the character of the Big Switch; for this is in part what is meant by specialization. Nevertheless, if the tendency is extreme—e.g., a unique method per problem—and the diagnostic routine sufficiently superficial—e.g., on the name of the problem—then the system seems not a general problem solver at all, but simply a collection of special problem solvers hidden in a single black box. Thus, the way parts of GPS operate conjointly on the different tasks provides a supplemental view of the generality of GPS.

The issue can be examined by looking at how the subparts of the problem solver are used in the tasks. In our case the obvious subpart to consider is the method. Figure 90 shows which methods were used in each of the eleven tasks. We see that each task uses some of the methods, but not all; on the average each uses about half. Thus, on this evidence, GPS was indeed a single problem solver, and not just a collection of special-purpose problem solvers.

There are some disadvantages to using the method as the unit of comparison. Some of the methods employ much of the same code. For example, both the MOVE-OPERATOR-METHOD and the MATCH-DIFF-METHOD use a common large subroutine that applies a TEST to an OBJECT-SCHEMA. In addition, considerable detail disappears at the method level. Since the methods themselves are conditional, not all of the subparts of a method need be used in any given task.

In Fig. 90 the methods are categorized according to the basic processes (described in Fig. 36) that they perform. There are additional basic processes that GPS performs that are not in the list of basic functions because they were already completely task indepen-

Basic Processes	Methods	Missionaries and Cannibals	Integration	Tower of Hanoi	Predicate Calculus	Father and Sons	Monkey	Three Coins	Water Jug	Bridges of Königsberg	Parsing	Letter Series
Object comparison, Object difference	TRANSFORM-METHOD	X	X	X	X	X	X	X	X	X	X	X
	MATCH-DIFF-METHOD	X	X	X	X	X	X	X	X	X	X	X
Operator application, Operator difference, Feasibility selection	MATCH-DIFF-METHOD		X		Y						X	
	MOVE-OPERATOR-METHOD	X		X		X	X	Y	X	X	X	Y
	FORM-OPERATOR-METHOD		X		Y						X	
	FORM-OPERATOR-TO-SET-METHOD											
	TWO-INPUT-OPERATOR-METHOD				Y							
	SET-OPERATOR-METHOD			X								
Desirability selection	REDUCE-METHOD	X	X	X	X	X	X	X	X	X	X	X
Canonization	IDENTITY-MATCH-METHOD	X	X	X	X	X	X	X	X	X	X	X
Other processes	TRANSFORM-SET-METHOD	X				X	X		X			
	SELECT-BEST-MEMBERS-METHOD	X	X			X	X		X			
	GENERATE-AND-TEST-METHOD											
	EXPANDED-TRANSFORM-METHOD	X					X		X			
	ANTECEDENT-GOAL-METHOD	X				X	X		X	X	X	
	TRY-OLD-GOALS-METHOD								X			

Fig. 90. Methods and processes used by GPS in solving the eleven tasks. X denotes that the method and basic processes were used in solving the task; Y that the method and basic processes, except for *operator difference*, were used.

dent. The basic process for selecting a member from a SET (the methods for achieving a SELECT goal) are independent of the representation (although the criterion is not). Other basic processes depend only on the goal structures of GPS. For example, GPS has processes for generating new things to do when it gets into trouble (e.g., generating an unfinished goal). All of these processes contribute to the common part of GPS that is used on all tasks.

Since the X's and Y's in Fig. 90 are scattered somewhat randomly, the methods do not appear to be specialized by task. However, much of the code in GPS is specialized by kinds of representation. This can be seen in the figure by noting what methods for applying an operator are used on the various tasks. In fact, two methods—FORM-OPERATOR-TO-SET-METHOD and GENERATE-AND-TEST-METHOD—are not used on any of the tasks, because they are specialized to a particular aspect of the representation that does not arise in these tasks. (They were used for logic in GPS-2-5.) However, specialization by representation is not the same as specialization by task, as demonstrated by the Parsing task, which uses both the FORM-OPERATOR-METHOD and the MOVE-OPERATOR-METHOD.

All of the basic processes (described in Fig. 36) except *operator difference* are used in attempting each of the eleven tasks, which shows that means–ends analysis is applicable to all of the tasks. (Note, however, that its efficacy varied widely: compare the Tower of Hanoi and the Water Jug tasks.) *Operator difference* does not occur in tasks that are so simple that GPS finds a solution before attempting to apply an operator that is initially inapplicable. Similarly, the TRY-OLD-GOALS-METHOD is used on solving the Water Jug task, because that is the only task in which GPS is hard pressed for something to do.

LEARNING VERSUS PERFORMANCE

Recall that in the beginning we distinguished three approaches to generality according to what aspect of a crude model of a problem solver we focused on: the external representation, the internal representation, or the problem-solving techniques. We did not consider an approach to generality through learning—that is, through the processes for becoming capable of performing tasks, even though initially not capable. However, one segment of the artificial intelligence field has taken learning as the point of primary concern, sometimes under the label of *learning machines*, sometimes of *self-organizing systems*.

There is little doubt that learning mechanisms will play a substantial role in the achievement of generality. The present effort on GPS, representing a concern with performance programs, can be viewed as expressing a tactical decision on where prior concern should be placed. Although there is little need to argue such preferences, it is worthwhile in analyzing the logic of this GPS case study to set out clearly the relationship of performance to learning.

Given a system X, the process of learning is to transform it into a new system X', whose performance capabilities are enhanced. Thus learning is to be viewed as a transformation on performance programs. The two boundaries of the learning situation are first, the set of performance programs within which the learning transformations operate; and second, the information available about the task environment in terms of which to make appropriate transformations.

To take Samuel's early checker program (1959) as a well-known example, the space of checker programs corresponds to the space of evaluation polynomials. To each such polynomial, constructed from a fixed pool of features with arbitrary weights, there corresponds a checker program. All the other features of the program remain constant. The information that is available is a record of past play in terms of moves made and the final outcome. Samuel describes a rather sophisticated hill-climbing scheme in which this information is used to converge on a good polynomial—i.e., to transform the initial checker player into a better one.*

Before turning to work on a learning mechanism, it is of some importance to determine whether the proposed space of programs is appropriate. It might be thought that the space could be expanded at will, and thus would not be a real constraint. However, a moment's consideration will show that this is no more possible than playing chess by examining all continuations to the end. Every increase in size of the space of programs implies an increase in the selectivity of the learning mechanisms if successful learning is to occur. Thus, in fact we find that almost all the actual learning and self-organizing systems reported on in the literature have extremely simple spaces of performance programs associated with them.

From this viewpoint the work on GPS is to be viewed as an attempt to discover an appropriate shape for a performance program if it is to be capable of being general. Given that one felt a version of GPS to be suitable, one would still need to embed it in a class of such programs. That is, one would need to make various aspects variable, so that learning mechanisms could select variants that performed well. So far, only the differences have attracted any attention as possibilities for learning (Newell, 1962b; Newell et al., 1960b). Neither the methods nor the translation into internal representation have been considered, although their relevance to learning for generality is evident.

---

* Actually, Samuel has developed several learning schemes involving different features of the program, different information about performance, and different learning schemes. Thus, matters are not quite as simple as stated [e.g., Samuel (1967)].

CONCLUDING REMARKS—THE CENTRAL LESSON RESTATED

We have reviewed the course of the case study and examined its logical foundations. It remains to summarize the central lesson that has come out of this study.

We have described a problem solver as a collection of methods. Each method makes a set of demands for information: if it can get the appropriate information it can operate; if not, then it cannot be used (even in the former case, it may fail, of course). A problem solver can be general, within this view, in two (nonexclusive) ways. It can work on both problem X and problem Y because it has one method proper to X and another method proper to Y and can evoke them appropriately. In the limit this leads to the Big Switch problem solver. Alternatively, it can have methods that apply to both the X and Y. This is unified problem solving.

If the same method is to be applied to several tasks, then the same kind of information (that demanded by the method) must be extracted from each of the tasks. The internal representation is the middle term between the methods and the tasks. It is defined with a view toward the methods, such that, if a task is expressible in the internal representation, the methods can always extract the information they need. Only when this condition is fulfilled do we talk about the structure as being "in" the internal representation.

The internal representation is generated also with an eye toward the tasks. In fact, each modification of the internal structure of GPS was triggered by some requirement of a particular task. DESCRIBED-OBJECTS were required by Integration; MOVE-OPERATORS were required by Missionaries and Cannibals. However, each augmentation of the internal representation increases in generality beyond the specific task that evoked it. Both MOVE-OPERATORS and DESCRIBED-OBJECTs for desired objects were used in many other tasks. Indeed, one could view the eleven example tasks as demonstrations that a modification has a reach beyond the single task that caused it.

We chose for this study a particular approach—extending an existing program centered about the method of heuristic search. Thus we accepted a number of boundary conditions: no translation from the naturally occurring external representation of a problem; no extension of the methods; and no tasks that could not be handled via heuristic search (actually via the means–ends analysis, characteristic of GPS).

Many of these boundaries could be pushed back, just for the effort of doing so. Thus, nothing in the present GPS is incompatible with an input-translation schema, say of the order of Bobrow's STUDENT. In fact, an examination of the mechanisms used there will show that nothing much new is needed. The power of STUDENT comes from matching input schemas to the external representation, something the GPS match could be adapted to do. The limitation on the methods was strictly self-imposed, and the method language would permit some relatively straightforward extensions. Whether additional problem-solving techniques could be added that significantly extend heuristic search and means–ends analysis is unexplored territory. Thus the technique boundary seems somewhat less fluid. The extensions of method that do seem plausible are those fitting the gross structure of a new class of tasks, such as game playing.

These extensions of GPS would undoubtedly add to both the appearance and the substance of its generality. However, it does not seem to us that they should necessarily be undertaken. As we remarked in the preface, GPS in its various versions has been doing duty as a vehicle for the study of problem solving, both artificial and human, since 1957. Thus, what should be extracted from GPS at this stage are the lessons of generality that have been put forward in the present work, and not the existing code as a kernel to receive further programming accretions.

THE VOCABULARY OF GPS EXTERNAL REPRESENTATION

1. META-WORDS

The following words are instructions to the process that translates the external representation into internal representation on how to interpret the text:

DECLARE   Sets the mode of the translator to DECLARE so that it will designate words to be a particular type of symbol or data structure.

END   Signifies the end of a task description.

LIST   Sets the mode of translation to LIST so that the words following it are translated as data structures consisting of strings of symbols to be converted into the internal representation after translation.

RENAME | Sets the mode of the translator to RENAME so that it can assign new names to the words in the basic vocabulary of GPS.

SKIP-WORDS | Sets the mode of the translator to SKIP-WORDS so that it will designate the words following it to be ignored.

TASK-STRUCTURES | Sets the mode of translator so that it will interpret the words following it as data structures.

, | In the LIST mode of translation is a text word. In the other modes, it marks the end of a group of words.

. | Marks the end of a group of words.

(| Marks the beginning of a group of words.

) | Marks the end of a group of words.

2. TEXT WORDS

The following words comprise that part of the basic vocabulary of GPS used in the representation of tasks. GPS understands each of these words; i.e., each corresponds to an IPL symbol that appears in some of the subroutines of GPS.

AMOUNT | Indicates that following it is the third argument, required by some OPERATIONs, of a TRANSFORMATION.

APPLY | Is the type of the GOAL of applying an operator to an object.

ATTRIBUTE | Is the type assigned to words that are attributes of nodes of OBJECT-SCHEMAs.

COMMON-DIFFERENCE | Stands for all types of difference.

COMP-FEAT-LIST | Is the list of difference types used

by the match. It occurs only in COMPARE-OBJECTS.

COMPARE-OBJECTS Is a parameter to the process that matches two objects.

CONSTRAINED-MEMBER Is a RELATION on three arguments. It requires that its third argument, which must be a TEST, be true and that its first argument be in the set designated by its second argument.

CONSTRAINT Precedes the third argument of a TEST whose RELATION is CONSTRAINED-MEMBER.

COPY Is the OPERATION that places a copy of its first argument at the FEATURE that is its second argument.

CREATION-OPERATOR Is the kind of MOVE-OPERATOR that creates new resultant objects.

DECREASE Is the OPERATION that decrements its first argument by its third argument and increments its second argument by its third argument. The first and second arguments must be FEATUREs, and the third argument follows AMOUNT.

DEFINED Is the RELATION that requires its first argument to have a value other than UNDEFINED. It has only one argument.

DESCRIBED-OBJ Is the type of object that is represented by a group of TESTs.

DIFF-ORDERING Orders the types of difference according to their relative difficulty.

EQUALS Is the RELATION that requires its two arguments to designate the same value.

EXCLUSIVE-MEMBER Is the RELATION that requires its

first argument to be a unique member of the SET designated by its second argument.

EXPRES   Is the type of data structure that is an arithmetic expression.

FEATURE   Is the type of data structure that designates a feature of an object.

FIRST   Is the LOC-PROG that designates the first subnode of the implied node of an OBJECT-SCHEMA.

FIRST-FIRST   Is the LOC-PROG that designates the FIRST node of the FIRST node of the implied node of an OBJECT-SCHEMA.

FIRST-FIRST-FIRST   Is the LOC-PROG that designates the FIRST node of the FIRST node of the FIRST node of the implied node of an OBJECT-SCHEMA.

FIRST-SECOND   Is the LOC-PROG that designates the SECOND node of the FIRST node of the implied node of an OBJECT-SCHEMA.

FOR-ALL   Signifies that the TEST in which it occurs contains a universally quantified variable. The quantified variable follows FOR-ALL, and the SET of values of the variables follows the variable.

FORM-OPERATOR   Is the type of operator that consists of an input form, which is an OBJECT-SCHEMA, and an output form, which is an OBJECT-SCHEMA.

FUNCTION   Indicates that following it is the name of a function.

GREATER-THAN   Is the RELATION that requires its first argument to be greater than its second argument.

INCREASE Is the OPERATION that increases the value of its second argument by the amount of its first argument.

IN-THE-SET Is the RELATION that requires its first argument to be in the SET designated by its second argument.

LESS-THAN Is the RELATION that requires its first argument to be less than its second argument.

LIST-OF-OPR Is a list of the FORM-OPERATORs in the task specification.

LIST-OF-VAR Is a list of the variables in the task specification.

LOC-PROG Is the type of the data structure that designates nodes of OBJECT-SCHEMAs relative to other nodes.

MOVE Is the OPERATION that removes the value of its first argument and makes it the value of its second argument. Both arguments must be FEATUREs.

MOVE-FUNCTION Is the OPERATION that removes the value of its first argument and makes the value of its second argument equal to a function of its first argument. The function follows FUNCTION.

MOVE-OPERATOR Is the type of operator that consists of several groups of TESTS and a group of TRANSFORMATIONs.

MOVES Signifies that a group of TRANSFORMATIONs will follow.

N-ARY-CONNECTIVE Is a type of symbol. Any node (of an OBJECT-SCHEMA) that has this type of symbol as the value of an ATTRIBUTE has more than one subnode. This information is used by the routines that convert objects and operators into their internal representation.

NOT-A-CONSTRAINED-MEMBER Is the RELATION that is the negation of CONSTRAINED-MEMBER.

NOT-AN-EXCLUSIVE-MEMBER Is the RELATION that is the negation of EXCLUSIVE-MEMBER.

NOT-EQUAL Is the RELATION that is the negation of EQUALS.

NOT-GREATER-THAN Is the RELATION that is the negation of GREATER-THAN.

NOT-IN-THE-SET Is the RELATION that is the negation of IN-THE-SET.

NOT-LESS-THAN Is the RELATION that is the negation of LESS-THAN.

OBJ-ATTRIBUTE Is a list of all the words that are ATTRIBUTEs.

OBJECT-SCHEMA Is the type of an object that is represented as a tree structure. OBJECT-SCHEMAs can contain variables, in which case they represent a class of objects.

OPERATION Is the type of symbol that designates the function of a TRANSFORMATION.

PARTICULAR Precedes the name of the node to which the FEATURE (in which it occurs) is applied. PARTICULAR always occurs within the scope of a FEATURE that is not a function of the implied node.

POST-TESTS Signifies that the group of TESTs that follow it must be satisfied by the resultant object. This word occurs only in a MOVE-OPERATOR.

PRETESTS Signifies that following it is the group of TESTs that represents the class of objects to which the operator can be applied. This word occurs only in a MOVE-OPERATOR.

QUOTE Indicates that the word following it stands for itself.

REDUCE Is the type of the GOAL of reducing a difference on an object.

REMOVE Is the OPERATION that deletes the value of its first argument. It has only one argument.

RELATION Is the type of symbol that designates the function of a TEST.

SELECT Is the type of the GOAL of selecting an element of a SET.

SET Is the type of data structure that is a set of items.

SET-SIZE Is a type of difference that is produced by the commutative match used in the Integration task. SET-SIZE is not a FEATURE.

SECOND Is the LOC-PROG that designates the second subnode of the implied node of an OBJECT-SCHEMA.

SECOND-FIRST Is the LOC-PROG that designates the FIRST node of the SECOND node of the implied node of an OBJECT-SCHEMA.

SECOND-SECOND Is the LOC-PROG that designates the SECOND node of the SECOND node of the implied node of an OBJECT-SCHEMA.

SIGN Is an ATTRIBUTE of the Integration task and the Predicate Calculus task. The routine that converts objects and operators into their internal representation knows the meaning of SIGN.

SUBEXPRESSIONS   Designates that the match should detect differences at all nodes of OBJECT-SCHEMAs. It occurs only in COMPARE-OBJECTS.

SUBEXPRESSION-TESTS   Signifies that the set of TESTs that follows it must be true of every node of an OBJECT-SCHEMA. It occurs only in a DESCRIBED-OBJ.

SYMBOL   Is an ATTRIBUTE of the Integration task and the Predicate Calculus task. The routine that converts objects and operators into their internal representation knows the meaning of SYMBOL.

TABLE-OF-CONNECTIONS   Associates with each type of difference the desirable operators.

TEST   Is the type of data structure consisting of a RELATION and its arguments.

THIRD   Is the LOC-PROG that designates the third subnode of the implied node of an OBJECT-SCHEMA.

TOP-GOAL   Is a statement of the problem.

TOP-NODE   Is the LOC-PROG that designates the implied node of an OBJECT-SCHEMA.

TRANSFORM   Is the type of the GOAL of transforming one object into another.

TRANSFORMATION   Is the type of data structure consisting of an OPERATION and its arguments.

TRUE   Is a RELATION on a single argument. A TEST whose RELATION is TRUE is satisfied if one or more of the TESTs in the argument, which must be a set of TESTs, is satisfied.

UNARY-CONNECTIVE   Is a type of symbol. Any node (of an OBJECT-SCHEMA) that has this type of symbol as the value of an ATTRIBUTE has one subnode. This information is used by the routines that convert objects and operators into their internal representation.

UNDEFINED Is the RELATION that requires that its first argument have the value UNDEFINED. It has only one argument. UNDEFINED can also be the value of either a FEATURE, an ATTRIBUTE, or a LOC-PROG.

VAR-DOMAIN Indicates that following it is a group of TESTs that must be satisfied in order for the variables to have legitimate values. It occurs only in MOVE-OPERATORS.

V-TESTS Is the type of a group of TESTs that follows TRUE.

YIELDS Separates the input form and the output form of a FORM-OPERATOR.

\+ Is an arithmetic operator that appears in EXPRESS.

, In the LIST mode of translation is the text-word that separates the OBJECT SCHEMAS in a SET of OBJECT-SCHEMAS, and separates the input forms in a FORM-OPERATOR that has two objects as an input. In the other modes of translation, it is processed as a meta-word.

− Is the value of the ATTRIBUTE "SIGN." The routine that converts the operators and objects of certain tasks into their internal representation knows this.

3. SKIP WORDS

The following words are ignored by the translator unless otherwise specified:

A	DO	ON	2.
ADD	DOES	ONE	3.
ALL	FOR	ONES	4.
AN	FROM	OR	5.
AND	IN	SHOULD	6.
ANY	INTO	THAN	7.
ARE	IS	THAT	8.
AT	IT	THE	9.
BE	NOT	-----	10.
BY	OF	1.	

APPENDIX B

THE OPERATORS OF THE
LOGIC TASK

This appendix contains the specification of the one-input operators in the formulation of logic in Fig. 7. They are expressed as FORM-OPERATORs in the first section and as MOVE-OPERATORs in the second. The two input operators of the logic task are not included in this appendix because there is no provision for expressing two-input operators as MOVE-OPERATORs. The names used for the operators in Fig. 7 are also used in this appendix. Some of the operators in Fig. 7 can be expressed only as several FORM-OPERATORs, each of which is assigned a local name, e.g., a, b,.... In Section 2, the MOVE-OPERATORs are assigned the same names. For example, the MOVE-OPERATOR R1: a, b is equivalent to the two FORM-OPERATORs R1: a and R1: b.

1. FORM-OPERATORs

The logical connectives *conjunction, disjunction, implication,* and *negation* are symbolized as ., v, ɪ, and —, respectively.* *A, B, C* and *X* are free variables that stand for propositions.

° The limitations of computer character sets prohibit using ⊃ for implication, ∨ for disjunction, and ~ for negation.

R1: a. $(A \vee B)$ YIELDS $(B \vee A)$
 b. $(A \cdot B)$ YIELDS $(B \cdot A)$

R2: $(A \text{ I } B)$ YIELDS $(- B \text{ I} - A)$

R3: a. $(A \vee A)$ YIELDS A
 b. $(A \cdot A)$ YIELDS A

R4: a. $(A \vee (B \vee C))$ YIELDS $((A \vee B) \vee C)$
 b. $(A \cdot (B \cdot C))$ YIELDS $((A \cdot B) \cdot C)$
 c. $((A \vee B) \vee C)$ YIELDS $(A \vee (B \vee C))$
 d. $((A \cdot B) \cdot C)$ YIELDS $(A \cdot (B \cdot C))$

R5: a. $(A \vee B)$ YIELDS $- (- A \cdot - B)$
 b. $- (- A \cdot - B)$ YIELDS $(A \vee B)$

R6: a. $(A \text{ I } B)$ YIELDS $(- A \vee B)$
 b. $(- A \vee B)$ YIELDS $(A \text{ I } B)$

R7: a. $(A \vee (B \cdot C))$ YIELDS $((A \vee B) \cdot (A \vee C))$
 b. $(A \cdot (B \vee C))$ YIELDS $((A \cdot B) \vee (A \cdot C))$
 c. $((A \vee B) \cdot (A \vee C))$ YIELDS $(A \vee (B \cdot C))$
 d. $((A \cdot B) \vee (A \cdot C))$ YIELDS $(A \cdot (B \vee C))$

R8: a. $(A \cdot B)$ YIELDS A
 b. $(A \cdot B)$ YIELDS B

R9: A YIELDS $(A \vee X)$

2. MOVE-OPERATORs

The notation used in the MOVE-OPERATORs is the same as above, with the exception that PERIOD is used for conjunction because "." is used as punctuation in the specification of MOVE-OPERATORs. Additional information must be given for specifying the logic operators as MOVE-OPERATORs:

a. LEFT and RIGHT are used as the names of the LOC-PROGs FIRST and SECOND, respectively.

b. SYMBOL and SIGN are the ATTRIBUTE of a node of an OBJECT-SCHEMA.

c. $<\vee,.>$ is the set of two elements, V and PERIOD.

d. <v,ɪ> is the set of two elements, v and ɪ.

e. [−+,+−] is the FUNCTION whose value is + if the input is − and
− if the input is +.

f. [vɪ,ɪv] is the FUNCTION whose value is ɪ if the input is v and v if
the input is ɪ.

g. [v.,.v] is the FUNCTION whose value is PERIOD if the input is v
and v if the input is PERIOD.

The MOVE-OPERATOR representation of R1–R9 follows:

R1: a, b. (PRETESTS
    THE SYMBOL IS IN-THE-SET <v,. > .
    MOVES
    1. MOVE THE LEFT TO THE RIGHT .
    2. MOVE THE RIGHT TO THE LEFT .)

R2:   (PRETESTS
    THE SYMBOL EQUALS ɪ .
    MOVES
    1. MOVE THE LEFT TO THE RIGHT .
    2. MOVE THE RIGHT TO THE LEFT .
    3. MOVE-FUNCTION OF THE LEFT SIGN TO THE RIGHT
       SIGN, THE FUNCTION IS [−+,+−] .
    4. MOVE-FUNCTION OF THE RIGHT SIGN TO THE LEFT
       SIGN, THE FUNCTION IS [−+,+−] .)

R3: a, b. (PRETESTS
    THE SYMBOL IS IN-THE-SET <v,. > .
    MOVES
    MOVE THE LEFT TO THE TOP-NODE .)

R4: a, b, (PRETESTS
    1. THE SYMBOL IS IN-THE-SET <v,. > .
    2. THE SYMBOL EQUALS THE RIGHT SYMBOL .
    MOVES
    1. MOVE THE LEFT TO THE LEFT-LEFT .
    2. MOVE THE RIGHT-LEFT TO THE LEFT-RIGHT .
    3. MOVE THE RIGHT-RIGHT TO THE RIGHT .)

c, d. (PRETESTS
    1. THE SYMBOL IS IN-THE-SET <v,. > .
    2. THE SYMBOL EQUALS THE LEFT SYMBOL .
    MOVES

1. MOVE THE LEFT-LEFT TO THE LEFT .
2. MOVE THE LEFT-RIGHT TO THE RIGHT-LEFT .
3. MOVE THE RIGHT TO THE RIGHT-RIGHT .)

R5: a, b. (PRETESTS

    1. THE SYMBOL IS IN-THE-SET $<$ V,. $>$.

    MOVES

    1. MOVE-FUNCTION OF THE SYMBOL TO THE SYMBOL , THE FUNCTION IS [V.,.V] .

    2. MOVE-FUNCTION OF THE SIGN TO THE SIGN , THE FUNCTION IS [−+,+−] .

    3. MOVE-FUNCTION OF THE LEFT SIGN TO THE LEFT SIGN , THE FUNCTION IS [−+,+−] .

    4. MOVE-FUNCTION OF THE RIGHT SIGN TO THE RIGHT SIGN , THE FUNCTION IS [−+,+−] .)

R6: a, b. (PRETESTS

    1. THE SYMBOL IS IN-THE-SET $<$V,I$>$.

    MOVES

    1. MOVE-FUNCTION OF THE SYMBOL TO THE SYMBOL , THE FUNCTION IS [VI,IV] .

    2. MOVE-FUNCTION OF THE LEFT SIGN TO THE LEFT SIGN , THE FUNCTION IS [−+,+−] .)

R7: a, b, (PRETESTS

    1. THE SYMBOL IS AN EXCLUSIVE-MEMBER OF $<$ V,. $>$.

    2. THE RIGHT SYMBOL IS AN EXCLUSIVE-MEMBER OF $<$ V,. $>$.

    MOVES

    1. MOVE THE SYMBOL TO THE LEFT SYMBOL .
    2. MOVE THE RIGHT SYMBOL TO THE SYMBOL .
    3. COPY THE SYMBOL AT THE RIGHT SYMBOL .
    4. MOVE THE LEFT TO LEFT-LEFT .
    5. COPY THE LEFT AT THE RIGHT-LEFT .
    6. MOVE THE RIGHT-LEFT TO THE LEFT-RIGHT .)

    c, d. (PRETESTS

    1. THE SYMBOL IS AN EXCLUSIVE-MEMBER OF $<$ V,. $>$.

    2. THE LEFT SYMBOL IS AN EXCLUSIVE-MEMBER OF $<$ V,. $>$.

    3. THE RIGHT SYMBOL EQUALS THE LEFT SYMBOL .

    4. THE LEFT-LEFT EQUALS THE LEFT-RIGHT .

    MOVES

    1. MOVE THE LEFT SYMBOL TO THE SYMBOL .
    2. MOVE THE SYMBOL TO THE RIGHT SYMBOL .

3. MOVE THE LEFT-LEFT TO THE LEFT .

4. MOVE THE LEFT-RIGHT TO THE RIGHT-LEFT .)

R8:   a. (PRETESTS

THE SYMBOL EQUALS PERIOD .

MOVES

MOVE THE LEFT TO THE TOP-NODE .)

b. (PRETESTS

THE SYMBOL EQUALS PERIOD .

MOVES

MOVE THE RIGHT TO THE TOP-NODE .)

R9:   (MOVES

1. MOVE THE TOP-NODE TO THE LEFT .)

2. COPY V AT THE SYMBOL .

3. COPY X AT THE RIGHT SYMBOL .)

BIBLIOGRAPHY

AMAREL, S. (1962). On the Automatic Formation of a Computer Program Which Represents a Theory, *in* "Self-Organizing Systems" (M. C. Yovits, G. Jacobi and G. Goldstein, eds.), 107–175. Spartan Books, Washington, D. C.

AMAREL, S. (1965). Problem Solving Procedures for Efficient Syntactic Analysis. RCA Laboratories, Princeton, New Jersey.

AMAREL, S. (1968). On Representations of Problems of Reasoning about Actions, *in* "Machine Intelligence 3" (D. Michie, ed.), pp. 131–173. Edinburgh Univ. Press, Edinburgh.

BAYLOR, G. W., and SIMON, H. A. (1966). A Chess Mating Combinations Program, *Proc. Spring Joint Comput. Conf.* **28**, 431–446.

BERNSTEIN, A., *et al.* (1958). A Chess-Playing Program for the IBM 704, *Proc. Western Joint Comput. Conf.*, pp. 157–159.

BLACK, F. (1964). A Deductive Question Answering System, Doctoral dissertation, Harvard University, Cambridge, Massachusetts.

BOBROW, D. G. (1964). Natural Language Input for a Computer Problem Solving System, Doctoral dissertation, M. I. T., Cambridge, Massachusetts.

CHOMSKY, A. N. (1957). "Syntactic Structures." Mouton and Co., The Hague.

CHURCH, A. (1956). "Introduction to Mathematical Logic." Princeton Univ. Press, Princeton, New Jersey.

DAVIS, M. (1958). "Computability and Unsolvability." McGraw-Hill, New York.

DAVIS, M., and PUTNAM, H. (1960). A Computing Procedure for Quantification Theory, *J. Assoc. Comput. Mach.* **7**, 201–215.

ERNST, G. W., and NEWELL, A. (1966). "GPS and Generality." Carnegie Inst. Technol., Pittsburgh, Pennsylvania.

ERNST, G. W., and NEWELL, A. (1967). Some Issues of Representation in a General Problem Solver, *Proc. Spring Joint Comput. Conf.* **30**, 583–600.

FEIGENBAUM, E. A. (1961). The Simulation of Verbal Learning Behavior, *Proc. Western*

Joint Comput. Conf., pp. 121–132 [reprinted in Feigenbaum and Feldman (1963)].

FEIGENBAUM, E. A., and FELDMAN, J., eds. (1963). "Computers and Thought." Mc-Graw-Hill, New York.

FELDMAN, J., TONGE, F., and KANTER, H. (1963). Empirical Explorations of a Hypothesis-Testing Model of Binary Choice Behavior, *in* "Symposium on Simulation Models" (A. C. Hoggott and F. E. Balderston, eds.), pp. 55–100. South-Western Publishing Co., Cincinnati, Ohio.

FILIPIAK, A. S. (1942). "100 Puzzles: How to Make and How to Solve Them," pp. 20–21. A. S. Barnes & Co., New York.

FLOYD, R. W. (1964). The Syntax of Programming Languages—A Survey, *IEEE Trans. Electronic Computers* **13**, 346–353.

FRIEDMAN, J. (1963). A Semidecision Procedure for the Functional Calculus, *J. Assoc. Comput. Mach.* **10**, 1–24.

GELERNTER, H. (1959). Realization of a Geometry-Theorem Proving Machine, *Proc. Internl. Conf. Information Processing*, pp. 273–282. UNESCO House, Paris [reprinted in Feigenbaum and Feldman (1963)].

GILBERT, W. L. (1966). Private communication.

GILMORE, P. C. (1960). A Proof Method for Quantification Theory, *IBM J. Res. Develop.* **4**, 28–35.

GREEN, B. B., WOLF, A. K., CHOMSKY, C., and LAUGHERY, K. (1961). BASEBALL: An Automatic Question Answerer, *Proc. Western Joint Comput. Conf.*, pp. 219–224 [reprinted in Feigenbaum and Feldman (1963)].

GREENBLATT, R. D., EASTLAKE, D. E., and CROCKER, S. D. (1967). The Greenblatt Chess Program, *Proc. Fall Joint Comput. Conf.* **30**, 801–810.

HORMANN, A. (1965). Gaku: an Artificial Student, *Behavioral Science* **10**, 88–107.

KATONA, G. (1940). "Organizing and Memorizing: Studies in the Psychology of Learning and Teaching." Columbia Univ. Press, New York.

KISTER, J., STEIN, P., ULAM, S., WALDEN, W., and WELLS, M. (1957). Experiments in Chess, *J. Assoc. Comput. Mach.* **4**, 174–177.

KOTOK, A. (1962). A Chess Playing Program for the IBM 7090, Bachelor's thesis, M. I. T., Cambridge, Massachusetts.

KRULEE, G. K., and KUCK, D. J. (1964). A Problem Solver with Formal Descriptive Inputs, *in* "Computer and Information Sciences" (J. T. Tou and R. H. Wilcox, eds.), pp. 344–374. Spartan Books, Washington, D. C.

LINDSAY, R. K. (1963). Inferential Memory as the Basis of Machines Which Understand Natural Language, *in* "Computers and Thought," (E. A. Feigenbaum and J. Feldman, eds.), pp. 219–233. McGraw-Hill, New York.

LUCHINS, A. S., and LUCHINS, E. H. (1959). "Rigidity and Behavior: A Variational Approach to the Effect of Einstellung." Univ. of Oregon Books, Eugene, Oregon.

McCARTHY, J. (1959). Programs with Common Sense, *Proc. Symp. Mech. Thought Processes*, pp. 75–84. H. M. Stationery Office, London.

McCARTHY, J. (1963). Situations, Actions, and Causal Laws, Stanford Artificial Intelligence Project Memo No. 2, Stanford University, Palo Alto, California.

McCARTHY, J. (1966). Private communication.

McCARTHY, J. *et al.* (1963). "LISP 1.5 Programmers Manual." M. I. T. Press, Cambridge, Massachusetts.

MOORE, O. K., and ANDERSON, S. B. (1954). Modern Logic and Tasks for Experiments on Problem-Solving, *J. Psychol.* **38**, 151–160.

MOREHEAD, A. H., and MOTT-SMITH, G. (1963). "Hoyle's Rules of Games." New American Library of World Literature, New York.

MOSES, J. (1967). Symbolic Integration, Doctoral dissertation, M. I. T., Cambridge, Massachusetts.

MOTT-SMITH, G. (1954). "Mathematical Puzzles for Beginners and Enthusiasts." Dover, New York.

NEWELL, A. (1962a). Some Problems of Basic Organization in Problem-Solving Programs, *in* "Self-Organizing Systems" (M. C. Yovits, G. T. Jacobi, and G. D. Goldstein, eds.), pp. 393–425. Spartan Books, Washington, D. C.

NEWELL, A. (1962b). Learning, Generality and Problem-Solving, *Proc. IFIP Congr., 1962*, pp. 407–412. North Holland Publ., Amsterdam.

NEWELL, A. (1963). A Guide to the General Problem-Solver Program GPS-2-2, RM-3337-PR, RAND Corp., Santa Monica, California.

NEWELL, A. (1965). Limitations of the Current Stock of Ideas about Problem Solving, *in* "Electronic Information Handling" (A. Kent and U. Taulbee, eds.), pp. 195–208. Spartan Books, Washington, D. C.

NEWELL, A., and ERNST, G. (1965). The Search for Generality, *Proc. IFIP Congr., 1965* (W. A. Kalenich, ed.), 17–24. Spartan Books, Washington, D. C.

NEWELL, A., and SIMON, H. A. (1961a). The Simulation of Human Thought, *in* "Current Trends in Psychological Theory," pp. 152–179. Univ. of Pittsburgh Press, Pittsburgh, Pennsylvania.

NEWELL, A., and SIMON, H. A. (1961b). Computer Simulation of Human Thinking, *Science* **134**, 2011–2017.

NEWELL, A., and SIMON, H. A. (1961c). GPS, a Program That Simulates Human Thought, *in* "Lernende Automaten" (H. Billing, ed.), pp. 109–124, Munich, Germany [reprinted in Feigenbaum and Feldman (1963)].

NEWELL, A., and SIMON, H. A. (1962). Computer Simulation of Human Thinking and Problem Solving, *in* "Management and the Computer of the Future" (M. Greenberger, ed.), pp. 94–131. Wiley, New York.

NEWELL, A., SHAW, J. C., and SIMON, H. A. (1957a). Empirical Explorations with the Logic Theory Machine, *Proc. Western Joint Comput. Conf.*, pp. 218–239 [reprinted in Feigenbaum and Feldman (1963)].

NEWELL, A., SHAW, J. C., and SIMON, H. A. (1957b). Preliminary Description of General Problem Solving Program-I (GPS-1), CIP Working Paper No. 7, Carnegie Institute of Technology, Pittsburgh, Pennsylvania.

NEWELL, A., SHAW, J. C., and SIMON, H. A. (1958). Chess Playing Programs and the Problem of Complexity, *IBM J. Res. Develop.*, pp. 320–335 [reprinted in Feigenbaum and Feldman (1963)].

NEWELL, A., SHAW, J. C., and SIMON, H. A. (1960a). Report on a General Problem-Solving Program for a Computer, *Information Processing: Proc. Internl. Conf. Information Processing*, pp. 256–264, UNESCO, Paris (reprinted in *Computers and Automation*, July 1959).

NEWELL, A., SHAW, J. C., and SIMON, H. A. (1960b). A Variety of Intelligent Learning in a General Problem Solver, *in* "Self Organizing Systems" (M. C. Yovits and S. Cameron, eds.), pp. 153–189, Pergamon Press, Oxford.

NEWELL, A., TONGE, F. M., FEIGENBAUM, E. A., GREEN, B. F., and MEALY, G. H. (1961). "Information Processing Language-V Manual," 2nd ed. Prentice-Hall, Englewood Cliffs, New Jersey.

NEWELL, A., SHAW, J. C., and SIMON, H. A. (1962). The Processes of Creative Thinking, in "Contemporary Approaches to Creative Thinking" (H. E. Gruber, G. Terell, and M. Wertheimer, eds.), pp. 63–119. Atherton Press, New York.

NORTHROP, E. P. (1944). "Riddles in Mathematics: A Book of Paradoxes," pp. 65–66. Van Nostrand, Princeton, New Jersey.

OETTINGER, A. G. (1965). Automatic Processing of Natural and Formal Languages, Proc. IFIP Congr., 1965 (W. A. Kalenich, ed.), pp. 9–16. Spartan Books, Washington, D. C.

PIVAR, M., and FINKELSTEIN, M. (1964). Automation, Using LISP, of Inductive Inference on Sequences, in "The Programming Language LISP: Its Operation and Applications" (E. Berkeley and D. Bobrow, eds.). Information International, Cambridge, Massachusetts.

QUINLAN, J. R., and HUNT, E. B. (1968). The Fortran Deductive system, Dept. of Psychology, University of Washington, Seattle, Washington.

RAPHAEL, B. (1964). SIR: A Computer Program for Semantic Information Retrieval, Doctoral dissertation, M. I. T., Cambridge, Massachusetts.

ROBINSON, J. A. (1963). Theorem-Proving on the Computer, J. Assoc. Comput. Mach. 10, 163–174.

ROBINSON, J. A. (1965). A Machine-Oriented Logic Based on the Resolution Principle, J. Assoc. Comput. Mach. 12, 23–41.

ROBINSON, J. A. (1968). The Generalized Resolution Principle, in "Machine Intelligence 3" (D. Michie, ed.), pp. 77–93. Edinburgh Univ. Press, Edinburgh.

ROSEN, S. ed. (1967). "Programming Systems and Languages." McGraw-Hill, New York.

ROSENBLATT, F. (1962). "Principles of Neurodynamics." Spartan Books, Washington, D. C.

SAMUEL, A. L. (1959). Some Studies in Machine Learning Using the Game of Checkers, IBM J. Res. Develop. 3, 211–229 [reprinted in Feigenbaum and Feldman (1963)].

SAMUEL, A. L. (1967). Some Studies in Machine Learning Using the Game of Checkers II—Recent Progress, IBM J. Res. Develop. 11, 6, 601–617.

SIMON, H. A. (1963). Experiments with a Heuristic Compiler, J. Assoc. Comput. Mach. 10, 493–506.

SIMON, H. A., and KOTOVSKY, K. (1963). Human Acquisition of Concepts for Sequential Patterns, Psychol. Rev. 70, 534–546.

SLAGLE, J. R. (1963). A Heuristic Program That Solves Symbolic Integration Problems in Freshman Calculus, J. Assoc. Comput. Mach. 10, 335–337 [reprinted in Feigenbaum and Feldman (1963)].

SLAGLE, J. R. (1965). Experiments with a Deductive Question-Answering Program, Comm. ACM 8, 792–798.

TONGE, F. (1961). "A Heuristic Program for Assembly Line Balancing." Prentice-Hall, Englewood Cliffs, New Jersey.

TONGE, F. (1963). Balancing Assembly Lines Using the General Problem Solver, in "Symposium on Simulation Models" (A. C. Hoggott and F. E. Balderston, eds.), pp. 139–151. South-Western Publishing Co., Cincinnati, Ohio.

WANG, H. (1960). Proving Theorems by Pattern Recognition, I, *Comm. ACM* **3**, 220–234.

WANG, H. (1961). Proving Theorems by Pattern Recognition, II, *Bell System Tech. J.* **40**, 1–41.

WEIZENBAUM, J. (1962). How to Make a Computer Appear Intelligent, *Datamation* **8**, 24–26.

WILLIAMS, D. (1966). Unpublished research.

WILLIAMS. T. G. (1965). Some Studies in Game Playing with a Digital Computer, Doctoral dissertation, Carnegie Institute of Technology, Pittsburgh, Pennsylvania.

WOS, L., CARSON, D., and ROBINSON, G. (1964). The Unit Preference Strategy in Theorem Proving, *Proc. AFIPS Conf.* **26**, 615–621. Spartan Books, Washington, D. C.

INDEX